Gaylan A. Rasmussen

Transition Curves for Highways

By

JOSEPH BARNETT

Senior Highway Design Engineer
Division of Design
Public Roads Administration

Federal Works Agency

Public Roads Administration

UNITED STATES GOVERNMENT PRINTING OFFICE ● WASHINGTON ● 1940

For sale by the Superintendent of Documents, U.S. Government Printing Office
Washington, D.C. 20402 - Price $2.50

TRANSITION CURVES FOR HIGHWAYS

By JOSEPH BARNETT, *senior highway design engineer, Division of Design, Public Roads Administration*[1]

CONTENTS

[1] Acknowledgments are due John S. Biscoe, assistant highway engineer, and James Harold Williamson, senior engineering draftsman, for assistance with the computations.

1

INTRODUCTION

Transitions from tangents to horizontal curves have been universally adopted by railroads, but they have not been generally accepted for highways even though their use results in greater safety, smoother riding, and a more graceful alinement of the highway.

Among the reasons for this are reluctance to change existing practices and to revise standards; a belief that a vehicle using the highway is not confined to a track and is able to effect the change from a straight to a circular motion smoothly; a belief that widening at a sharp curve together with the gradual attainment of this widening accomplishes a satisfactory transition; and a belief that transitions involve tedious calculations both in the office and field, resulting in increased costs of engineering. There has also been considerable confusion as to what factors should determine the minimum length of a transition.

Some of these reasons were valid when road speeds were slower than at present but they do not apply now. At moderate speeds the average driver can traverse a satisfactory short transition path within the limits of a vehicle lane but with increased speeds longer transitions are required. These can be traversed only by hazardous crowding or occupation of adjoining lanes. The increase in the speeds at which vehicles are operated, the desire for increased speed with safety, and the mounting accident toll make it imperative that highways be constructed in such manner that a driver traveling at the safe speed for which the highway is designed will not only find it possible to confine his vehicle to the occupied lane but will be encouraged to do so.

In the following pages the relation of speed to highway design is discussed, and a method for determining the required lengths of transitions under various conditions is presented, together with tables from which the required transitions can be chosen and located without extensive calculations. Other factors related to transitions such as limiting curvature, superelevation, pavement widening, and right-of-way acquisition, are discussed. The use of the tables should make it as simple and inexpensive to design and locate curves with transitions as it is to design and locate simple curves. The methods employed and the use of the tables are illustrated by numerous examples.

SPEED IN RELATION TO HIGHWAY DESIGN

In urban areas motor vehicles are driven at speeds that vary over a wide range. Traffic control by officers or lights, density and variations in types of traffic, numerous intersections, changing roadway widths, grades, and pavement types, trolley cars, parked vehicles, eccentricities of other drivers and of pedestrians, and many other causes tend to make the driver vary his speed and stop frequently.

Once clear of urban areas, the average driver tends to settle down to a steady speed which in his mind is as great as the traffic and the physical characteristics of the highway permit. The speed is seldom the maximum speed of the vehicle since almost all passenger vehicles and some busses and trucks can attain speeds greater than that considered safe on existing highways and greater than that for which the public and highway engineers deem it economically advisable to construct most highways at the present time.

For the purposes of this discussion it is assumed that traffic is not dense enough to slow down a vehicle so that the steady speed adopted by the average driver depends largely upon the physical characteristics of the highway. The personal factor cannot be ignored. Some drivers choose a higher speed than do others. Some passengers feel comfortable at speeds higher than do others. Those physical characteristics of the highway that tend to make a fast driver slow down also tend to make a slow driver reduce speed. But an approximately uniform speed is generally the aim of all drivers.

The assumed design speed of a highway is the maximum approximately uniform speed that probably will be adopted by the faster group of drivers but not, necessarily, by the small percentage of reckless ones. The principal factor affecting the choice of a design speed is the character of the terrain. In general, rolling terrain justifies a higher design speed than mountainous country since the cost of constructing almost every highway detail for a higher speed is less. An important highway carrying a large volume of traffic may justify a higher design speed than a less important highway in similar topography because the increased expenditure for right-of-way and construction will be offset by the savings in vehicle operation, highway maintenance, and other operating costs. A low design speed should not be assumed for a secondary road if the topography is such that vehicle operators probably will travel at high speeds on the completed highway. Drivers do not adjust their speed to the importance of the road, but to the physical limitations such as curvature, grade, sight distance, and smoothness of surface. All other conditions being the same, a driver may use greater speed on a less important highway because of the absence of considerable traffic.

A balanced design requires that every critical detail of the highway, as far as economically possible, be designed for the assumed speed. For higher speeds, curve radii, superelevation, sight distances, widths of pavements and shoulders, set-backs for guard rails and walls, and widening at curves should be increased, slopes decreased, and other changes familiar to highway engineers should be made.

No unexpected detail requiring or encouraging a sudden reduction of speed or swerving from the occupied lane should be permitted. To

be confronted suddenly with such a detail is disconcerting and dangerous, especially if some other emergency imposes itself upon the thoughts
of the driver.   Where such a detail is unavoidable, a conspicuous
warning sign, visible night and day, should be erected well in advance
of the point of danger.   If such details are spaced closely, most drivers
will slow down instinctively and that section of highway should be
designed for a lower speed.

While designing for a given speed necessarily fixes a limit of curvature, there is no restriction or inhibition to the use of flatter curves if
they can be introduced as a part of economic design.   In fact such
procedure should be encouraged.   An occasional flat curve will not
encourage drivers to speed up but if a succession of flat curves is met,
drivers naturally will resort to greater speeds and that section of the
highway should be designed for a higher speed.   A section of highway
in which the assumed design speed is constant may be any reasonable
length and not, necessarily, the entire length of highway between
terminals.

An exceptional case may justify deliberately constructing a series
of curves of gradually decreasing radii to induce the drivers to slow
down before reaching a section of highway unsafe for high speeds.
Transitions from flat terrain to sharply rolling or hilly topography,
and entrances to cities with numerous intersections, are cases in point.
Such changes should be made as gradual as possible and advantage
should be taken of every change in topography to reduce any appearance of forced alinement.

Design speeds of 30, 40, 50, 60, and 70 miles per hour are used
throughout this discussion.

SAFE SPEED ON CURVES

A vehicle traveling around a curve of constant radius at a constant
velocity exerts a force outward known as centrifugal force which is
represented by $\dfrac{Wv^2}{gR}$, in which W represents the weight of the vehicle,
v the velocity in feet per second, g the acceleration of gravity in feet
per second per second, and R the radius of the curve in feet.   The centrifugal force is resisted by the component of the weight of the vehicle
parallel to the superelevated surface of road and the friction between
vehicle tires and road surface.   These are represented by WS and WF,
respectively, S being the superelevation slope or rate of superelevation
and F the friction factor.

If the vehicle is not skidding these forces are in equilibrium and may
be represented by the equation,

$$\frac{Wv^2}{gR} = WS + WF$$

Eliminating W, changing v in feet per second to V in miles per hour. and substituting 32.16 for g there results

$$S + F = \frac{0.067\,V^2}{R}$$

Superelevation must be limited for practical reasons. When traveling around a curve at low speed, large superelevation results in a tendency to slide down the incline since the centrifugal force is negligible. Friction will resist sliding but tests indicate that where ice is encountered the maximum frictional resistance that may be developed before sliding down the incline is 0.1 W. The frictional resistance required to prevent a vehicle on a superelevated cross section from sliding down the incline when traveling at little or no speed is represented by SW. The limiting superelevation recommended is numerically about the same as F for ice; namely, 0.10 foot per foot or about $1\frac{1}{4}$ inches per foot. As much as $1\frac{1}{2}$ inches may be used for skid-resistant surfaces in sections where freezing is infrequent.

A large number of driving tests [2] indicate that the amount of resistance to transverse sliding that may be developed with safety by a vehicle traveling around a curve is represented by a value of F of 0.16 for speeds of 30 to 60 miles per hour and by a value of 0.14 for a speed of 70 miles per hour. Resistance considerably in excess of that represented by these values may be developed without skidding; but it is inadvisable, when designing with safety a primary consideration, to use values which under certain conditions of road surface, etc., would closely approach those at impending skid. There is little difference in effect between applying a lower factor to a comfortably safe speed and applying a higher factor to a critical speed not used by most drivers.

MAXIMUM CURVATURE FOR VARIOUS DESIGN SPEEDS

Using a maximum superelevation slope of 0.10 and a maximum safe factor for frictional resistance of 0.16, $S + F = 0.26 = \dfrac{0.067\,V^2}{R}$

$$\therefore \text{ Minimum safe } R = 0.258\ V^2$$

For speeds of 30, 40, 50, and 60 miles per hour, curves with radii less than 232, 412, 644, and 928 feet, respectively, should not be used. These correspond to curves of 24.7°, 13.9°, 8.9°, and 6.2°, respectively.

---

[2] For an analysis of the reports of nearly 900 driving tests see paper, Safe Side Friction Factors and Superelevation Design, in the proceedings of the sixteenth annual meeting of the Highway Research Board, 1936.

For a speed of 70 miles per hour, the use of a lower friction factor of 0.14 and a maximum superelevation slope of 0.10 results in the equation

$$S + F = 0.24 = \frac{0.067 \ V^2}{R}$$

The safe minimum radius, therefore, is 1,370 feet, corresponding to a curvature of 4.2°.

SUPERELEVATION DESIGN

It has been common practice to superelevate pavements on curves to counteract all the centrifugal force of a vehicle traveling at an assumed speed. Because of practical limitations on the amount of superelevation it is not possible to compensate fully for centrifugal force on sharp curves and it becomes necessary to rely upon friction, in addition to superelevation, to prevent a vehicle from sliding outward. A vehicle traveling on a highway at the assumed vehicle speed will develop no friction rounding flat curves but will develop considerable friction on sharp curves.

There is little balance in a design in which no friction is developed rounding some curves and the maximum allowable amount is developed rounding other curves at the same speed. It seems desirable to develop a moderate amount of friction rounding the flat curves but the friction should not exceed that developed when rounding sharp curves superelevated by the above method. This may be accomplished by designing superelevation for a vehicle speed that is some fraction of the assumed design speed of the highway.

The practical maximum superelevation per unit of width is 0.10 and the maximum safe factor for frictional resistance is 0.16. For the sharpest permissible curve and at the assumed design speed about 39 percent of the centrifugal force will be counteracted by the effects of superelevation since $\frac{0.10}{0.10 + 0.16} = 0.39$. If exactly 39 percent is used, only the sharpest curves will be superelevated 0.10 foot per foot with proportionately lesser amounts of superelevation with decrease in curvature. This reduces the margin of safety to vehicles rounding the easier curves at speeds in excess of the design speed. Fully counteracting centrifugal force by superelevation wherever possible is objectionable because it results in all but the very flat curves being superelevated to the practical maximum slope of 0.10. Seventy-five percent is suggested as a compromise between the two extremes.[3] For example, the curves on a highway with an assumed design speed of 60 miles per

---

[3] For a discussion of the effects of designing superelevation for three-quarters of the assumed design speed see paper, Safe Side Friction Factors and Superelevation Design, in the proceedings of the sixteenth annual meeting of the Highway Research Board, 1936.

hour would be superelevated to compensate for the centrifugal force developed at 45 miles per hour except where the limitation of 0.10 foot per foot governed.

Slow-moving vehicles would be aided by this method of superelevation without inconvenience to fast-moving vehicles. The numerical value of the centrifugal force per unit of weight of a vehicle moving slowly around a flat curve may be less than the value of superelevation slope, in which case frictional resistance is required to prevent the vehicle sliding down the incline. If the assumed speed for designing superelevation is decreased the required friction is reduced or eliminated. This is a desirable effect since most vehicles will travel at speeds less than the assumed design speed. Fast-moving vehicles would not be subjected to danger because sharp curves would be super-elevated to the practical maximum in any case.

Possible future redesigns of the highway for somewhat higher speeds would not be made more difficult because a reduction in superelevation from that resulting from a design based on the total assumed design speed of the highway would be made only on the flatter curves that are safe for vehicle speeds considerably greater than the assumed design speed of the highway.

The superelevation values shown in table I are based on the assumption that all centrifugal force resulting from a speed of three-fourths of the design speed is counteracted by the effects of superelevation up to a maximum practicable limit of 0.10. When slopes are desired in inches per foot, each 0.01 foot may be considered equal to one-eighth inch without appreciable error.

TRANSITION CURVES IN RELATION TO SPEED

On highways without transitions the average driver traveling at the maximum speed for which a curve is designed finds it difficult to confine his vehicle to his traffic lane and maintain a uniform speed around the curve. On approaching such a curve he may choose one of several courses. If he can see well ahead around the curve or otherwise knows of its existence he may slow down so that he can swing into the curve and remain in the traffic lane; that is, give himself enough time to change from a straight to a circular course by turning his wheel on a short transition which may be created within the limits of his lane since the lane is wider than the vehicle. The smaller the difference between the widths of lane and vehicle, the shorter the transition that can be made within the limits of the lane. As an alternative to slowing down he may swing wide and encroach upon an adjacent traffic lane. In either case he is following a transition course selected by himself. Encroachment on adjacent traffic lanes creates a traffic hazard both to the driver and to others.

Transitions must be used if a uniform speed is to be maintained around a curve and the driver encouraged to keep within his traffic lane. The transitions should be long enough so that at the speed for which the curve is designed most drivers will have sufficient time to change from a straight to a circular motion by turning their wheels gradually and to swing into the circular curve within the limits of the occupied lane.

From another viewpoint, the transition must be sufficiently long that the driver feels the development of centrifugal force gradually. If the change from a tangent to a circular curve is made in a short distance, the driver is conscious of the sudden application of the full centrifugal force, and instinctively seeks to minimize this effect by driving on a longer transition obtained by occupying part of the adjoining lane. Long transition curves eliminate this tendency.

The required length of transition, L_s, may be determined as follows: If a vehicle travels on a curve at a constant speed of v in feet per second it is accelerating towards the center at the rate of $\frac{v^2}{R}$. The total time required to traverse the transition curve is $\frac{L_s}{v}$. The average rate at which the vehicle on the transition approaches this final constant centrifugal acceleration is therefore $\frac{v^2}{R} \div \frac{L_s}{v} = \frac{v^3}{RL_s}$.

This average rate will vary for different drivers and a great number and variety of tests and observations are needed to determine the maximum average rate that will accommodate almost all drivers. The few observations available indicate that a value of 2 for $\frac{v^3}{RL_s}$ will be satisfactory and is used herein. Equating these values and converting from feet per second to miles per hour we have

$$2 = \frac{v^3}{RL_s} = 3.16 \frac{V^3}{RL_s} \quad \text{and} \quad L_s = 1.6 \frac{V^3}{R}.$$

TRANSITION CURVES IN RELATION TO RUN-OFF

Transitions also are used to effect gradual changes from crowned or level sections to superelevated sections. To avoid the appearance that results from too rapid a change in superelevation, the transition should be long enough to permit the slope of the outer edge of pavement with respect to the center line to be no greater than 1 in 200. Where the topography or some other condition makes the use of shorter transitions advisable, shorter lengths corresponding to relative slopes of 1 in 150 and 1 in 175 may be used for design speeds of 30 and 40 miles per hours, respectively.

Where the grade and alinement are such as to accentuate depressing the inside edge of the road, it is preferable to keep this edge a fixed distance below the normal center-line grade and to raise both the center line and outside edge of the pavement. This results in minimum transition lengths nearly twice as long as are obtained by the method in which the center-line grade remains unchanged. The slope of the outside edge from normal to superelevated position is referred to the inside edge rather than to the center line.

Curvature begins at the T. S.,[4] at which point the outer half of the pavement should be level so that at no point on the curve will the surface slope downward toward the outside. Full superelevation should be attained at the S.C. where the radius of curvature is that for which the superelevation is designed. For simplicity, the change may be made uniformly between these points. Where the grade and alinement are such as to permit depression of the inner half of the pavement, this half should be symmetrical with the outer half except that it should be warped from a crowned section at the T.S. to a straight inclined section at a point where the changing superelevation of the outer half becomes equal to the crown. The whole cross section at this point will be a straight inclined line. The outer half will have to be warped from a crowned section at a point on the tangent some distance from the T.S. to a level section at the T.S. This distance should result in a slope of the outer edge of pavement with respect to the center line of about 1 in 400, requiring about 33 feet for each inch of crown. Where design speeds of 30 and 40 miles per hour are used, shorter distances may be used where necessary since the chosen design speeds indicate limited tangent distances.

Figure 1 shows recommended methods of attaining superelevation.

While vertical curves are desirable wherever slopes are changed, the slopes of the pavement edges with respect to the center line are so small that changes without vertical curves generally are not noticeable. If desired, however, the effect of a vertical curve can be produced by eye adjustments of the stakes or forms in the field. An exception is the high point or S.C.S. of a curve transitional throughout where a short section of full superelevation should be used if the relative slope is steeper than say, 1 in 400.

Where the S.T. of one curve and the T.S. of the next curve ahead are identical or a short distance apart, smoother riding and improved appearance may be obtained by the use of a level cross section midway between the points and straight line variations to the adjacent C.S. and S.C.

Rate of run-off, sometimes expressed in terms of the elevation of one tire with respect to the other and sometimes expressed by the rate of angular change or the rate of attaining superelevation slope, similar to the method often used for railroad transitions, has been advanced as

---

[4] Transition symbols and what they represent are listed on pp. 13 and 14.

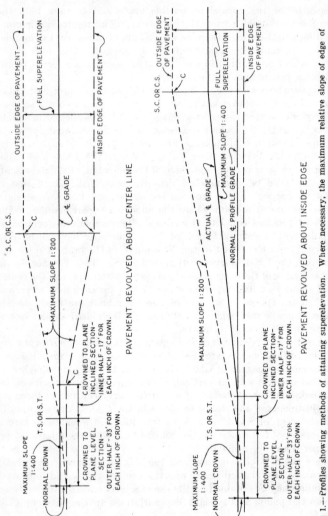
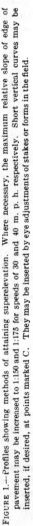

FIGURE 1.—Profiles showing methods of attaining superelevation. Where necessary, the maximum relative slope of edge of pavement may be increased to 1:150 and 1:175 for speeds of 30 and 40 m. p. h. respectively. Short vertical curves may be inserted, if desired, at points marked C. They may be inserted by eye adjustments of stakes or forms in the field.

a means for the determination of minimum transition lengths. Where the transition length is at least long enough to meet the requirements outlined above for the relative slope of the outer edge of pavement, the rate of run-off is moderate.

RECOMMENDED MINIMUM TRANSITION LENGTHS

Recommended minimum transition lengths for various degrees of curvature and assumed design speeds are shown in table I. Each transition is sufficiently long to satisfy the condition for speed as expressed by the formula, $L_s = 1.6\dfrac{V^3}{R}$, and to limit the slope of the outer edge of a pavement 20 feet wide with respect to the normal center line to 1 in 150 for an assumed design speed of 30 miles per hour, 1 in 175 for 40 miles per hour, and 1 in 200 for higher speeds. In general, the slope requirement governs for the flatter curves and the speed requirement governs for the sharper curves. Where the width of pavement used in the determination of the minimum transition length to meet slope requirements is more than 10 feet, as in four-lane pavements, or in two-lane pavements in which the inside edge is kept a constant distance below the normal center line, the slope requirement will always govern. The minimum transition length for such a case is determined by the superelevation slope, the governing width of pavement, and the slope limitation of 1 in 150, 175, or 200, as the case may be. Traffic lanes for modern traffic should be at least 11 feet wide. Transition lengths to meet slope requirements are slightly greater than for lanes 10 feet wide but differences are not great enough to consider changes in the few values in table I affected thereby.

All transition lengths are shown to the nearest 50 feet for ease of design and location. The reason for this becomes apparent when the use of the tables is described. A transition length less than 150 feet is considered impractical. A length of 100 feet satisfies the speed requirement and the requirement that the slope of the outer edge of pavement with respect to the center line of a two-lane pavement be not steeper than 1 in 200 for curves of 8°, 5°, 3°, and 1° 30', or less, for assumed design speeds of 30, 40, 50, and 60 miles per hour, respectively. Because of this limited application and the improved appearance resulting from the use of a 150-foot transition, it was considered inadvisable to increase the bulk of the tables by inserting data for $L_s = 100$ feet.

It may be inferred that transitions should be omitted where the length necessary to meet speed and slope requirements is less than 100 feet, but this is not advocated because the appearance of the alinement is improved when any superelevated curve has transition. Very few curves would be affected in any case. Where a low design speed is necessary there are few opportunities for flat curves.

Table I shows neither superelevation nor transitions for curves of 1° or less. A vehicle rounding the outside of a 1° curve crowned 1 inch in 10 feet at the maximum assumed design speed of 70 miles per hour will develop friction represented by a factor of 0.06, well within safe limits, the length of transition required is less than 100 feet, and the break at the P.C. of a simple 1° curve is not noticeable.

DESIGN OF CURVES WITH EQUAL TRANSITIONS BY USE OF TABLES

TYPE OF TRANSITION USED

In the preceding discussion controlling conditions to be met in the design of transition curves have been presented. A method of design meeting these conditions will now be described. For simple curves with equal lengths of transition at the ends, the design may be made directly from data presented in the tables. Data needed for staking a curve can be taken largely from the tables. Except for simple interpolations, few or no calculations are required.

In this publication the complete mathematical derivations are not given. The necessary formulas and tables with only enough of the derivation to aid in understanding their application are shown.

The transition curve used is one in which the degree of curvature (arc definition) varies directly as the length of transition, being zero at the beginning of the transition and equal to D_c at the S.C. (See list of symbols following.) It is the same form of transition used by Arthur N. Talbot in The Railway Transition Spiral except that Professor Talbot used the chord definition and his tables were developed around the symbol a which represents the rate of change of degree of curve per 100 feet of length and equals the degree of curvature at a point 100 feet from the T.S., $a = \dfrac{100\,D_c}{L_s}$.

The American Railway Engineering Association spiral is the same form of transition as used herein except that the chord definition of degree of curve is used and the spiral is always divided into 10 equal chords. It is known commonly as the 10-chord spiral and became very popular due to the ease with which it is located in the field, despite the fact that even stations are not readily located by this method. The transition used by T. F. Hickerson in Highway Surveying and Planning is the same in form as the one used herein. In the Searles spiral the transition is effected by a series of compound circular curves in which each curve is sharper than the preceding curve. In England the lemniscate advanced by F. G. Royal-Dawson in his book, Road Curves, has been used to some extent.

As regards riding qualities, safe speeds, or rates of change of super-elevation, no one form of transition has any particular advantage over other forms. The principal shortcoming of the treatises in which transitions have been presented heretofore is that the tables have not been prepared with the thought in mind that the transition is part of a complete curve which must fit between two tangents with a measured intersection angle and at the same time meet possible limitations of tangent and external distances in addition to those of speed, rate of run-off, superelevation, and appearance. A laborious method of trial and error had to be used when specific limitations were imposed, often resulting in odd lengths of transition and odd values of degree of curvature that materially increased the time required for computing and staking the work.

TRANSITION SYMBOLS

Figure 2 and the following list of symbols show the meaning of terms and symbols used in the discussion.

P.I.	Point of intersection of the main tangents.
T.S.	Tangent spiral, common point of tangent and spiral of near transition.
S.C.	Spiral curve, common point of spiral and circular curve of near transition.
C.S.	Curve spiral, common point of circular curve and spiral of far transition.
S.T.	Spiral tangent, common point of spiral and tangent of far transition.
S.C.S.	Spiral curve spiral, common point of both spirals or midpoint of a curve transitional throughout. (Except where special reference is advisable, the S.C.S. will not be mentioned hereafter since a curve transitional throughout is the same as any other curve with transitions in which $\Delta_c = 0$ and the S.C.S. may by considered the S.C.)
R_c	Radius of the circular curve.
L_s	Length of spiral between T.S. and S.C.
L	Length between T.S. and any other point on spiral.
L_1	Length between any two points on spiral.
T_s	Tangent distance P.I. to T.S. or S.T., or tangent distance of the complete curve.
E_s	External distance P.I. to center of circular curve portion, or to S.C.S. of a curve transitional throughout.
$L.T.$	Long tangent distance of spiral only.
$S.T.$	Short tangent distance of spiral only.
$L.C.$	Straight line chord distance T.S. to S.C.
p	Offset distance from the tangent of P.C. of circular curve produced.

k	Distance from T.S. to point on tangent opposite the P.C. of the circular curve produced.
Δ	Intersection angle between tangents of entire curve.
Δ_c	Intersection angle between tangents at the S.C. and at the C.S. or the central angle of the circular curve portion of the curve.
θ_s	Intersection angle between the tangent of the complete curve and the tangent at the S.C., the spiral angle.
θ	Intersection angle between the tangent of the complete curve and the tangent at any other point on the spiral, the spiral angle of any other point.
D_c	Degree of the circular curve same as degree of curvature of spiral at the S.C. (arc definition).
D	Degree of curvature of spiral at any other point on spiral (arc definition).
ϕ_c	Deflection angle from tangent at T.S. to S.C.
ϕ	Deflection angle from tangent at any point on spiral to any other point on spiral.
x_c, y_c	Coordinates of S.C. from the T.S.
x, y	Coordinates of any other point on spiral from the T.S.

USE OF TABLES IN DESIGN

In designing highway alinement the angle between intersecting tangents is usually known as well as the limiting lengths of tangents and external distances.

Table IV gives tangent distances, T_s, and external distances, E_s, for numerous combinations of transition length, L_s, and degree of curvature, D_c. Each section of the table represents one value of the intersection angle Δ. All combinations above and to the right of a zigzag line are safe for the speed indicated at the end of the line. The designs that fit the limiting conditions of T_s or E_s or both may be obtained directly from the table corresponding to the measured angle Δ.

After the combination of L_s and D_c is decided upon the value of T_s may be taken from the tables to the nearest hundredth of a foot and used to establish and locate the station of the T.S. by subtracting T_s from the station of the P.I. The central angle of the circular curve portion of the curve may be calculated by subtracting the central angle occupied by both transitions from the total central angle Δ. Thus $\Delta_c = \Delta - 2\theta_s = \Delta - \dfrac{L_s D_c}{100}$. Note that this is the only calculation required thus far and since L_s is always a multiple of 50 feet and D_c is in even degrees, except for values less than 4° when it is in even half

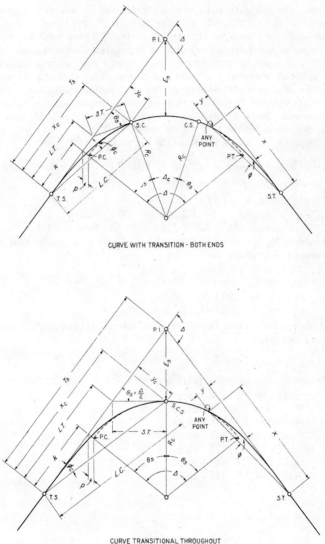

CURVE WITH TRANSITION - BOTH ENDS

CURVE TRANSITIONAL THROUGHOUT

FIGURE 2.—Typical curves with transitions.

1:1:1 Ratio used by Engineers.
1:2:1   "   Better for our uses

degrees, the calculation may be made mentally. The S.T. may be located on the far tangent, distance T_s from the P.I., and its station established by adding to the station of the T.S. the total length of curve which is 2 L_s plus the length of the central circular curve.

When Δ is not in even degrees, as is usually the case, the table for the value of Δ nearest the measured Δ is used for choosing the combination of L_s and D_c which best fits the limiting conditions. Then the exact value of T_s may be obtained by simple interpolation between the tangent distances read for the same combinations of L_s and D_c from the tables for the two nearest values of Δ.

Examples 1, 2, and 3 illustrate the use of table IV.

EXAMPLE 1.—*Illustration of use of table IV where external distance controls*

Given: Design speed 40 m.p.h.

Measured $\Delta = 56°$ P.I. station $436 + 89.20$

Line should be located about 92 feet from the P.I.

In table IV for $\Delta = 56°$ it may be observed at a glance that the following combinations fit:

$D_c = 11°$ $L_s = 500$ feet.
$D_c = 10°$ $L_s = 400$ feet.
$D_c = 9°$ $L_s = 300$ feet.
$D_c = 9°$ $L_s = 350$ feet.

If the combination of $D_c = 9°$ and $L_s = 300$ feet is chosen, $T_s = 491.35$ is read directly.

$$\Delta_c = \Delta - \frac{L_s D_c}{100} = 56° - 3 \times 9° = 29°$$

Length of circular curve portion $= 100 \times 29° \div 9° = 322.22$ feet.

Station of P.I. $436 + 89.20$
T_s 4   91.35
Station of T.S. $431 + 97.85$
Station of S.C. $434 + 97.85$
                  3   22.22
Station of C.S. $438 + 20.07$
Station of S.T. $441 + 20.07$

EXAMPLE 2.—*Illustration of use of table IV where interpolation is necessary*

Given: Same as example 1 except that $\Delta = 56°14'$.

Table IV for $\Delta = 56°$ is used to find the combinations which fit requirements. If the combination of $D_c = 9°$ and $L_s = 300$ feet is chosen T_s is found by simple interpolation between 491.35 from the table for $\Delta = 56°$ and 498.57 for the same combination from the table for $\Delta = 57°$ resulting in $T_s = 491.35 + \dfrac{14}{60} \times 7.22 = 493.03$.

$$\Delta_c = \Delta - \frac{L_s D_c}{100} = 56°14' - 3 \times 9° = 29°14'.$$

Length of circular curve portion $= 100 \times 29°14' \div 9° = 324.81$.

Station of P.I. $436 + 89.20$
T_s 4   93.03
Station of T.S. $431 + 96.17$
Station of S.C. $434 + 96.17$
                    3   24.81
Station of C.S. $438 + 20.98$
Station of S.T. $441 + 20.98$

As a check for the requirement that E_s be about 92 feet it may be interpolated between 91.1 from table for $\Delta = 56°$ and 94.5 from the table for $\Delta = 57°$ resulting in $E_s = 91.9$ feet.

EXAMPLE 3.—*Illustration of use of table IV where tangent distance is limited*

Given: Design speed 60 m. p. h.

Measured $\Delta = 42°48'$ P.I. station $87 + 37.24$.

Not more than 700 feet available for total tangent.

In table IV for $\Delta = 43°$ it may be observed at a glance that the following combinations fit:

$D_c = 6°$ $L_s = 350, 400, 500,$ and 600 feet.
$D_c = 5°$ $L_s = 300, 350,$ and 400 feet.
$D_c = 4°$ $L_s = 250.$

If the requirement that the line be not less than 85 feet and not more than 95 feet from the P.I. be added the choice narrows down to the following combinations:

$D_c = 6°$ $L_s = 600$ feet.
$D_c = 5°$ $L_s = 300, 350,$ and 400 feet.

If the combination of $D_c = 5°$ and $L_s = 400$ feet is chosen T_s is found by simple interpolation between 641.90 from the table for $\Delta = 42°$ and 653.47 from the table for $\Delta = 43°$ resulting in $T_s = 641.90 + \dfrac{48}{60} \times 11.57 = 651.16.$

$$\Delta_c = 42°48' - 4 \times 5° = 22°48'$$

Length of circular curve $= 100 \times 22°48' \div 5° = 456.00$.

Station of P.I. $87 + 37.24$
T_s 6 51.16
Station of T.S. $80 + 86.08$
Station of S.C. $84 + 86.08$
            4 56.00
Station of C.S. $89 + 42.08$
Station of S.T. $93 + 42.08$

Values for central angles less than 6° are not shown in table IV. The design of curves to fit small intersection angles is governed by the appearance of the highway. A curve of relatively short length even with proper transitions has the appearance of a sharp bend. For a central angle of 5° the curve should be at least 500 feet long and for each decrease of 1° in the central angle the curve should be at least 100 feet longer. These curve lengths are obtained with simple curves of 1° or less which require no transition. For intersection angles of 6° and 7° the curves should be at least 400 feet long, and for intersection angles of 8°, 9°, and 10° the curves should be at least 350 feet long. These may be simple curves of 1° or less or sharper curves with proper transitions chosen from table IV. The suggested minimum lengths of curves for small intersection angles should not be construed as both minimum and maximum. Nothing adds more to the pleasing appearance and graceful alinement of a highway than long, flowing curves. Where topography permits, an effort should be made to accomplish this by the use of 20', 30' or 40' curves for intersection angles equal to or greater than those indicated above.

Curves transitional throughout are those in which the two transitions occupy the entire curve. They may be treated like any other curves with transitions in which $\Delta_c=0$. $\theta_s=\dfrac{\Delta}{2}$ and $\Delta=2\theta_s=\dfrac{L_sD_c}{100}$. In table IV E_s distances for those curves transitional throughout are shown to two decimals (for example see entries at bottom of columns for $\Delta=30°$) for convenience of locating the S.C.S. from which, if it is desired, both transitions may be located. Curves transitional throughout also may be designed by the use of table III which gives T_s and E_s for various values of Δ for transitions 1 foot long. Where T_s or E_s controls the design and a curve transitional throughout is desired, L_s may be found by dividing T_s or E_s by the factor for transitions 1 foot long adjacent to the measured Δ interpolating if necessary. The resulting curve must be tested for safe speed. Curves transitional throughout generally result in odd values for L_s or D_c or both. The advantage of confining designs to combinations shown in table IV will become apparent later.

LOCATING THE CHOSEN CURVE WITH TRANSITIONS

After designing the curve with transitions by choosing a combination of L_s and D_c shown in table IV, the curve may be located by the use of data from table V. It is desirable to locate the control points of the curve, the T.S., S.C., C.S., and S.T., to the precision required of the line as a whole so that no appreciable errors are carried forward, thus permitting other points on the transitions to be located with less precision.

Table V (left page) gives the details of all transitions shown in table IV. Table V (right page) gives the deflection angles for all transitions shown in table IV for a set-up on the T.S. from the tangent to points on the transition dividing it into 10 equal lengths. Facing pages give the data for one value of L_s. Thus if the curve chosen in table IV is $L_s=300$ feet and $D_c=9°$, the pages of table V for $L_s=300$ feet apply. The details of the transition are found on the left page along the line for $D_c=9°$, and the deflection angles for a set-up on the T.S. from the main tangent to the division points of the transition divided into 10 equal lengths are found on the right page, also along the line for $D_c=9°$.

There are several methods of locating the S.C. of a curve with transitions. In illustrating methods, use will be made of the data of a previous example in which $\Delta = 56°$ and the combination chosen to fit conditions was $D_c = 9°$ and $L_s = 300$ feet.

(a) *By long chord.*—L.C. $= 299.26$ read directly from table V for $L_s = 300$, left page, and deflection angle to S.C. or point 10 $= 4°30'$ read directly on the opposite page. When set up on the S.C. the transit zero may be set on the common tangent by backsighting on the T.S. with the vernier set for the deflection angle to the T.S. from the local tangent. This deflection angle equals θ_s minus the deflection angle from the T.S., in this case $13°30' - 4°30' = 9°00'$.

(b) *By spiral tangents.*—Long tangent $= 200.58$, short tangent $= 100.53$, and $\theta_s = 13°30'$ are all read directly from table V for $L_s = 300$, left page. In this method a set-up is made on the intersection of the spiral tangents which is on the main tangent a distance from the T.S. equal to the long tangent.

Sta. of T.S. _____ 431 + 97.85
Long tangent _____ 2 + 00.58
                                                    _____
Sta. of intersection of spiral tangents _ 433 + 98.43

The angle θ_s is turned off the main tangent and the short tangent distance measured from the point of set-up to the S.C. By setting up on the S.C. and backsighting on the intersection of the spiral tangents the telescope will be on the tangent common to both spiral and circular curves.

(c) *By coordinates.*—$x_c = 298.34$ and $y_c = 23.47$ are read directly from table V for $L_s = 300$, left page, and measured from the T.S.

(d) *By measuring from the P.I.*—This method can be used only where the curve is visible from the P.I. A simple trigonometric calculation is required. The line from P.I. to S.C. is the hypotenuse of a right triangle of which one side is $y_c = 23.47$ and the other is $T_s - x_c = 491.35 - 298.34 = 193.01$. Using a table of trigonometric functions, the deflection angle from the tangent at the P.I. is found to be $6°56'$ and the distance to the S.C. is computed to be 194.43. When set up on the S.C. the transit zero may be set on the local tangent by backsighting on the P.I. with the vernier set for the deflection angle to the P.I. which equals θ_s plus the deflection angle from the P.I. in this case $13°30' + 6°56' = 20°26'$. When the curve is transitional throughout the angular deflection to the S.C.S. from the tangent at the P.I. is $90° - \dfrac{\Delta}{2}$ and the distance is E_s. The common tangent at the S.C.S. is perpendicular to the line from the P.I.

If the entire transition is visible from the T.S. it may be located from a set-up on the T.S. by locating the division points on the transition divided into 10 equal lengths using a chord length of one-tenth

L_s and deflection angles read directly from table V, right page, checking out on the S.C., point 10.

For all practical purposes the chord length equals the arc length except for transition lengths 400 feet and longer and then the exception applies only for comparatively sharp curves. The true chord length may be obtained by the use of any standard table using the arc length and the average degree of curvature. The average degree of curvature may be computed mentally to the nearest degree, being 0.95 D_c for the chord next to the S.C., 0.85 D_c for the next chord, etc. For the transitions shown in table IV the maximum discrepancies between chord and arc lengths are found for $L_s = 600$ feet and $D_c = 16°$, being 0.06 for the last chord, 0.05 for the next chord, etc. The discrepancies for $L_s = 500$ and $D_c = 20°$ are about the same and those for $L_s = 400$ and $D_c = 25°$ are about 0.01 less in each case.

Example 4 illustrates the use of table V, right page, in determining deflection angles from the T.S.

EXAMPLE 4.—*Deflection angles from the T.S.*

Given: $D_c = 9°$ $L_s = 300$.   Sta. of T.S. 431+97.85

Deflections read directly from table V, right page, for $L_s = 300$

Transit on T.S. station	431+97.85	
To point 1	432+27.85	0°03′
2	+57.85	0°11′
3	+87.85	0°24′
4	433+17.85	0°43′
5	+47.85	1°08′
6	+77.85	1°37′
7	434+07.85	2°12′
8	+37.85	2°53′
9	+67.85	3°39′
10 = S.C.	+97.85	4°30′

The deflection angles in table V are shown to tenths of minutes for use in interpolating when the deflection angle is desired to a point other than a chord point, such as an even station. Simple interpolation leads to small errors which may be corrected by the use of column A in the table which gives the correction in minutes for each foot of the distance from the nearest chord point. In all cases the correction is deducted from the interpolated value.

For example, assume that the deflection angle is desired to Sta. 433+00 in example 4.

Point 3, Station 432 + 87.85 deflection angle $\phi = 0°24.4′$
Point 4, Station 433 + 17.85 deflection angle $\phi = 0°43.2′$
Station 433+00 by simple interpolation $= 0°32.0′$
Correction 0.05′ × 12 feet $=   0.6′$
Final deflection angle $= 0°31.4′$ or 0°31′

Other methods for locating the transition, as well as computations for the transition when it is not visible from the T.S. and an intermediate set-up is required, are described later. A method of locating the transition from the S.C. is also described.

The method that has been described is based on the use of table IV which is predicated on the assumption that the intersection angle is the first condition controlling design and in which the tangent and external distances for the entire curve with transitions may be read at a glance. The combinations of L_s and D_c shown are believed to be sufficient to meet all reasonable sets of conditions. If values of L_s or D_c or combinations of both other than those shown in table IV are desired, table IV may be used as a guide, the approximate values of T_s and E_s being obtained from combinations close to the one desired. The amount of trial and error may be reduced but the correct value of T_s to locate the T.S. and the S.T., for example, will require some calculation. The details of the general transition and the methods of making the calculations when the L_s and D_c values in table IV are not chosen are given in succeeding pages.

SUPPLEMENTARY TABLES FOR SHARP CURVES

The main body of the tables gives data for curves up to and including 25°, the maximum safe curvature for an assumed speed of 30 miles per hour. The range of curves is sufficient for practically all situations met in practice except in mountainous topography where sharper curves may be required. The supplementary tables in the appendix give data for curves from 26° to 38° inclusive for transition lengths of 150, 200, and 250 feet. Data for longer transitions are considered to be unnecessary since where sharp curvature is required it is improbable that tangent distances will be long enough to accommodate transitions longer than 250 feet.

The tables in the appendix are presented as supplements to the main tables. They are extensions of the main tables and may be used in the same way. Zigzag speed lines are not shown in the supplement to table IV. All combinations of D_c and L_s shown are safe for speeds of 25 to 30 miles per hour when the pavements are superelevated to the practical maximum of 0.10 foot (1¼ inches) per foot.

Table X shows maximum degrees of curvature considered safe for various combinations of rate of superelevation, S, and speed, V, based on the relation, $S + F = \dfrac{0.067 \ V^2}{R}$.

The friction factor, F, used in each case is that considered safe for the assumed design speed and is shown at the head of each column. This table has no direct relation to the tables for transitions. It is included to show directly the relation between the various factors entering into the design of circular curves. It may be used to determine safe speeds on existing curves, but it should be remembered that a transition is required at each end of each curve for safe operation at the speed shown.

DESIGN OF CURVES WITH TRANSITIONS—GENERAL CASE

GENERAL PROCEDURE

In the transition used throughout this discussion the degree of curvature varies directly as the length of spiral, being zero at the T.S. and D_c at the S.C.

$$D = \frac{L}{L_s} \times D_c$$

The spiral angle, θ_s, at the S.C. equals the central angle of the circular curve for a length just half the length of the spiral.

$$\theta_s = \frac{L_s}{200} \times D_c$$

The spiral angle varies as the square of the length of spiral from the T.S. so that at any other point the spiral angle,

$$\theta = \frac{L^2}{L_s^2} \times \theta_s.$$

The coordinates x and y are expressed in terms of geometric series not shown here. However, the values of the coordinates for any given value of the spiral angle θ vary directly as the length of the spiral from the T.S. Table II gives values of x and y for a unit length of spiral for different values of θ. To obtain x or y for any point multiply the value in the table for the θ at that point by the length of spiral from the T.S. to the point.

The distance k is equal to $\frac{L_s}{2}$ approximately and the spiral almost exactly bisects p.

Values of p and k for a unit length of transition are given in table II for various values of θ so that p and k for any particular transition may be obtained by multiplying the table coefficients opposite $\theta = \theta_s$ by the length of spiral.

Values of p and k are required when adjusting an alinement of tangents and simple curves to provide for the insertion of transitions. The circular curve must be made sharper or moved inward so that the P.C. of the circular curve is the distance p from the tangent and there must be sufficient tangent distance between curves to increase the tangent of the simple curve by a length approximately equal to k. When it is proposed to use two transitions of equal length the shift or other adjustment of the circular curve is made without difficulty. However, when local conditions control the alinement to the extent that transitions of unequal length must be used the circular curve must be adjusted until the p at each end is that required to fit D_c and the corresponding L_s.

Often in rugged topography, a location is made without first establishing both tangents to the curve. In an alinement without transitions the tangent may be carried forward only to the P.C. from which point the degree of curvature is estimated or assumed and the curve carried forward. The transition length should be established at that time to avoid the difficulties encountered in adjusting the curve later to accommodate the transition. The details of the transition should be calculated, the S.C. established as outlined, and the circular curve carried forward from that point. When leaving the curve a similar procedure should be followed. In this method nothing is gained by making both transitions alike except that equal transitions avoid new computations for establishing the S.T. and the transition leading to the S.T.

Table IV is not used when a location is made in this manner. Table I is useful in choosing a transition length and table II may be used in calculating the details of the transition. Tables VI and VIII may be used to locate the transition after it is designed. If the chosen curvature is in even degrees (or half degrees for curves flatter than 4°) and the chosen transition length is a multiple of 50 feet, the details of the transition may be read directly from table V and also the deflection angles from the tangent at the T.S. to points dividing the transition into 10 equal lengths.

Most curves are designed with equal transitions for which the tangent and external distances for the entire curve are computed, as follows:

$$T_s = (R_c + p)\tan\frac{\Delta}{2} + k$$

$$E_s = (R_c + p)\operatorname{exsec}\frac{\Delta}{2} + p$$

The use of the tangents for each transition and for the circular curve, if any, is often found advantageous. The P.I. of the complete curve may be inaccessible whereas the P.I.'s of the transitions and the section of circular curve are much nearer the center line and therefore more likely to be accessible. Sometimes conditions make it advisable to use unequal transitions for which the computations for the tangents for the complete curve are laborious. Sometimes it may be advantageous to carry the line forward by the use of the long chord.

Values of L.T., long tangent (fig. 2), S.T., short tangent, and L.C., long chord, for a unit length of transition are given in table II for various values of θ so that the values for any transition may be obtained by multiplying the coefficients in the table opposite $\theta = \theta_s$ by the length of the transition. If the chosen curvature is in even degrees (or half degrees for curvatures less than 4°) and the chosen transition length is a multiple of 50 feet, these distances may be read directly from table V.

The central angle of the circular curve portion is the total central angle less the angles occupied by both transitions,

$$\Delta_c = \Delta - 2\theta_s = \Delta - \frac{L_s D_c}{100}.$$

The total length of curve is the sum of the lengths of both transitions and the length of the central circular curve.

$$\text{Total length of curve} = 2L_s + 100\frac{\Delta_c}{D_c}$$

The deflection angle, ϕ, at a set-up on the T.S. from the tangent to any point on the spiral is the angle whose tangent is $\frac{x}{y}$. It is unnecessary to compute x and y since the deflection angle is very nearly equal to one-third of the spiral angle, the correction being small for small values of the spiral angle, and less than half a minute for values less than 21°.

$$\phi = \frac{\theta}{3} - C$$

Table VII gives corrections to be deducted for various values of θ.

When a set-up on an intermediate point on the spiral is required, as when an obstruction makes it impossible to locate the entire spiral from the T.S. and a forward movement of the transit is required, it is necessary to set the zero of the transit on the tangent at the point of set-up and to compute a new set of deflection angles. The deflection angles are computed as follows:

The degree of curve at the point of set-up is first computed by the formula, $D = \frac{L}{L_s} \times D_c$. The length to any other point on the transition for which the deflection angle is desired is known and may be designated L_1. The deflection angle for a circular curve of degree D for length L_1 is computed. The deflection angle from the T.S. to a point on the transition distance L_1 from it is computed. The desired deflection angle equals the circular curve deflection plus or minus the transition deflection. If the point is towards the T.S. from the set-up, the transition deflection is deducted and if the point is towards the S.C. it is added. The foregoing follows from the fact that the spiral leaves the circular curve at any point at the same rate that it leaves the tangent at the T.S.

To set the zero of the transit on the local tangent any other known point on the spiral may be used as a backsight by setting the vernier for the deflection angle to the point of backsight. The deflection angle may be computed as described above. Usually the T.S. is a convenient backsight point. The deflection angle from the local tangent to the T.S. equals, by geometry, $\theta - \phi$ in which θ represents the spiral angle and ϕ the deflection angle from the T.S. for the point of set-up. Since $\phi = \dfrac{\theta}{3}$ very closely, except for large angles, the back deflection angle to the T.S. equals, very closely, $2\,\phi$.

If a spiral is divided into any number of equal parts the deflection angle to or from any point of division to any other such point is the same for a value of the spiral angle θ_s regardless of the length of spiral. Tables VI and VIII give coefficients which when multiplied by the spiral angle θ_s give the deflection angles from any point to any other point of a spiral divided into 10 and 20 equal parts, respectively. For a set-up on the T.S. the coefficients in the column headed 0 are used. For a set-up on the S.C. the coefficients in the column headed 10 or 20 are used. It is believed that with these tables the deflection angles can be computed and a spiral located as readily as a circular curve, the only disadvantage being that the points located are not even stations.

The results obtained by the use of tables VI and VIII are correct except that since each deflection is made up of a circular curve deflection and a spiral deflection the latter should be corrected in accordance with table VII. For rough work the correction can be ignored and for more accurate work it can be ignored for all values of θ less than 21° so that it will rarely be used. To compute the correction, θ is first computed by multiplying the spiral angle θ_s by the "Constant for θ" located within the same diagonal zigzag lines as the coefficient in table VI or VIII. θ is then used in table VII to obtain directly the correction to be subtracted or added as indicated in table VI or VIII.

USE OF TABLES IN LOCATING THE CHOSEN CURVE

From the design of any curve whether made in the field or office the following are usually known: Δ, Δ_c, L_s, θ_s, D_c, T_s, and E_s. The station of the T.S. is known or may be computed by deducting T_s from the station of the P.I.

Four methods are given for locating the transition. A set-up may be required on the T.S. or on the S.C. or on an intermediate point depending on the method used. If the transitions are located by tangent offsets the x distances are measured from the T.S. and S.T. and may be lined in from one set-up on the P.I. or from separate set-ups on other points on the main tangents. If chords and deflection angles are used both the transition and the circular curve may be located from a set-up on the S.C. and both transitions of a curve transitional throughout may be located from a set-up on the S.C.S.

When set up on the S.C. the zero of the transit may be set on the local tangent at the point by backsighting on the T.S. with the vernier set for the deflection angle to the T.S. This deflection angle equals $\theta_s - \phi_c$. Since ϕ_c is very closely $\frac{1}{3} \theta_s$ the deflection angle to the T.S. is closely $\frac{2}{3} \theta_s$. For a large value of θ_s a correction should be applied as described in the preceding chapter.

When set up on the S.C.S. of a curve transitional throughout the local tangent is perpendicular to a line from the P.I.

METHOD 1.—*Deflection angles to points of equal division (the 10- or 20-chord spiral).*—A simple method for locating a transition is to divide the length into 10 or 20 equal parts, set up on the T.S. or on the S.C. and locate the spiral by deflection angles and equal chords in the same manner as when locating a circular curve from a set-up on the P.C. or P.T. The zero of the transit should always be set on the tangent at the point of set-up and deflection angles to the points to be located may be computed by means of table VI for the 10-chord spiral or table VIII for the 20-chord spiral. The coefficients under the point of set-up and across from the points to be sighted on, when multiplied by θ_s, give the deflection angles. In some cases corrections are required as heretofore described. When set up on the T.S., column 0 is used. When set up on the S.C., column 10 of table VI or column 20 of table VIII is used. The transition is located by successive equal arc lengths beginning at either end. For all practical purposes the arc length equals the chord length except for transition lengths 400 feet and longer and then the exception applies only to comparatively sharp curvatures. The true chord length may be obtained from any standard table using the arc length and the average degree of curvature. The average degree of curvature may be computed to the nearest degree mentally, being 0.95 D_c for the chord next to the S.C., 0.85 D_c for the next chord, etc.

When a part of the transition is not visible from either end an intermediate set-up generally is necessary, and, unlike locating a circular curve, a new set of deflection angles must be computed. These may be computed easily, however, by multiplying the coefficients in table VI or VIII under the point of set-up by θ_s. The deflection angle to some known point on the transition, preferably the T.S. or S.C. also may be computed in the same manner and may be used to set the zero of the transit on the local tangent by backsighting on the point with the vernier set for the deflection angle to the point.

Where it is desired to set even stations this method is not used.

The computations for a set-up on the T.S. with the entire spiral visible and the computations for a set-up on an intermediate point are shown in example 5.

EXAMPLE 5.—*Computations for a set-up on the T.S. with entire spiral visible and for an intermediate set-up*

Given: $D_c = 9°$ $L_s = 300$ $\theta_s = 13°30'$ T.S. at station 431+97.85

[Chord length for 10-chord spiral 30 feet.—Coefficients read from table VI.]

Point	Station	Deflection angles ϕ	
		Set up on T.S.	Set up on point 6
T.S.	431+97.85		$0.2400 \times 13.5° = 3°14'$
1	432+27.85	$0.0033 \times 13.5° = 0°03'$	
2	+57.85	$.0133 \times 13.5° = 0°11'$	
3	+87.85	$.0300 \times 13.5° = 0°24'$	
4	433+17.85	$.0533 \times 13.5° = 0°43'$	
5	+47.85	$.0833 \times 13.5° = 1°08'$	
6	+77.85	$.1200 \times 13.5° = 1°37'$	
7	434+07.85	$.1633 \times 13.5° = 2°12'$	$.0633 \times 13.5° = 0°51'$
8	+37.85	$.2133 \times 13.5° = 2°53'$	$.1333 \times 13.5° = 1°48'$
9	+67.85	$.2700 \times 13.5° = 3°39'$	$.2100 \times 13.5° = 2°50'$
S.C.	+97.85	$.3333 \times 13.5° = 4°30'$	$.2933 \times 13.5° = 3°58'$

The deflection angles of example 5 for a set-up on the T.S. may be read directly in table V, right pages, since the combination of $D_c = 9°$ and $L_s = 300$ feet is included in that table.

Example for computing corrections:

Correction for ϕ from T.S. to point 9.

Constant for θ between zigzag lines $= 0.81$ $\therefore$ $\theta = 0.81 \times 13.5° = 11°$.

This is too small to require correction but, if large enough, the correction to be subtracted would be obtained from table VII.

METHOD 2.—*Deflection angles to even stations.*—Where it is desired to set even stations, deflection angles from the T.S. may be computed by the formula $\phi = \frac{1}{3} \times \theta = \frac{1}{3} \times \frac{L^2}{L_s^2} \times \theta_s$ (deducting a correction where the resulting deflection is greater than 7°).

Where an intermediate set-up is necessary, the degree of curvature at the point of set-up is computed by simple proportion. Circular curve deflection angles for this curvature for the lengths from the set-up to all other points are computed and to them are added (or subtracted) deflection angles for the spiral from the T.S. for the same lengths. The deflection angle from the point of set-up back to the T.S. may be more easily computed by $\theta - \phi$ for that point.

The deflection angles for a set-up on the S.C. may be computed in the same manner as for a set-up on an intermediate point, the degree of circular curve for this set-up being D_c.

Example 6 shows the computations where the entire spiral is visible from the T.S. and example 7 shows the computations for the same numerical example where an intermediate set-up is necessary. All but one or two calculations were made with a 10-inch slide rule with which results accurate to the nearest minute are obtained.

EXAMPLE 6.—*Computations where the entire spiral is visible from the T.S.*

Given: $D_c=9°$ $L_s=300$ $\theta_s=13°30'$ T.S. at station $431+97.85$

$$\frac{1}{3}\times\frac{\theta_s}{L_s{}^2}=\frac{1}{3}\times\frac{13.5}{300^2}=0.00005$$

Set-up on T.S.

Station	$L=$distance from T.S.	L^2	Deflection angle $\phi=\frac{L^2}{L_s{}^2}\times\frac{\theta_s}{3}=L^2\times0.00005$
T.S. $431+97.85$			
$432+00$	2.15	5	$0.000°=0°00'$
$432+50$	52.15	2720	$.136°=0°08'$
$433+00$	102.15	10450	$.522°=0°31'$
$433+50$	152.15	23150	$1.158°=1°09'$
$434+00$	202.15	40900	$2.045°=2°03'$
$434+50$	252.15	63600	$3.180°=3°11'$
S.C. $434+97.85$			$\dfrac{\theta_s}{3}=4.5=4°30'$

EXAMPLE 7.—*Computations where part of spiral is not visible from T.S.*

[Assume that all points ahead of $433+50$ in example 6 could not be seen from the T.S.]

$$D=\frac{152.15}{300}\times9°=4.565°$$

Set-up on $433+50$

Station	$L_1=$distance from $433+50$	$L_1{}^2$	ϕ for spiral $L_1{}^2\times0.00005$	ϕ for circular curve $\dfrac{L_1}{200}\times4.565$	Deflection angle ϕ
T.S. $431+97.85$	152.15	23150	$1.158°$	$3.475°$	$2.317°=2°19'$
$433+50$	0				
$434+00$	50	2500	$.125°$	$1.142°$	$1.267°=1°16'$
$434+50$	100	10000	$.500°$	$2.282°$	$2.782°=2°47'$
S.C. $434+97.85$	147.85	21850	$1.093°$	3.375	$4.468°=4°28'$

METHOD 3.—*Offsets from the tangent.*—To locate a transition by offsets from the tangent the x distances are measured from the T.S. along the main tangent and the corresponding perpendicular y distances are measured from these points. The x and y distances may be computed by first computing θ for each point,

$$\theta=\frac{L^2}{L_s{}^2}\times\theta_s$$

and then obtaining the x and y coefficients for θ for each point from table II. The x and y distances for each point are the products of the coefficients and the lengths along the transition from the T.S. as illustrated in example 8.

EXAMPLE 8.—*Computation of offsets from tangent*

Given: $D_c = 9°$ $L_s = 300$ $\theta_s = 13°30'$ T.S. at station $431+97.85$

$$\frac{\theta_s}{L_s^2} = \frac{13.5}{300^2} = 0.00015$$

Station	$L =$ distance from T.S.	L^2	$\theta = \frac{L^2}{L_s^2} \times \theta_s =$ $L^2 \times 0.00015$	Coordinates			
				x coef- ficient	x	y coef- ficient	y
T.S. 431+97.85							
432+00	2.15	5	0.00°	1.00000	2.15	0.00000	0.00
432+50	52.15	2720	.41	.99999	52.15	.00239	.12
433+00	102.15	10450	1.57	.99992	102.14	.00914	.93
433+50	152.15	23150	3.48	.99963	152.09	.02024	3.08
434+00	202.15	40900	6.13	.99885	201.92	.03563	7.21
434+50	252.15	63600	9.54	.99723	251.45	.05539	13.97
S.C. 434+97.85	300		13.50	.99446	298.34	.07823	23.47

METHOD 4.—*Offsets from the tangent and circular curve.*—In this method points on the first half of the spiral are located by offsets from the tangent, by method 3, and points on the second half are located by offsets from the circular curve carried back from the S.C. to the P.C. This is possible since the spiral leaves the circular curve at the same rate that it leaves the tangent and offsets from the circular curve are the same as from the tangent except that the x distances are measured along the circular curve from the S.C. The circular curve between the P.C. and the S.C. may be located from either end. If the spiral tangents or the spiral long chord (L.C.) are used to set the S.C. it may be easier to locate the circular curve from the S.C. The P.C. may also be set from the T.S. by the use of k and p from which point the circular curve may be located not only to the S.C. but beyond it.

An advantage of this method over method 3 is that the offsets are small. In example 9 the same data are used as in example 8. The largest offset is 2.82 feet as against 13.97 feet for method 3.

EXAMPLE 9.—*Computations of offsets from tangent and from circular curve* [1]

Given: $D_c=9°$ $L_s=300$ $\theta_s=13°30'$ T.S. at station 431+97.85

$$\frac{\theta_s}{L_s^2}=\frac{13.5}{300^2}=0.00015$$

Station of P.C. $431+97.85+\dfrac{300}{2}=433+47.85$

$p=0.01960$ (table II) $\times300=5.88$

$k=0.49908$ (table II) $\times300=149.72$

Tan angle T.S. to P.C. $=\dfrac{p}{k}=\dfrac{5.88}{149.72}=0.03927$ Angle$=2°15'$

Distance T.S. to P.C. $=k\div\cos$ of angle T.S. to P.C. $=149.72\div0.99923=149.84$

Station	L above line from T.S. below line from S.C.	L^2	$\theta=\dfrac{L^2}{L_s^2}\times\theta_s=$ $L^2\times0.00015$	Coordinates			
				x coefficient	x	y coefficient	y
T.S. 431+97.85							
432+00	2.15	5	0.00°	1.00000	2.15	0.00000	0.00
432+50	52.15	2720	.41	.99999	52.15	.00239	.12
433+00	102.15	10450	1.57	.99992	102.14	.00914	.93
433+50	147.85	21850	3.28			.01907	2.82
434+00	97.85	9580	1.44			.00838	.82
434+50	47.85	2290	.34			.00198	.09
S.C. 434+97.85							

[1] In using this method the x-distances, in most cases, may be made equal to L.

PARALLEL TRANSITIONS

Sometimes it is necessary to stake a line parallel to the center line of the roadway.   Generally this is done by offsets from the center line. When this is impractical the parallel line may be treated as a separate alinement with each circular curve concentric with the corresponding curve of the center line with a radius equal to the radius of the center line circular curve plus or minus the offset distance.   The value of p is the same as that of the center line and the P.C. of the circular curve produced is opposite that of the center line but the transition for a curve inside of the center line must be shorter due to the increase in D_c and the transition for a curve outside of the center line must be longer due to the decrease in D_c.   The length of transition may be found by trial, using the ratio of the values of D_c as a guide in choosing the length for first trial, as illustrated in example 10.

Example 10.—*Calculations for transition curve parallel to center line with transition. Calculations made with slide rule*

The following assumptions are those used in the example on page 19.

$L_s = 300$ feet, $D_c = 9°$, $R = 636.62$ feet.

$\theta_s = 13°30'$ and $p = 300 \times 0.01960$ (table II) $= 5.88$ feet.

Design a parallel line 30 feet inside the center line.

$R = 606.62$ $D_c = 9.45°$.

Try L_s a little larger than $\dfrac{9.00}{9.45} \times 300$.

Try $L_s = 290$ $\theta_s = 1.45 \times 9.45° = 13.70°$ $p = 290 \times 0.01989 = 5.76$.

Try $L_s = 292$ $\theta_s = 1.46 \times 9.45° = 13.80°$ $p = 292 \times 0.02003 = 5.85$.

Try $L_s = 293$ $\theta_s = 1.465 \times 9.45° = 13.84°$ $p = 293 \times 0.02009 = 5.89$ O.K.

The T.S. of the offset curve is forward of the T.S. of the center-line curve a distance equal to the difference of the k distances. For this example

k for center line $= 300 \times 0.49908$ (table II) $= 149.72$

k for offset line $= 293 \times 0.49903$ $= 146.22$

The resulting curve is very nearly but not exactly parallel to the center line and is as smooth and graceful in appearance as the center line with transition.

When pavements are widened on curves the inside edge may be given transition by the method illustrated in example 10 except that the throw, p, is the sum of the p of the center line and the widening of the pavement on the inside of the curve. This procedure results in a smooth curve without any break at the S.C. but a transition much longer than the center-line transition is required. The central circular portion and the tangents leading to the center line T.S. and S.T. must be long enough to permit inserting the extra length of transition.

TRANSITIONS FOR COMPOUND CURVES

GENERAL PROCEDURE

Transitions are used between curves of different radii to change gradually from one circular motion to another of greater or less degree and to permit a corresponding change in superelevation. The sharper curve must necessarily lie inside the flatter curve.

The length of transition required is the difference between the lengths required for changing from a longitudinal to a circular motion for each curve so that

$$L_s = 1.6\, \frac{V^3}{R_2} - 1.6\, \frac{V^3}{R_1}$$

where R_1 and R_2 represent the larger and smaller radii of the two curves Substituting $5{,}730 \div D$ for each radius there results

$$L_s = 1.6 V^3 \times \frac{(D_2 - D_1)}{5,730}$$

The last term of the equation is the reciprocal of the radius for a curve of a degree equal to the difference of the degrees of the two curves so that

$$L_s = 1.6 \frac{V^3}{R_a}$$

which is essentially the formula for the length of any transition except that R_a represents the radius of a curve of a degree equal to the difference between the degrees of the two curves.

To change gradually from the superelevation of one curve to that of another the slope of the outer edge of pavement with respect to the center line should not be steeper than 1 in 200 so that the minimum length of transition should be at least 200 times the difference between the full superelevation of the two curves.

The transition in superelevation may be effected by straight-line variation throughout the transition in curvature. While vertical curves are desirable wherever slopes are changed, the difference between the slope of the pavement edge and that of the center line is so small that generally changes without vertical curves are not noticeable. If desired, the effect of a vertical curve can be produced by eye adjustment of the stakes in the field.

Compounding two curves that differ in radius by more than 50 percent of the smaller radius results in a sudden change of curvature which is noticeable if the transition is omitted. A transition at least 100 feet long should be inserted. Where two curves differ in radius by less than 50 percent and the preceding methods of design result in transitions less than 100 feet long they may be omitted and such change in superelevation as may be required can be effected on the flatter curve.

As an illustration of methods recommended, assume a design speed of 40 miles per hour and that it is required to determine L_s for a transition between curves of 8° and 14°. For

$D = 14° - 8° = 6°$
$R = 955$ feet
$L_s = 1.6 \times \dfrac{40^3}{955} = 107$ feet

For a pavement 20 feet wide the difference in elevation between the center line and the edge of the fully superelevated section is (table I)

$(0.10 - 0.08) \times 10$ feet $= 0.2$ feet

$200 \times 0.2 =$ less than 107 feet $\therefore L_s = 107$ feet (minimum value).

If the change in curvature were from 4° to 10°, L_s, determined by the radius of a 6° curve, would be the same as above, namely, 107 feet (minimum value); but the rate of change of superelevation would govern, resulting in $L_s = (0.10 - 0.04) \times 10 \times 200 = 120$ feet (minimum value).

As another illustration, assume a design speed of 40 miles per hour and that a transition is to be provided between curves of 9° and 14°.

R for $D = 5° = 1,146$ feet

$$L_s = 1.6 \times \frac{40^3}{1,146} = 89 \text{ feet}$$

L_s required to effect change of superelevation in a 20-foot pavement is less than the above so that ordinarily a transition may be omitted. However, the radius of a 9° curve is more than 50 percent greater than the radius of a 14° curve and a transition at least 100 feet long should be inserted for appearance.

SYMBOLS FOR TRANSITIONS FOR COMPOUND CURVES

All subscripts 1 refer to the flatter curve and subscripts 2 to the sharper curve (fig. 3).

C.S.$_1$ and C.S.$_2$	Common points of curves and spiral. Curve spiral.
R_1 and R_2	Radii of the circular curves.
L_a	Length of transition C.S.$_1$ to C. S.$_2$.
I	Point of intersection of tangents at C.S.$_1$ and C.S.$_2$.
T_1 and T_2	Tangent distances C.S.$_1$ and C.S.$_2$ to I.
p_a	Offset distance between the circular curves produced at the common radius.
Δ_1 and Δ_2	Intersection angles between the tangents at C.S.$_1$ and C.S.$_2$ and the parallel tangents of the circular curves produced at the common radius.
D_1 and D_2	Degrees of curvature of the circular curves.
R_a	Radius of curve of degree $D_2 - D_1$.
θ_a	"Equivalent" spiral angle. (See text.)

DETAILS OF THE TRANSITION FOR COMPOUND CURVES

The transition connecting two curves of different radii has the same characteristics as a transition connecting a tangent and curve except that the degree of curve is the difference of the degrees of curvature of the circular curves.

Thus, if D_1 is the degree of curvature of the flatter curve and D_2 that of the sharper curve $\theta_a = \frac{L_a}{200} \times (D_2 - D_1)$. This is termed the "Equivalent" spiral angle since it is not the central angle of the actual spiral. The common radius bisects the spiral so that the actual central angle may be computed by adding the central angle for each curve for half the length of spiral

$$\Delta_1 = \frac{L_a}{200} \times D, \qquad \Delta_2 = \frac{L_a}{200} \times D_2$$

$$\Delta_1 + \Delta_2 = \frac{L_a}{200}(D_1 + D_2)$$

The equivalent spiral angle may be used in table II to find p_a, the offset between the two circular curves at the common radius.

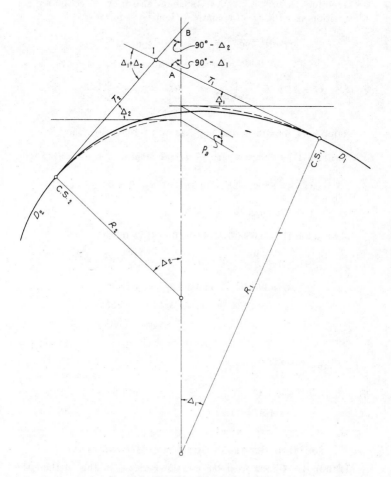

FIGURE 3.—Transition for compound curves.

Where compound curves are required the center line is often located without first establishing the normal tangents. To avoid the laborious work of adjusting the circular curves to permit insertion of transitions, allowance should be made for a transition at each change of curvature before proceeding with the circular curve ahead. At the P.C. and P.T. this may be done by means of the spiral tangents or long chord as heretofore described. Spiral tangents also may be computed for a transition at a P.C.C. of a compound curve as follows:

$$\Delta_1 = \frac{L_a}{200} \times D_1 \qquad \Delta_2 = \frac{L_a}{200} \times D_2$$

$$AB = R_2 \text{ exsec } \Delta_2 - R_1 \text{ exsec } \Delta_1 - p_a$$

$$AI = AB \times \frac{\cos \Delta_2}{\sin (\Delta_1 + \Delta_2)} \qquad BI = AB \times \frac{\cos \Delta_1}{\sin (\Delta_1 + \Delta_2)}$$

$$T_1 = R_1 \times \tan \Delta_1 + AI \qquad T_2 = R_2 \times \tan \Delta_2 - BI$$

Example 11 illustrates the application of these formulas.

EXAMPLE 11.—*Computations of spiral tangents for a transition at P.C.C.*

Given: $D_1 = 2° \ R_1 = 2864.79 \ D_2 = 6° \ R_2 = 954.93 \ L_a = 140$ feet.

$$\theta_a = \frac{140}{200} (6 - 2) = 2.8°$$

p_a (table II) $= 0.00406 \times 140 = 0.5684$ or 0.568

$$\Delta_1 = \frac{140}{200} \times 2° = 1.4° \qquad \Delta_2 = \frac{140}{200} \times 6° = 4.2°$$

$$AB = 954.93 \times \text{ exsec } 4.2° \quad = +2.571$$

$$-2864.79 \times \text{exsec } 1.4° = -0.855$$

$$-p_a = -0.568$$

$$+1.148 \qquad AB = 1.148$$

$$AI = 1.148 \times \frac{\cos 4.2°}{\sin 5.6°} = 11.73 \qquad BI = 1.148 \times \frac{\cos 1.4°}{\sin 5.6°} = 11.76$$

$$T_1 = 2864.79 \times \tan 1.4° = 70.01 \qquad T_2 = 954.93 \times \tan 4.2° = 70.13$$

$$+ AI = 11.73 \qquad\qquad\qquad - BI = 11.76$$

$$\overline{81.74} \qquad\qquad\qquad\qquad \overline{58.37}$$

LOCATING THE TRANSITION FOR COMPOUND CURVES

METHOD 1.—*Offsets from the circular curves.*—In this method the spiral is located by offsets from both circular curves which are located first. The offset at the midpoint of the spiral is $\frac{p_a}{2}$ and the offset at any other point is equal to $\frac{p_a}{2}$ multiplied by the cube of the proportion of the distance from the nearer C.S. Offsets from the sharper curve are, of course, outward and from the flatter curve inward.

METHOD 2.—*Deflection angles to even stations.*—When using this method the deflection angles may be computed in the same manner as for a set-up on an intermediate point of a spiral connecting tangent and circle. The deflections for a circular curve of the degree of curve at the point of set-up are first calculated. If set-up on C.S.$_1$, D_1 is the degree of curve, if set up on C.S.$_2$, D_2 is the degree of curve, and if set up on an intermediate point distance L from the C.S.$_1$, $D = D_1 + \dfrac{L}{L_a} \times (D_2 - D_1)$. If L is measured from the C.S.$_2$ of the sharper curve, $D = D_2 - \dfrac{L}{L_a} \times (D_2 - D_1)$. These formulas follow from the fact that the degree of curvature varies directly as the length of spiral beginning with D_1 at C.S.$_1$ and increasing uniformly to D_2 at C.S.$_2$

Spiral deflections computed in the same manner as for any other spiral using the equivalent spiral angle are then added to or subtracted from the circular curve deflections. They must be added if sighting toward the sharper curve and subtracted if sighting toward the flatter curve.

EXAMPLE 12.—*Computations for location of spiral by offsets from compound curve*

Given: $D_1 = 2°$ $D_2 = 6°$ $L_a = 140$ feet S.C.$_1$ at station $35 + 40.10$ and stations increasing towards S.C.$_2$

$$\theta_a = \frac{140}{200}\,(6 - 2) = 2.8°$$

From table II $p_a = 0.00406 \times 140 = 0.568$ $\dfrac{p_a}{2} = 0.284$

$$\frac{\dfrac{p_a}{2}}{\left[\dfrac{L_a}{2}\right]^3} = \frac{0.284}{343000} = 0.000000828$$

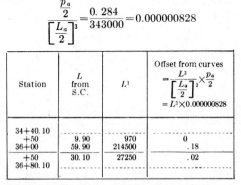

Station	L from S.C.	L^3	Offset from curves $= \dfrac{L^3}{\left[\dfrac{L_a}{2}\right]^3} \times \dfrac{p_a}{2}$ $= L^3 \times 0.000000828$
34+40.10	....	....	....
+50	9.90	970	0
36+00	59.90	214500	.18
+50	30.10	27250	.02
36+80.10	....	....	....

Offsets above line are measured inward from 2° curve.
Offsets below line are measured outward from 6° curve.

EXAMPLE 13.—*Computations for deflections to even stations from a set-up on C.S.₁ of the flatter curve*

Given: $D_1 = 2°$ $D_2 = 6°$ $L_a = 140$ feet. S.C.₁ at station 35+40.10 and stations increase towards S.C.₂

$$\theta_a = \frac{140}{200} (6-2) = 2.8°$$

$$\frac{1}{3} \times \frac{\theta_a}{L_a^2} = \frac{1}{3} \times \frac{2.8}{19,600} = 0.0000476$$

Set-up on S.C.₁

Station	L from S.C.₁	L^2	ϕ for spiral $= \dfrac{L^2}{L_a^2} \times \dfrac{\theta_a}{3}$ $= L^2 \times 0.0000476$	ϕ for $D = 2°$	Deflection angle ϕ
35+40.10					
+50	9.90	98	0	0.099°	0.099° = 0°06′
36+00	59.90	3,590	.171°	.599	.770 = 0°46′
+50	109.90	12,080	.575	1.099	1.674 = 1°40′
36+80.10	140.00	19,600	.933	1.400	2.333 = 2°20′

METHOD 3.—*Deflection angles to a 10- or 20-chord spiral.*—This method is similar to method 2 except that the spiral is divided into 10 or 20 equal parts and the spiral deflections which are added to or subtracted from the circular curve deflections are more easily computed by the use of the first column of either table VI or table VIII using the equivalent spiral angle. The first column, which gives deflections from a set-up on the T.S., is used regardless of the point of set-up since the spiral deflections desired are those from the T.S. of an equivalent simple transition. The circular curve deflections are computed for the curvature at the point of set-up as in method 2.

In examples 14 and 15 a 10-chord spiral is used. In example 14 the entire curve is visible from the S.C.₁ and in example 15 an intermediate set-up is required.

EXAMPLE 14.—*Computations of deflection angles for 10-chord spiral. Entire curve visible from S.C.₁*

Given: $D_1=2°$ $D_2=6°$ $L_a=140$ feet. S.C.₁ at station 35+40.10 and stations increase towards S.C.₂

$$\theta_a=\frac{140}{200}(6-2)=2.8°. \quad \text{Chord}=\frac{140}{10}=14.0 \text{ feet.}$$

ϕ for spiral computed by multiplying coefficients in first column of table VI by 2.8°.

Set-up on S.C.₁

Point	Station	L from S.C.₁	ϕ for spiral	ϕ for $D=2°$	Deflection angle ϕ
S.C ₁	35+40. 10				
1	+54. 10	14	0. 0033×2. 8=0. 009°	0. 140°	0. 149°=0°09′
2	+68. 10	28	. 0133×2. 8= . 037	. 280	. 317 =0°19′
3	+82. 10	42	. 0300×2. 8= . 084	. 420	. 504 =0°30′
4	+96. 10	56	. 0533×2. 8= . 149	. 560	. 709 =0°43′
5	36+10. 10	70	. 0833×2. 8= . 234	. 700	. 934 =0°56′
6	+24. 10	84	. 1200×2. 8= . 336	. 840	1. 176 =1°11′
7	+38. 10	98	. 1633×2. 8= . 457	. 980	1. 437 =1°26′
8	+52. 10	112	. 2133×2. 8= . 597	1. 120	1. 717 =1°43′
9	+66. 10	126	. 2700×2. 8= . 757	1. 260	2. 017 =2°01′
S.C.₂	36+80. 10	140	. 3333×2. 8= . 933	1. 400	2. 333 =2°20′

EXAMPLE 15.—*Same conditions as example 14 except that beyond point 6 curve cannot be seen from S.C.₁*

$$D \text{ at point } 6=2°+\frac{6}{10}(6°-2°)=4.4°$$

Set-up on point 6.

Point	Station	Points from point 6	L from point 6	ϕ for spiral	ϕ for $D=4.4°$	Deflection angle ϕ
S.C.	35+40. 10	6	84	0. 1200×2. 8=0. 336°	1. 850°	1. 514°=1°31′
6	36+24. 10	0	0	0	0	0
7	+38. 10	1	14	. 0033×2. 8= . 009°	. 308°	. 317°=0°19′
8	+52. 10	2	28	. 0133×2. 8= . 037	. 616	. 653 =0°39′
9	+66. 10	3	42	. 0300×2. 8= . 084	. 924	1. 008 =1°01′
S.C.₂	36+80. 10	4	56	. 0533×2. 8= . 149	1. 232	1. 381 =1°23′

ADJUSTING ALINEMENTS OF SIMPLE CURVES FOR TRANSITIONS

The practice of first projecting an alinement of simple curves and tangents and later adjusting it to permit insertion of transitions is not recommended: This method is not only laborious but may upset the original design, especially if long transitions are necessary. Shifting the center of the simple curve appreciably or changing its degree is required. Additional difficulties are encountered if the length of tangent between simple curves is too short to permit insertion of transitions.

Some of these difficulties may be alleviated to some extent by mentally making allowances in the initial field work or paper projection for the future insertion of transitions. Allowance may be made for an increase in the tangent distance of a simple curve by an amount approximately equal to distance k, which is closely one-half the length of the transition. Allowance may be made for an increase in the external distance by an amount equal to the throw, p, if the center of the simple curve is retained and the radius reduced to permit insertion of the transitions. If the radius of the simple curve is retained and the curve shifted bodily, the allowance for an increase in the external distance is $p \div \cos \dfrac{\Delta}{2}$.

In adjusting simple curves to permit insertion of transitions the following cases are encountered frequently:

(a) *Simple curve, equal transitions.*—If the radius of the curve is unchanged in length, p and k may be computed directly by the use of table II and the center moved bodily along the bisector of the central angle an amount equal to $p \div \cos \dfrac{\Delta}{2}$. This also represents the increase in E_s. The increase in $T_s = k + p \tan \dfrac{\Delta}{2}$.

If the center of the curve is retained the radius must be reduced, generally, resulting in an odd value of D_c. In this case p is computed for the revised D_c and the desired L_s. It must equal the decrease in the radius. If it does not a new radius is tried. Trial and error may be reduced by first computing p for the original D_c and desired L_s and using it as a guide in reducing the radius. When p, D_c, and L_s conform to one another k may be computed. E_s is increased by an amount equal to p. T_s is increased by an amount equal to k.

(b) *Simple curve, unequal transitions.*—If the radius of the curve is retained, p and k may be computed for each transition and the center of the curve moved until the P.C. and P.T. are off-set from the respective tangents by distances equal to the respective values of p. This adjustment may be made by first moving the center of curve perpendicular to the tangent at the P.C. an amount equal to p for the transition at the P.C. and then moving the center of curve parallel to the same tangent until the P.T. of the curve is offset from its tangent a distance equal to the corresponding p. The amount of the second shift may be found by geometry to be equal to $\dfrac{p_2 - p_1 \cos \Delta}{\sin \Delta}$ in which p_1 is the p-distance at the P.C. and p_2 the p-distance at the P.T. If Δ is greater than $90°$ it should be recognized that the cosine is negative, making the expression above the line a sum instead of a difference. The change in each T_s may be computed readily, but the change in E_s which is not required to the nearest hundredth of a foot may be more readily measured from a scaled lay-out.

Where unequal transitions are necessary the center of the curve cannot be retained. It may be retained temporarily and the radius adjusted to fit the p and L_s at the P.C. after which the p at the P.T. may be computed. The center of the circle must then be moved parallel to the tangent at the P.C. until the P.T. is offset from its tangent a distance equal to the corresponding p. The amount of this movement may be found by geometry to be equal to $\dfrac{p_2 - p_1}{\sin \Delta}$ in which p_1 is the p-distance at the P.C. and p_2 the p-distance at the P.T. If the result is positive the center of the curve is moved away from the P.I. If it is negative the center of curve is moved closer to the P.I.

(c) *Compound curves.*—Laborious geometry is required to adjust an alinement of tangents and compound circular curves to permit inserting transitions at the P.C., P.T., and each P.C.C. The curves must be adjusted so that each curve is offset from each tangent a distance equal to the corresponding p and the circular curves at each P.C.C. are separated by a distance equal to the corresponding p_a with the sharper curve inside the flatter curve. Care must be exercised in choosing transitions to see that they do not overlap.

One method of adjusting compound curves to permit insertion of transitions is to retain the degrees of curvature of all curves, calculate the offset distances p and p_a and adjust all centers of circles starting at one main tangent and proceeding around to the other. This may best be illustrated by assuming an alinement consisting of two main tangents between which are three circular compound curves which may be labeled A, B, and C, curve A being adjacent to the P.C. and curve C adjacent to the P.T. The steps are as follows:

(1) Move centers of all curves perpendicular to the tangent at the P.C. a distance equal to the distance p for the transition at the P.C.

(2) Move centers of curves B and C parallel to the common radius for curves A and B a distance equal to the distance p_a at that P.C.C.

(3) Move center of curve C parallel to the common radius for curves B and C a distance equal to the distance p_a at that P.C.C.

(4) Calculate the new position of the P.T. with respect to the tangent at the P.T. in view of all shifts made thus far. A scale diagram of the shifts aids considerably.

(5) Move all centers parallel to the tangent at the P.C. until the P.T. is offset from its tangent a distance equal to the corresponding p.

The amount of this move may be found by geometry to be $\dfrac{p_2 \pm d}{\sin \Delta}$ in which p_2 is the p-distance at the P.T. and d is the perpendicular distance from the P.T. to the tangent found by step (4). The plus sign is used when the P.T. prior to this move falls outside the tangent and the minus sign is used when it falls inside the tangent.

The change in each T_s may be computed readily but the change in E_s may be found more readily by scale from a drawing. Trial and error methods are not used in adjusting compound curves as outlined above. If, however, this procedure results in an unsatisfactory position of the center line and a shift is required by changing one or more radii, trial and error may be required to fit the alinement to the location desired.

(d) *Reverse curves separated by tangent.*—When simple curves of opposite direction are separated by a tangent, each curve may be treated as a separate problem and adjusted to permit insertion of a transition between it and the fixed tangent. It may be impracticable, however, to move or change the radii of the curves. With this condition imposed, space for inserting transitions may be provided by lengthening both curves so that the tangents at the new P.C. of one curve and new P.T. of the other are parallel to each other and a distance apart equal to the sum of the p-distances for both transitions. The problem and its solution are shown in figure 4.

(e) *Simple curves separated by tangent (broken back curves).*—Simple curves in the same direction separated by a tangent should be avoided as dangerous since many drivers will not expect successive curves in the same direction. Also, when both curves and tangent are visible at one time they are particularly unsightly. If a transition is inserted between each curve and the tangent some improvement results but a more effective method is to connect both curves by another curve. The radius of the connecting curve then may be increased to provide a distance, p_a, at each P.C.C. for the insertion of transitions. The problem is simplified by assuming a value for the radius of the connecting curve. The solution is shown in figure 5.

WIDENING PAVEMENTS ON CURVES

Extra width of pavement is provided on curves because a vehicle or train of vehicles occupies extra width and because it is difficult to keep vehicles to the center of the occupied lane. Minimum required sight distance has also been offered as a reason for providing extra width, but this might better be provided by removing obstacles outside the pavement limits.

When a vehicle travels on a curve at the speed at which the effects of superelevation counteract exactly all centrifugal force, no friction in a radial direction occurs, the rear axle is radial, and the rear wheels track inside the front wheels. At greater speeds friction is required to counteract centrifugal force and the rear wheels assume a position farther out in order to provide the "slip angle" necessary to develop the required friction. As the speed is increased a point is approached where the rear wheels track outside the front wheels.

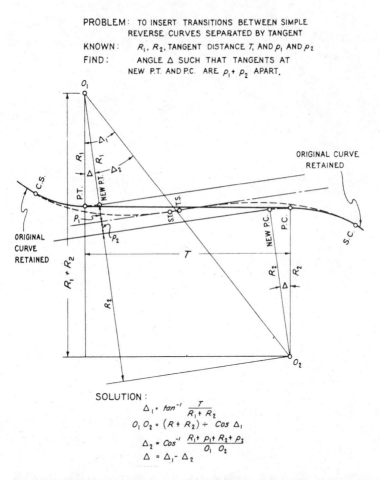

PROBLEM: TO INSERT TRANSITIONS BETWEEN SIMPLE REVERSE CURVES SEPARATED BY TANGENT

KNOWN: R_1, R_2, TANGENT DISTANCE T, AND p_1 AND p_2

FIND: ANGLE Δ SUCH THAT TANGENTS AT NEW P.T. AND P.C. ARE $p_1 + p_2$ APART.

SOLUTION:

$$\Delta_1 = \tan^{-1} \frac{T}{R_1 + R_2}$$

$$O_1 O_2 = (R + R_2) \div \cos \Delta_1$$

$$\Delta_2 = \cos^{-1} \frac{R_1 + p_1 + R_2 + p_2}{O_1 O_2}$$

$$\Delta = \Delta_1 - \Delta_2$$

FIGURE 4.—Transitions for reverse curves. Sum of both spiral lengths for which p_1 and p_2 are calculated should be somewhat less than twice the original tangent distance T or S.T. and T.S. will overlap.

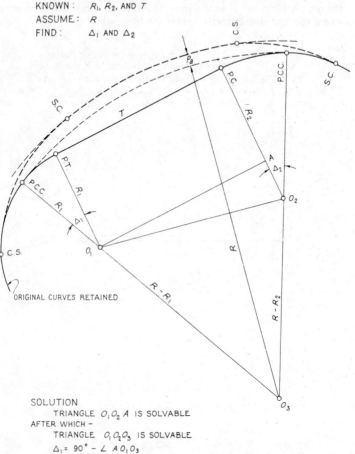

PROBLEM: TO SUBSTITUTE TRIPLE COMPOUND CURVE FOR
A BROKEN BACK CURVE HOLDING ORIGINAL CURVES,
THEN INCREASING R TO INSERT TRANSITIONS

KNOWN: R_1, R_2, AND T

ASSUME: R

FIND: Δ_1 AND Δ_2

ORIGINAL CURVES RETAINED

SOLUTION
TRIANGLE $O_1 O_2 A$ IS SOLVABLE
AFTER WHICH —
TRIANGLE $O_1 O_2 O_3$ IS SOLVABLE
$\Delta_1 = 90° - \angle A O_1 O_3$
$\Delta_2 = 180° - \angle A O_2 O_3$

FIGURE 5.—Transitions for broken back curves.

Trailers are usually pulled with flexible connections so that, at speeds
at which the effects of superelevation counteract all centrifugal force,
the trailer wheels track inside the rear wheels of the tractor, adding to

the extra width required. As the speed is increased the trailer assumes positions farther out on the curve to a point where it may line up with the driving vehicle and at excessive speeds the longitudinal axes of the driving vehicle and trailer may form a bend opposite to the curve of the road. Certain conditions, such as a piece of rough pavement or jerks on the tongue of the trailer, tend to correct this tendency to slip outwards for short periods of time resulting in the "whipping" action noted when trailers travel at high speeds. This whipping action is further increased with an increase in the number of trailers. Improvements in couplings, springs, etc., have decreased this tendency and further improvements may be expected. On icy pavements the small friction factor requires a large slip angle to develop the required frictional resistance so that the positions assumed by the rear wheels of the driving vehicle and the trailer wheels tend to be farther out than when traveling at the same speeds on rougher pavements.

The committee on road design of the American Association of State Highway Officials recommends the following formula for computing the widening for a two-lane pavement,

$$W = 2[R - \sqrt{R^2 - L^2}] + \frac{35}{\sqrt{R}}$$

in which L is the wheel base of the vehicle in feet. A value of 20 feet for L is recommended by the committee.

By simple geometry $R - \sqrt{R^2 - L^2}$ represents the additional width required for each lane because the rear wheels track inside the front wheels when the speed of the vehicle in rounding the curve is that for which the pavement is superelevated. The use of 20 feet for L appears to be reasonable in view of the fact that the wheelbases of less than 10 percent of all busses manufactured in 1931 to 1937, inclusive, exceeded 20 feet in length and practically no 1937 trucks exceeded this dimension. Of 583 commercial vehicles of various makes and body types described in the July 1935 issue of the Commercial Car Journal only 11 had a wheelbase exceeding 20 feet and but 1 exceeded 21 feet.

Other factors affecting widening pavements on curves cannot be evaluated readily. At low speeds slippage of rear wheels increases the extra width occupied by a vehicle and trailer wheels track farther inside the rear wheels of the pulling vehicle than when traveling at the speed for which the effects of superelevation exactly counteract all centrifugal force. These extra widths, however, are small compared to the extra width required because of the difficulty of keeping a vehicle to the center of the occupied lane at high speeds, and due to the sideslip of the rear wheels and trailer wheels at high speeds to develop the friction necessary to counteract centrifugal force. It may be stated, however, that the required extra widths as described increase with an increase in speed. It is therefore suggested that the second half of the expression for widening, which was probably based on a design speed of 35 miles per hour, be changed to $\dfrac{V}{\sqrt{R}}$ resulting in the following formula,

$$W = n[R - \sqrt{R^2 - 400}] + \frac{V}{\sqrt{R}}$$

in which n represents the number of lanes and V represents the speed in miles per hour.

Theoretically the entire expression should be multiplied by the number of lanes but it has been arbitrarily restricted to the first part of the expression due to the improbability of more than two large trucks or trains of trucks and trailers passing each other at the same time.

Present practice regarding the degree of curvature below which no widening is required varies between 5° and 8°. It is suggested that no pavement requiring less than 2 feet of widening in accordance with the above formula be widened. This results in no widening on two-lane pavements on curves flatter than 4° for 70 miles per hour, 5° for 60 miles per hour, 6° for 50 miles per hour, 7° for 40 miles per hour, and 8° for 30 miles per hour.

Table IX shows widening for pavements on curves to the nearest foot. For simplicity the table is limited to one column for two-lane pavements and one column for four-lane pavements, the speed used in each case being the maximum of the assumed design speeds used herein for each degree of curvature. The lower values resulting when computing widening for some of the curvatures at lower speeds are lost when rounding to the nearest foot.

Tests and observations of driving habits indicate that for safe and comfortable driving a traffic lane should be at least 11 feet wide. It is not intended to delve into this subject in this discussion but to point out that the table of widening is reasonable for pavements 22 feet and 44 feet wide for two and four lanes, respectively. If wider lanes are adopted the figures in the table should be reduced by the standard widths in excess of 22 and 44 feet. Likewise if lanes narrower than 11 feet are used, the figures in the table should be increased by the amounts 22 and 44 feet are in excess of the standard widths.

Under existing practice where transitions are either not used at all or if used are often entirely too short, widening on curves is always placed entirely on the inside. This is usually combined with some form of gradual change from the standard width to create, in effect, a short transition.

Widening may be placed entirely on the inside where the curves are properly transitioned. A separate transition may be designed as described on page 32. The widening may also be effected by making the widening zero at the T.S. and a maximum at the S.C. or at the S.C.S. of a curve transitional throughout. The widening at intermediate points may be proportional to the distances from the T.S. Maximum widening should be used for the entire length of the circular portion of the curve. In the field the normal center line is first located and the edges of pavement located from it by perpendicular distances which are equal to half the standard width of pavement for the outside edge and half the standard width of pavement plus the widening for the inside edge. The actual center line of the pavement will fall inside the normal center line. It may be located from the normal center line by perpendicular distances equal to half the widening. This method results in smooth curves for the edges of pavement except at the S.C. and more especially at the S.C.S. of a curve transitional throughout where a break at the inside edge of the pavement may be noticeable. This may be remedied, however, by making the widening at this point the mean of the computed widening 20 feet or so each side of the point or by eye adjustments of the stakes or forms in the field.

Where curves are properly transitioned widening may be divided equally on both sides of the normal center line. This results in a slight reduction in the length of transition for the outer half of the pavement but this is not important where adequate transition lengths are used. As in the case of applying widening entirely on the inside, widening may be made zero at the T.S., a maximum at the S.C. or at the S.C.S., and proportional to the distances from the T.S. at intermediate points. Maximum widening should be used for the entire length of circular curve. In the field the normal center line is first located and the edges of pavement located from it by perpendicular distances which, for both edges of pavement, are half the normal width of pavement plus half the widening. Breaks may be noticed at both the inside and outside edges of pavement at the S.C. or S.C.S. but they are much less noticeable than the break at the inside edge where the entire widening is applied on the inside.

Where the widening is divided evenly on both sides of the normal center line a reverse curve will result for the outer edge of pavement near the T.S. This should be avoided by extending the tangent on the outer edge of pavement past the T.S. to a point where the curve falls inside of it. In field practice this can be done when locating the outer edge of pavement by moving any stakes which fall outside the tangent produced in to this line. The loss in widening near the T.S. will be negligible and the break at the point where the tangent produced meets the curve of the outer edge of pavement will be imperceptible.

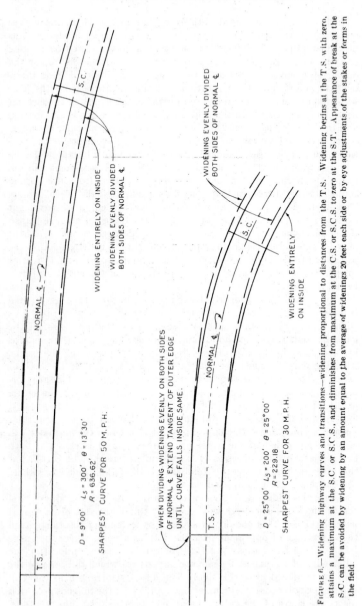

FIGURE 6.—Widening highway curves and transitions—widening proportional to distances from the T.S. Widening begins at the T.S. with zero, attains a maximum at the S.C. or S.C.S., and diminishes from maximum at the C.S. or S.C.S. to zero at the S.T. Appearance of break at the S.C. can be avoided by widening by an amount equal to the average of widenings 20 feet each side or by eye adjustments of the stakes or forms in the field.

Figure 6 shows both methods of widening for the sharpest permissible circular curves and the shortest transitions for these curves for assumed design speeds of 30 and 50 miles per hour.

RIGHT-OF-WAY LINES IN RELATION TO TRANSITIONS

There are three general methods of purchasing and describing right-of-way for highway improvements: (1) By purchasing irregular areas and describing the enclosing right-of-way lines by metes and bounds referenced to existing property lines, (2) by purchasing to right-of-way lines parallel to and at designated distances from the highway center line and referencing them to the center line, and (3) by purchasing to right-of-way lines parallel to and at designated distances from the highway center line and describing the right-of-way lines by metes and bounds.

(1) This method is not affected by transitions. Generally the required right-of-way is marked by monuments and the described area tied in to existing property lines.

(2) This method requires no special treatment due to the use of transitions. If the plans of the State highway department define the transition as a curve in which the degree of curve (arc definition) varies as the distance from the beginning of the transition, the center line is located definitely by the usual information shown on the plans.

(3) Right-of-way lines parallel to a center line that consists of tangents and curves with transitions cannot readily be described by metes and bounds; and if a description of this character is desired, it is necessary to substitute a center line consisting of tangents and simple compound curves, which at no point will vary materially from the established center line. When the substitute center line is established, right-of-way lines may be handled by the same methods used for any alinement consisting of tangents and simple curves.

A substitute center line may be fixed by replacing each transition with a curve of constant radius tangent to the normal tangent and compounded with the central circular curve at the S.C. which becomes the P.C.C. The calculations for each substitute curve are relatively simple, the central angle being θ_s and the tangent distance being equal to the short tangent of the transition The radius may be computed by the formula $R = S.T. \div \tan \frac{\theta_s}{2}$

The station of the P.C. may be computed by adding to the station of the T.S. the difference between the long tangent and the short tangent of the transition as illustrated in example 16.

EXAMPLE 16.—*Method of substituting simple curves for transitions for purposes of describing right-of-way*

$D_c = 9°$, $L_s = 300$ feet, L.T. = 200.58, S.T. = 100.53
$\theta_s = 13°30'$ and station of T.S. = 431+97.85
R of substitute curve = 100.53 ÷ tan 6°45′ = 849.37.
Station of P.C. = 431+97.85+(200.58−100.53) = 432+97.90

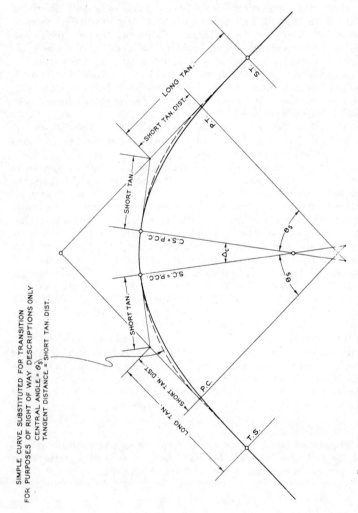

SIMPLE CURVE SUBSTITUTED FOR TRANSITION
FOR PURPOSES OF RIGHT OF WAY DESCRIPTIONS ONLY
CENTRAL ANGLE = θ_S
TANGENT DISTANCE = SHORT TAN. DIST.

FIGURE 7.—A method of substituting simple curves for transitions for purposes of right-of-way descriptions.

Figure 7 shows the suggested method for substituting constant radius curves for transitions. The simplicity of this method is counterbalanced by the fact that, for long transitions and relatively sharp curves, the central portion of each substitute curve of constant radius may be a few feet outside the normal transition center line. For the maximum curvature of 25° used in the accompanying tables for transition lengths of 150, 200, 250, 300, 350, and 400 feet the central portion of the substitute curve falls outside the transition maximum distances of about 1, 2, 3, 5, 6, and 8 feet, respectively. For a transition 500 feet long and a curve of 20°, the maximum shown for that length, the maximum distance is about 9 feet and for a transition 600 feet long and a curve of 16° the maximum distance is about 10 feet. Account may have to be taken of such conditions in some cases when deciding on the distance from the substitute center line to the proposed right-of-way line, increasing the distance on the inside and decreasing it on the outside of the curve. Any variation in this distance should be confined to the limits of each substitute curve and is not required for the tangent or for the central circular curve portion of the normal center line.

Where curves are transitional throughout the same method may be used resulting in a single curve of constant radius.

TABLES

EXPLANATION OF TABLES

Table I.—S is the recommended superelevation slope. Up to the practical maximum of 0.10 foot per foot S is sufficient for its effect to counteract all centrifugal force when a vehicle travels at three-quarters of the assumed design speed.

L_s is the recommended minimum transition length in feet. Lengths shown are at least sufficient to limit rate of approaching centrifugal acceleration to 2 feet per second cubed and to limit slope of outer edge of two-lane pavement with respect to the center line to 1 in 150 for 30 miles per hour, 175 for 40 miles per hour, and 200 for higher assumed speeds.

Curves sharper than those for which values are shown are considered unsafe for the respective assumed speeds. Friction, in addition to the effects of superelevation, required to counteract centrifugal force would be greater than that represented by a factor of 0.16 for speeds up to 60 miles per hour and 0.14 for 70 miles per hour.

Table II.—p, k, x, y, L.T., S.T., and L.C. are shown for a transition 1 foot long. To obtain the lengths for any transition multiply the values shown adjacent to the corresponding θ by the length of transition. If θ is any value other than an even 0.1° lengths may be obtained by interpolation with negligible error. x and y at any point distance L

from the T.S. may be obtained in a similar manner by computing θ at the point and multiplying the values adjacent to θ by L.

$$\theta_s = \frac{L_s D_c}{200} \qquad \theta = \left(\frac{L}{L_s}\right)^2 \theta_s$$

Table III.—T_s and E_s are shown for curves transitional throughout in which each transition is 1 foot long. To obtain the lengths for any curve transitional throughout multiply the values adjacent to the corresponding Δ by the length of each transition. If Δ is any value other than an even degree lengths may be obtained by interpolation with negligible error.

If the location of the highway is controlled by a T_s or E_s distance and a curve transitional throughout is desired, L_s to fit may be computed by dividing T_s or E_s by the corresponding value in the table adjacent to the measured Δ, interpolating if necessary.

Table IV.—Each page shows T_s and E_s for various combinations of L_s and D_c for one value of Δ. All combinations above and to the right of a zigzag line, indicating an assumed design speed, are safe for that speed or a higher speed. In addition to the assumed design speed highway location is controlled generally by an approximate E_s or T_s or both. To find the combination of D_c and L_s which fits, turn to the table for that value of Δ nearest to the measured Δ and from the area above and to the right of the zigzag line representing the assumed design speed, choose a combination such that the T_s or E_s or both shown are as close as possible to the value or values which control the location.

If the measured Δ is in even degrees T_s and E_s are read without computations. If the measured Δ is not in even degrees T_s and E_s may be interpolated between the values in the two nearest tables for the same combinations of D_c and L_s with negligible error. Thus if the measured Δ is $21°14'$ and the table for $\Delta = 21°$ shows that the combination of $D_c = 5°$ and $L_s = 300$ feet very nearly fits conditions, T_s may be interpolated between 362.90 taken from the table for $\Delta = 21°$ and 373.29 taken from the table for $\Delta = 22°$ resulting in $T_s = 365.32$ feet. When interpolating, D_c and L_s remain unchanged, the variation in Δ being taken up in Δ_c.

T_s, being given to the nearest 0.01 foot, may be subtracted from the station of the P.I. to obtain the station of the T.S. The functions of the chosen transition may be read directly from table V and the transition may be located with the aid of tables V, VI, or VIII.

$$\theta_s = \frac{L_s D_c}{200} \text{ or it may be read directly from table V.}$$

$$\Delta_c = \Delta - 2\theta_s$$

Table V.—The functions of the transitions for the various combinations of D_c and L_s shown in table IV may be read directly, each page covering one value of L_s. After the T.S. is established by the use of T_s obtained from table IV the S.C. may be located by means of x_c and y_c or L.T., S.T., and θ_s or L.C. and ϕ_s. ϕ_s may be obtained directly from the right page of table V, being the deflection angle from the T.S. to point 10, the S.C.

The right page of table V shows deflection angles for the transitions for the various combinations of D_c and L_s, shown in table IV. The deflections are from the T.S. to points on the transition obtained by dividing L_s into 10 equal chords, each chord being equal to the length of arc for all practical purposes.

Deflection angles to stations other than chord points may be obtained by interpolation with very small error. These small errors may be practically eliminated by subtracting from the interpolated value the value in column A in minutes for each foot of the distance from the station to the nearest chord point.

Table VI.—Deflection angles from any chord point to any other chord point on a transition divided into 10 equal chords, each chord being equal to the length of arc for all practical purposes, may be obtained by multiplying the factors in this table by θ_s. This method is especially useful when locating a transition which is not entirely visible from the T.S. and intermediate set-ups are necessary. It may be advisable sometimes to set up on an S.C. or C.S. and locate a transition and the circular curve portion from the same set-up. Deflection angles from the S.C. or C.S. (point 10) may be computed using the last column of factors.

Corrections are rarely necessary since results to the nearest minute are close enough for all practical purposes. Corrections, when desired, may be read from table VII after computing θ for the point of set-up, θ being the product of θ_s and the factor between the zigzag lines on the sides of table VI.

Table VII.—Corrections in minutes are shown for various values of θ in the formula $\phi = \dfrac{\theta}{3} - C$.

Table VIII.—This table is similar to table VI except that the transition is divided into 20 equal lengths or chords.

Table IX.—This table shows recommended widening of pavements for various degrees of curvature for two-lane and four-lane pavements.

Table X.—This table shows maximum degrees of curvature considered safe for various combinations of rate of superelevation, S, and speed, V, based on the relation,

$$S + F = \frac{0.067\ V^2}{R}$$

The friction factor F used in each case is that considered safe for the assumed design speed and is shown at the head of each column.

Table X bears no direct relation to the tables for transitions. It is included to show, directly, the relation between the various factors entering into the design of circular curves. This table may be used, also, to determine safe speeds on existing curves.

Extensions of tables IV and V for values of D_c of 26° to 38°, inclusive, for $L_s = 150$, 200, and 250 feet will be found in the appendix.

D_c	R	30 mph		40 mph		50 mph		60 mph		70 mph	
		S	L_s	S	L_s	S	L_s	S	L_s	S	L_s
1-00	5729.58	0	0	0	0	0	0	0	0	0	0
1-30	3819.72	.01	150	.02	150	.02	150	.04	150	.05	150
2-00	2864.79	.01	"	.02	"	.03	"	.05	150	.06	200
2-30	2291.83	.01	"	.03	"	.04	"	.06	150	.08	250
3-00	1909.86	.02	"	.03	"	.05	"	.07	200	.09	300
3-30	1637.02	.02	"	.04	"	.06	"	.08	200	.10	350
4	1432.39	.02	"	.04	"	.06	"	.09	250	.10	400
5	1145.92	.03	"	.05	"	.08	150	.10	300		
6	954.93	.03	"	.06	"	.10	200	.10	350		
7	818.51	.04	"	.07	"	.10	250				
8	716.20	.05	"	.08	"	.10	300				
9	636.62	.05	"	.09	150	.10	300				
10	572.96	.06	"	.10	200						
11	520.87	.06	"	"	200						
12	477.46	.07	"	"	200						
13	440.74	.07	"	"	250						
14	409.26	.08	"	.10	250						
15	381.97	.09	"								
16	358.10	.09	"								
17	337.03	.10	"								
18	318.31	"	"								
19	301.56	"	"								
20	286.48	"	"								
21	272.84	"	"								
22	260.44	"	"								
23	249.11	"	150								
24	238.73	"	200								
25	229.18	.10	200								

RECOMMENDED SUPERELEVATIONS ft/foot AND MINIMUM TRANSITION LENGTHS TABLE I

Table II — Functions of Transition for $L_s=1$

θ	p	k	χ	y	L.T.	S.T.	L.C.	θ
0.0	.00000	.50000	1.00000	.00000	.66667	.33333	1.00000	0.0
.1	015	000	1.00000	058	67	33	1.00000	.1
.2	029	000	1.00000	116	67	34	1.00000	.2
.3	044	000	.99999	175	67	34	1.00000	.3
.4	058	000	999	233	67	34	1.00000	.4
.5	073	000	999	291	67	34	1.00000	.5
.6	088	000	999	349	67	34	1.00000	.6
.7	102	000	998	407	68	34	.99999	.7
.8	117	000	998	465	68	34	.99999	.8
0.9	.00131	.50000	.99997	.00524	.66668	.33334	.99999	0.9
1.0	.00146	.49999	.99997	.00582	.66668	.33334	.99999	1.0
.1	161	999	996	640	68	35	98	.1
.2	175	999	995	698	68	35	98	.2
.3	190	999	995	756	69	35	98	.3
.4	204	999	994	814	69	35	97	.4
.5	219	999	993	873	69	36	97	.5
.6	233	999	992	931	69	36	97	.6
.7	248	998	991	.00989	70	36	96	.7
.8	262	998	990	.01047	70	37	96	.8
1.9	.00277	.49998	.99989	.01105	.66671	.33337	.99995	1.9
2.0	.00291	.49998	.99988	.01163	.66671	.33337	.99995	2.0
.1	305	998	987	222	71	38	94	.1
.2	320	997	985	280	72	38	93	.2
.3	334	997	984	338	72	39	93	.3
.4	349	997	982	396	73	39	92	.4
.5	363	997	981	454	73	39	92	.5
.6	377	996	979	512	74	40	91	.6
.7	392	996	978	571	75	40	90	.7
.8	406	996	976	629	75	41	90	.8
2.9	.00421	.49996	.99975	.01687	.66676	.33341	.99989	2.9
3.0	.00435	.49995	.99973	.01745	.66676	.33342	.99988	3.0
.1	450	995	971	803	77	43	87	.1
.2	464	994	969	861	78	43	86	.2
.3	479	994	967	919	78	44	85	.3
.4	493	994	965	.01978	79	45	84	.4
.5	508	994	963	.02036	80	45	83	.5
.6	523	993	961	094	81	46	82	.6
.7	537	993	958	152	81	47	81	.7
.8	552	993	956	210	82	47	80	.8
3.9	.00566	.49992	.99953	.02268	.66683	.33348	.99979	3.9
4.0	.00581	.49992	.99951	.02326	.66684	.33349	.99978	4.0
.1	596	991	948	384	85	50	77	.1
.2	610	991	946	443	86	50	76	.2
.3	625	991	943	501	86	51	75	.3
.4	639	990	941	559	87	52	74	.4
.5	654	990	938	617	88	53	73	.5
.6	669	989	935	675	89	54	71	.6
.7	683	989	932	733	90	55	70	.7
.8	698	988	930	791	91	56	69	.8
4.9	.00712	.49988	.99927	.02849	.66692	.33357	.99967	4.9
5.0	.00727	.49987	.99924	.02907	.66693	.33358	.99966	5.0

Coef X lgm. spiral .

θ	p	k	χ	y	L.T.	S.T.	L.C.	θ
5.0	.00727	.49987	.99924	.02907	.66693	.33358	.99966	5.0
.1	742	987	921	.02965	694	359	965	.1
.2	756	986	918	.03023	696	360	963	.2
.3	771	986	914	082	697	361	962	.3
.4	785	985	911	140	698	362	961	.4
.5	800	985	908	198	699	363	959	.5
.6	814	984	904	256	700	364	958	.6
.7	829	984	901	314	701	365	956	.7
.8	843	983	897	372	703	366	954	.8
5.9	.00858	.49983	.99894	.03430	.66704	.33367	.99953	5.9
6.0	.00872	.49982	.99890	.03488	.66705	.33368	.99951	6.0
.1	887	981	886	546	706	369	950	.1
.2	901	981	882	604	708	371	948	.2
.3	916	980	879	662	709	372	946	.3
.4	930	979	875	720	710	373	944	.4
.5	945	979	871	778	712	374	943	.5
.6	960	978	867	836	713	376	941	.6
.7	974	977	863	894	715	377	939	.7
.8	989	976	859	.03952	716	378	937	.8
6.9	.01003	.49976	.99855	.04010	.66717	.33380	.99936	6.9
7.0	.01018	.49975	.99851	.04068	.66719	.33381	.99934	7.0
.1	033	974	846	126	720	382	932	.1
.2	047	973	842	184	722	384	930	.2
.3	062	973	838	242	724	385	928	.3
.4	076	972	833	300	725	386	926	.4
.5	091	971	829	358	727	388	924	.5
.6	105	970	824	416	728	389	922	.6
.7	120	969	819	474	730	391	920	.7
.8	134	969	815	532	732	392	918	.8
7.9	.01149	.49968	.99810	.04590	.66733	.33394	.99916	7.9
8.0	.01163	.49967	.99805	.04648	.66735	.33395	.99913	8.0
.1	178	966	800	706	737	397	911	.1
.2	192	965	795	764	738	399	909	.2
.3	207	965	790	822	740	400	907	.3
.4	221	964	785	879	742	402	904	.4
.5	236	963	780	937	744	403	902	.5
.6	250	962	775	.04995	745	405	900	.6
.7	265	961	770	.05053	747	407	897	.7
.8	279	961	764	.05111	749	409	895	.8
8.9	.01294	.49960	.99759	.05169	.66751	.33410	.99893	8.9
9.0	.01308	.49959	.99754	.05227	.66753	.33412	.99890	9.0
.1	323	958	748	285	755	414	888	.1
.2	337	957	742	342	757	416	885	.2
.3	352	956	737	400	759	417	883	.3
.4	366	955	731	458	761	419	880	.4
.5	381	954	725	516	763	421	878	.5
.6	395	953	719	574	765	423	875	.6
.7	410	952	713	632	767	425	873	.7
.8	424	951	708	690	769	427	870	.8
9.9	.01439	.49950	.99702	.05747	.66771	.33428	.99867	9.9
10.0	.01453	.49949	.99696	.05805	.66773	.33430	.99865	10.0

10°-15°	TABLE II - FUNCTIONS OF TRANSITION FOR L_s = 1							
θ	p	k	x	y	L.T.	S.T.	L.C.	θ
10.0	.01453	.49949	.99696	.05805	.66773	.33430	.99865	10.0
.1	468	948	690	863	776	432	862	.1
.2	482	947	684	921	778	434	859	.2
.3	497	946	677	.05978	780	436	856	.3
.4	511	945	671	.06036	782	438	854	.4
.5	526	944	665	094	784	440	851	.5
.6	540	943	658	152	787	442	848	.6
.7	555	942	652	210	789	444	845	.7
.8	569	941	645	267	791	447	842	.8
10.9	.01584	.49940	.99639	.06325	.66794	.33449	.99839	10.9
11.0	.01598	.49939	.99632	.06383	.66796	.33451	.99836	11.0
.1	613	938	625	440	798	453	833	.1
.2	627	937	618	498	801	455	830	.2
.3	642	935	612	556	803	457	827	.3
.4	656	934	605	614	806	460	824	.4
.5	671	933	598	671	808	462	821	.5
.6	685	932	591	729	811	464	818	.6
.7	700	931	584	787	813	466	815	.7
.8	714	929	576	844	816	469	812	.8
11.9	.01729	.49928	.99569	.06902	.66818	.33471	.99808	11.9
12.0	.01743	.49927	.99562	.06959	.66821	.33473	.99805	12.0
.1	757	926	555	.07017	823	476	802	.1
.2	772	924	547	075	826	478	799	.2
.3	786	923	540	132	828	480	795	.3
.4	801	922	532	190	831	483	792	.4
.5	815	921	525	248	834	485	789	.5
.6	829	919	517	305	836	488	785	.6
.7	844	918	509	363	839	490	782	.7
.8	858	917	502	420	842	493	778	.8
12.9	.01873	.49915	.99494	.07478	.66845	.33495	.99775	12.9
13.0	.01887	.49914	.99486	.07535	.66847	.33498	.99771	13.0
.1	902	913	478	593	850	500	768	.1
.2	916	911	470	650	853	503	764	.2
.3	931	910	462	708	856	505	761	.3
.4	945	909	454	765	859	508	757	.4
.5	960	908	446	823	862	511	753	.5
.6	974	906	438	880	865	513	750	.6
.7	.01989	905	430	938	868	516	746	.7
.8	.02003	904	421	.07995	871	519	742	.8
13.9	.02018	.49902	.99413	.08053	.66874	.33521	.99739	13.9
14.0	.02032	.49901	.99405	.08110	.66877	.33524	.99735	14.0
.1	046	900	396	168	880	527	731	.1
.2	061	898	387	225	883	530	727	.2
.3	075	897	379	282	886	532	723	.3
.4	090	895	370	340	889	535	720	.4
.5	104	894	362	397	892	538	716	.5
.6	118	892	353	455	895	541	712	.6
.7	133	891	344	512	898	544	708	.7
.8	147	889	335	569	901	547	704	.8
14.9	.02162	.49888	.99326	.08627	.66904	.33550	.99700	14.9
15.0	.02176	.49886	.99317	.08684	.66908	.33553	.99696	15.0

FUNCTIONS OF TRANSITION FOR $L_s=1$ TABLE II   15°-20°

θ	p	k	χ	y	L.T.	S.T.	L.C.	θ
15.0	.02176	.49886	.99317	.08684	.66908	.33553	.99696	15.0
.1	190	884	308	741	911	556	692	.1
.2	205	883	299	799	914	559	688	.2
.3	219	881	289	856	918	561	683	.3
.4	234	880	280	913	921	564	679	.4
.5	248	878	271	.08970	924	567	675	.5
.6	262	876	261	.09028	928	571	671	.6
.7	277	875	252	085	931	574	667	.7
.8	291	873	242	142	934	577	662	.8
15.9	.02306	.49872	.99233	.09200	.66938	.33580	.99658	15.9
16.0	.02320	.49870	.99223	.09257	.66941	.33583	.99654	16.0
.1	335	868	213	314	945	586	649	.1
.2	349	867	203	371	948	589	645	.2
.3	364	865	194	428	952	593	641	.3
.4	378	864	184	485	955	596	636	.4
.5	393	862	174	543	959	599	632	.5
.6	407	860	164	600	962	602	627	.6
.7	422	859	154	657	966	606	623	.7
.8	436	857	143	714	970	609	618	.8
16.9	.02451	.49856	.99133	.09771	.66973	.33612	.99614	16.9
17.0	.02465	.49854	.99123	.09828	.66977	.33615	.99609	17.0
.1	479	852	113	885	981	619	605	.1
.2	494	850	102	942	984	622	600	.2
.3	508	849	092	.09999	988	626	595	.3
.4	522	847	081	.10056	992	629	591	.4
.5	537	845	071	113	995	632	586	.5
.6	551	843	060	170	.66999	636	581	.6
.7	565	841	050	227	.67003	639	576	.7
.8	579	840	039	284	.67007	643	572	.8
17.9	.02594	.49838	.99029	.10341	.67011	.33646	.99567	17.9
18.0	.02608	.49836	.99018	.10398	.67015	.33650	.99562	18.0
.1	622	834	.99007	455	019	654	557	.1
.2	637	832	.98996	512	023	657	552	.2
.3	651	830	985	569	027	661	547	.3
.4	666	828	974	626	031	664	542	.4
.5	680	827	962	683	035	668	537	.5
.6	694	825	951	740	039	672	532	.6
.7	709	823	940	797	043	675	527	.7
.8	723	821	929	854	047	679	522	.8
18.9	.02738	.49819	.98917	.10910	.67051	.33683	.99517	18.9
19.0	.02752	.49817	.98906	.10967	.67055	.33687	.99512	19.0
.1	766	815	894	.11024	059	690	507	.1
.2	781	813	883	081	063	694	502	.2
.3	795	811	871	138	067	698	497	.3
.4	810	809	860	194	072	702	491	.4
.5	824	808	848	251	076	706	486	.5
.6	838	806	836	308	080	709	481	.6
.7	853	804	824	364	084	713	476	.7
.8	867	802	812	421	089	717	470	.8
19.9	882	800	.98800	.11478	.67093	.33721	.99465	19.9
20.0	.02896	.49798	.98788	.11535	.67097	.33725	.99460	20.0

θ	p	k	x	y	L.T.	S.T.	L.C.	θ
20.0	.02896	.49798	.98788	.11535	.67097	.33725	.99460	20.0
.1	910	796	776	591	102	729	454	.1
.2	925	794	764	648	106	733	449	.2
.3	939	791	752	705	111	737	443	.3
.4	954	789	740	761	115	741	438	.4
.5	968	787	728	818	119	745	432	.5
.6	982	785	715	875	124	749	427	.6
.7	.02997	783	703	931	128	753	421	.7
.8	.03011	781	690	.11988	133	758	415	.8
20.9	.03026	.49779	.98678	.12044	.67137	.33762	.99410	20.9
21.0	.03040	.49777	.98665	.12101	.67142	.33766	.99404	21.0
.1	054	775	652	157	147	770	399	.1
.2	068	773	639	214	151	774	393	.2
.3	083	770	627	270	156	779	387	.3
.4	097	768	614	327	161	783	381	.4
.5	111	766	601	383	165	787	376	.5
.6	125	764	588	439	170	791	370	.6
.7	140	762	575	496	175	796	364	.7
.8	154	759	562	552	180	800	358	.8
21.9	.03169	.49757	.98549	.12609	.67184	.33804	.99352	21.9
22.0	.03183	.49755	.98536	.12665	.67189	.33809	.99346	22.0
.1	197	753	523	721	194	813	340	.1
.2	211	751	509	777	199	818	334	.2
.3	226	749	496	834	204	822	328	.3
.4	240	747	482	890	208	826	322	.4
.5	254	745	469	.12946	213	831	316	.5
.6	268	743	455	.13002	218	835	310	.6
.7	283	740	442	059	223	840	304	.7
.8	297	738	428	115	228	844	298	.8
22.9	.03312	.49735	.98415	.13172	.67233	.33849	.99292	22.9
23.0	.03326	.49733	.98401	.13228	.67238	.33854	.99286	23.0
.1	340	731	387	284	243	858	279	.1
.2	354	728	373	340	248	863	273	.2
.3	369	726	359	396	254	868	267	.3
.4	383	723	345	452	259	872	261	.4
.5	397	721	331	508	264	877	254	.5
.6	411	719	316	564	269	882	248	.6
.7	426	716	302	621	274	886	242	.7
.8	440	714	288	677	280	891	235	.8
23.9	.03455	.49711	.98274	.13733	.67285	.33896	.99229	23.9
24.0	.03469	.49709	.98260	.13789	.67290	.33901	.99222	24.0
.1	483	707	245	845	295	906	216	.1
.2	497	704	231	901	301	910	209	.2
.3	512	702	216	.13957	306	915	203	.3
.4	526	699	202	.14012	311	920	196	.4
.5	540	697	187	068	317	925	190	.5
.6	554	694	172	124	322	930	183	.6
.7	568	692	157	180	328	935	177	.7
.8	583	689	143	236	333	940	170	.8
24.9	.03597	.49687	.98128	.14292	.67339	.33945	.99163	24.9
25.0	.03611	.49684	.98113	.14348	.67344	.33950	.99157	25.0

θ	p	k	χ	y	L.T.	S.T.	L.C.	θ
25.0	.03611	.49684	.98113	.14348	.67344	.33950	.99157	25.0
.1	625	681	098	404	350	955	150	.1
.2	640	679	083	459	355	960	143	.2
.3	654	676	068	515	361	965	136	.3
.4	669	674	053	571	366	970	129	.4
.5	683	671	038	627	372	975	123	.5
.6	697	668	022	682	378	981	116	.6
.7	711	666	.98007	738	383	986	109	.7
.8	725	663	.97991	794	389	991	102	.8
25.9	.03739	.49661	.97976	.14849	.67395	.33996	.99095	25.9
26.0	.03753	.49658	.97960	.14905	.67400	.34001	.99088	26.0
.1	767	656	945	.14961	406	007	081	.1
.2	782	653	929	.15016	412	012	074	.2
.3	796	651	913	072	418	017	067	.3
.4	811	648	898	128	424	023	060	.4
.5	825	646	882	183	430	028	053	.5
.6	839	643	866	239	435	033	046	.6
.7	853	640	850	294	441	039	038	.7
.8	868	638	834	350	447	044	031	.8
26.9	.03882	.49635	.97818	.15405	.67453	.34049	.99024	26.9
27.0	.03896	.49632	.97802	.15461	.67459	.34055	.99017	27.0
.1	910	629	786	516	465	060	.99009	.1
.2	924	626	770	571	471	066	.99002	.2
.3	939	624	753	627	477	071	.98995	.3
.4	953	621	737	682	483	077	987	.4
.5	967	618	721	738	490	083	980	.5
.6	981	615	704	793	496	088	973	.6
.7	.03995	613	688	848	502	094	965	.7
.8	.04009	610	671	903	508	099	958	.8
27.9	.04023	.49608	.97655	.15959	.67514	.34105	.98950	27.9
28.0	.04037	.49605	.97638	.16014	.67520	.34111	.98943	28.0
.1	051	602	621	069	527	116	935	.1
.2	065	599	604	124	533	122	928	.2
.3	080	596	588	180	539	128	920	.3
.4	094	593	571	235	546	134	913	.4
.5	108	590	554	290	552	139	905	.5
.6	122	587	537	345	558	145	897	.6
.7	136	584	520	400	565	151	890	.7
.8	151	582	503	455	571	157	882	.8
28.9	.04165	.49579	.97486	.16510	.67578	.34163	.98874	28.9
29.0	.04179	.49576	.97469	.16565	.67584	.34169	.98866	29.0
.1	193	573	452	620	591	165	859	.1
.2	207	570	434	675	597	171	851	.2
.3	222	567	417	730	604	177	843	.3
.4	236	564	399	785	610	193	835	.4
.5	250	561	382	840	617	199	827	.5
.6	264	558	364	895	623	205	819	.6
.7	278	555	346	.16950	630	211	811	.7
.8	293	552	329	.17005	637	217	803	.8
29.9	.04307	.49549	.97311	.17060	.67643	.34223	.98795	29.9
30.0	.04321	.49546	.97293	.17114	.67650	.34229	.98787	30.0

θ	p	k	x	y	L.T.	S.T.	L.C.	θ
30.0	.04321	.49546	.97293	.17114	.67650	.34229	.98787	30.0
.1	335	543	275	169	657	235	779	.1
.2	349	540	257	224	664	241	771	.2
.3	363	537	239	279	670	248	763	.3
.4	377	534	221	333	677	254	755	.4
.5	391	531	203	388	684	260	746	.5
.6	405	528	185	443	691	266	738	.6
.7	419	525	167	498	698	273	730	.7
.8	434	522	148	552	705	279	722	.8
30.9	.04448	.49519	.97130	.17607	.67712	.34285	.98713	30.9
31.0	.04462	.49516	.97112	.17661	.67719	.34292	.98705	31.0
.1	476	513	094	716	726	298	697	.1
.2	490	510	075	770	733	304	688	.2
.3	504	506	057	825	740	311	680	.3
.4	518	503	038	879	747	317	672	.4
.5	532	500	020	934	754	324	663	.5
.6	546	497	.97001	.17988	761	330	655	.6
.7	560	494	.96982	.18043	768	337	646	.7
.8	574	490	.96963	.18097	775	343	638	.8
31.9	.04588	.49487	.96944	.18152	.67783	.34350	.98629	31.9
32.0	.04602	.49484	.96926	.18206	.67790	.34356	.98621	32.0
.1	616	481	907	260	797	363	612	.1
.2	630	478	887	315	804	370	603	.2
.3	645	475	868	369	812	376	595	.3
.4	659	472	849	424	819	383	586	.4
.5	673	469	830	478	826	390	577	.5
.6	687	466	811	532	834	397	569	.6
.7	701	462	791	586	841	403	560	.7
.8	715	459	772	640	849	410	551	.8
32.9	.04729	.49455	.96752	.18694	.67856	.34417	.98542	32.9
33.0	.04743	.49452	.96733	.18748	.67863	.34424	.98534	33.0
.1	757	449	713	803	871	431	525	.1
.2	771	445	694	857	878	438	516	.2
.3	785	442	674	911	886	444	507	.3
.4	799	438	655	.18965	894	451	498	.4
.5	813	435	635	.19019	901	458	489	.5
.6	827	432	615	073	909	465	480	.6
.7	841	429	595	127	916	472	471	.7
.8	855	425	576	181	924	479	462	.8
33.9	.04869	.49422	.96556	.19234	.67932	.34486	.98453	33.9
34.0	.04883	.49419	.96536	.19288	.67939	.34493	.98444	34.0
.1	897	415	516	342	947	500	435	.1
.2	911	412	496	396	955	508	425	.2
.3	925	408	475	450	963	515	416	.3
.4	939	405	455	504	971	522	407	.4
.5	953	401	435	557	979	529	398	.5
.6	967	398	414	611	987	536	389	.6
.7	981	395	394	665	.67994	544	379	.7
.8	.04995	391	373	718	.68002	551	370	.8
34.9	.05009	.49388	.96353	.19772	.68010	.34558	.98361	34.9
35.0	.05023	.49385	.96332	.19826	.68018	.34565	.98351	35.0

θ	p	k	x	y	L.T.	S.T.	L.C.	θ
35.0	.05023	.49385	.96332	.19826	.68018	.34565	.98351	35.0
.1	037	381	311	879	026	573	342	.1
.2	051	378	291	933	034	580	333	.2
.3	065	374	270	.19987	042	587	323	.3
.4	079	371	250	.20040	051	595	314	.4
.5	093	367	229	.20094	059	602	304	.5
.6	107	363	208	147	067	610	295	.6
.7	121	360	187	201	075	617	285	.7
.8	135	356	166	254	083	625	276	.8
35.9	.05149	.49353	.96145	.20307	.68092	.34632	.98266	35.9
36.0	.05163	.49349	.96124	.20361	.68100	.34640	.98257	36.0
.1	177	345	103	414	108	647	247	.1
.2	191	342	081	467	116	655	237	.2
.3	204	338	060	521	125	663	227	.3
.4	218	335	038	574	133	670	218	.4
.5	232	331	.96017	627	141	678	208	.5
.6	246	327	.95996	680	150	686	198	.6
.7	260	324	.95974	734	158	693	188	.7
.8	273	320	.95953	787	167	701	179	.8
36.9	.05287	.49317	.95931	.20840	.68175	.34709	.98169	36.9
37.0	.05301	.49313	.95910	.20893	.68184	.34717	.98159	37.0
.1	315	309	888	.20946	192	725	149	.1
.2	329	306	866	.20999	201	732	139	.2
.3	343	302	844	.21052	210	740	129	.3
.4	357	299	822	105	218	748	119	.4
.5	371	295	800	158	227	756	109	.5
.6	385	291	778	211	236	764	099	.6
.7	399	287	756	264	244	772	089	.7
.8	413	284	734	317	253	780	079	.8
37.9	.05427	.49280	.95712	.21370	.68262	.34788	.98069	37.9
38.0	.05441	.49276	.95690	.21423	.68271	.34796	.98059	38.0
.1	455	272	668	475	279	804	049	.1
.2	469	268	645	528	288	812	038	.2
.3	482	264	623	581	297	820	028	.3
.4	496	260	601	634	306	829	018	.4
.5	510	256	578	686	315	837	.98008	.5
.6	524	252	556	739	324	845	.97997	.6
.7	538	249	533	792	333	853	987	.7
.8	551	245	511	844	342	861	977	.8
38.9	.05565	.49242	.95488	.21897	.68351	.34870	.97967	38.9
39.0	.05579	.49238	.95466	.21949	.68360	.34878	.97956	39.0
.1	593	234	443	.22002	369	886	946	.1
.2	607	230	420	054	379	895	935	.2
.3	620	226	397	107	388	903	925	.3
.4	634	222	374	159	397	911	914	.4
.5	648	218	351	212	406	920	904	.5
.6	662	214	328	264	415	928	893	.6
.7	676	210	305	316	424	937	883	.7
.8	690	207	281	369	434	945	872	.8
39.9	.05704	.49203	.95258	.22421	.68443	.34954	.97861	39.9
40.0	.05718	.49199	.95235	.22473	.68452	.34962	.97851	40.0

θ	p	k	x	y	L.T.	S.T.	L.C.	θ
40.0	.05718	.49199	.95235	.22473	.68452	.34962	.97851	40.0
.1	732	195	212	526	462	971	840	.1
.2	745	191	188	578	471	980	829	.2
.3	759	187	165	630	481	988	819	.3
.4	772	183	141	682	490	.34997	808	.4
.5	786	179	118	734	500	.35006	797	.5
.6	800	175	094	786	509	014	786	.6
.7	814	171	071	838	519	023	775	.7
.8	827	167	047	890	528	032	765	.8
40.9	.05841	.49163	.95023	.22942	.68538	.35041	.97754	40.9
41.0	.05855	.49159	.95000	.22994	.68547	.35049	.97743	41.0
.1	869	155	.94976	.23046	557	058	732	.1
.2	883	151	952	098	567	067	721	.2
.3	896	146	928	150	577	076	710	.3
.4	910	142	904	202	586	085	699	.4
.5	924	138	880	254	596	094	688	.5
.6	938	134	856	306	606	103	677	.6
.7	952	130	832	358	616	112	666	.7
.8	965	126	807	409	626	121	655	.8
41.9	.05979	.49122	.94783	.23461	.68635	.35130	.97643	41.9
42.0	.05993	.49118	.94759	.23513	.68645	.35139	.97632	42.0
.1	.06007	114	734	564	655	148	621	.1
.2	020	110	710	616	665	158	610	.2
.3	034	105	685	667	675	167	599	.3
.4	047	101	661	719	685	176	587	.4
.5	061	097	636	771	695	185	576	.5
.6	075	093	612	822	706	194	565	.6
.7	089	088	587	874	716	204	553	.7
.8	102	084	562	925	726	213	542	.8
42.9	.06116	.49079	.94538	.23976	.68736	.35222	.97531	42.9
43.0	.06130	.49075	.94513	.24028	.68746	.35232	.97519	43.0
.1	144	071	488	079	756	241	508	.1
.2	157	067	463	130	767	250	496	.2
.3	171	062	438	182	777	260	485	.3
.4	184	058	413	233	787	269	473	.4
.5	198	054	388	284	798	279	462	.5
.6	212	050	363	335	808	288	450	.6
.7	226	045	337	387	818	298	438	.7
.8	239	041	312	438	829	307	427	.8
43.9	.06253	.49036	.94287	.24489	.68839	.35317	.97415	43.9
44.0	.06267	.49032	.94262	.24540	.68850	.35327	.97404	44.0
.1	281	028	236	591	860	336	392	.1
.2	294	024	211	642	871	346	380	.2
.3	308	019	185	693	882	356	368	.3
.4	321	015	160	744	892	365	357	.4
.5	335	011	134	795	903	375	345	.5
.6	349	007	108	846	914	385	333	.6
.7	362	.49003	082	896	924	395	321	.7
.8	376	.48998	057	947	935	405	309	.8
44.9	.06389	.48994	.94031	.24998	.68946	.35415	.97297	44.9
45.0	.06403	.48990	.94005	.25049	.68957	.35424	.97285	45.0

FUNCTIONS OF TRANSITION FOR $L_s=1$ TABLE II 45°-50°

θ	p	k	x	y	L.T.	S.T.	L.C.	θ
45.0	.06403	.48990	.94005	.25049	.68957	.35424	.97285	45.0
.1	416	985	.93979	100	967	434	273	.1
.2	430	981	953	150	978	444	261	.2
.3	443	976	927	201	.68989	454	249	.3
.4	457	972	901	251	.69000	464	237	.4
.5	470	967	875	302	011	474	225	.5
.6	484	963	849	353	022	485	213	.6
.7	497	958	823	403	033	495	201	.7
.8	511	954	796	454	044	505	189	.8
45.9	.06524	.48949	.93770	.25504	.69055	.35515	.97177	45.9
46.0	.06538	.48945	.93744	.25555	.69066	.35525	.97165	46.0
.1	552	940	717	605	078	535	152	.1
.2	565	936	691	655	089	546	140	.2
.3	579	931	664	705	100	556	128	.3
.4	592	927	638	756	111	566	116	.4
.5	606	922	611	806	122	576	103	.5
.6	620	918	584	856	134	587	091	.6
.7	633	913	558	907	145	597	079	.7
.8	647	909	531	.25957	156	608	066	.8
46.9	.06660	.48904	.93504	.26007	.69168	.35618	.97054	46.9
47.0	.06674	.48900	.93477	.26057	.69179	.35629	.97041	47.0
.1	688	895	450	107	191	639	029	.1
.2	701	890	423	157	202	650	016	.2
.3	715	885	396	207	214	660	.97004	.3
.4	728	881	369	257	225	671	.96991	.4
.5	742	876	342	307	237	681	979	.5
.6	755	871	315	357	248	692	966	.6
.7	768	866	288	407	260	703	954	.7
.8	782	862	260	457	272	714	941	.8
47.9	.06795	.48857	.93233	.26506	.69283	.35724	.96928	47.9
48.0	.06809	.48852	.93206	.26556	.69295	.35735	.96916	48.0
.1	822	847	178	606	307	746	903	.1
.2	836	843	151	656	318	757	890	.2
.3	849	838	123	705	330	768	877	.3
.4	863	834	096	755	342	778	865	.4
.5	876	829	069	805	354	789	852	.5
.6	890	824	041	854	366	800	839	.6
.7	903	819	.93013	904	378	811	826	.7
.8	917	815	.92985	.26953	390	822	813	.8
48.9	.06930	.48810	.92958	.27003	.69402	.35833	.96800	48.9
49.0	.06944	.48805	.92930	.27052	.69414	.35844	.96787	49.0
.1	957	800	902	101	426	855	774	.1
.2	970	796	874	151	438	867	761	.2
.3	983	791	846	200	450	878	748	.3
.4	.06997	786	818	250	463	889	735	.4
.5	.07010	782	790	299	475	900	722	.5
.6	023	777	762	348	487	911	709	.6
.7	037	772	733	397	499	923	696	.7
.8	050	767	705	446	512	934	683	.8
49.9	.07064	.48762	.92677	.27495	.69524	.35945	.96670	49.9
50.0	.07078	.48757	.92649	.27544	.69536	.35957	.96656	50.0

TABLE III	T_s and E_s for $L_s = 1$ for CURVES TRANSITIONAL THROUGHOUT							
Δ	T_s	E_s	Δ	T_s	E_s	Δ	T_s	E_s
6	1.00064	.01747	38	1.02682	.11599	70	1.10214	.24203
7	1.00087	.02040	39	1.02832	.11936	71	1.10561	.24681
8	1.00114	.02332	40	1.02987	.12275	72	1.10917	.25167
9	1.00144	.02625	41	1.03146	.12617	73	1.11281	.25660
10	1.00178	.02918	42	1.03310	.12962	74	1.11654	.26161
11	1.00216	.03212	43	1.03479	.13309	75	1.12036	.26669
12	1.00257	.03507	44	1.03653	.13660	76	1.12427	.27186
13	1.00302	.03802	45	1.03831	.14012	77	1.12828	.27710
14	1.00350	.04098	46	1.04015	.14370	78	1.13240	.28244
15	1.00402	.04396	47	1.04204	.14730	79	1.13661	.28786
16	1.00458	.04693	48	1.04399	.15094	80	1.14092	.29337
17	1.00518	.04992	49	1.04598	.15460	81	1.14535	.29898
18	1.00581	.05292	50	1.04804	.15831	82	1.14988	.30468
19	1.00648	.05593	51	1.05014	.16206	83	1.15453	.31048
20	1.00719	.05895	52	1.05230	.16584	84	1.15930	.31639
21	1.00794	.06198	53	1.05452	.16966	85	1.16418	.32241
22	1.00873	.06502	54	1.05680	.17352	86	1.16919	.32854
23	1.00955	.06808	55	1.05913	.17742	87	1.17433	.33478
24	1.01042	.07115	56	1.06153	.18137	88	1.17960	.34115
25	1.01132	.07424	57	1.06399	.18536	89	1.18500	.34763
26	1.01226	.07734	58	1.06651	.18940	90	1.19054	.35425
27	1.01324	.08045	59	1.06909	.19348	91	1.19623	.36099
28	1.01427	.08358	60	1.07174	.19762	92	1.20207	.36788
29	1.01533	.08674	61	1.07446	.20181	93	1.20806	.37490
30	1.01644	.08990	62	1.07724	.20604	94	1.21421	.38207
31	1.01758	.09309	63	1.08010	.21034	95	1.22052	.38940
32	1.01877	.09630	64	1.08302	.21468	96	1.22700	.39688
33	1.02000	.09952	65	1.08602	.21908	97	1.23366	.40453
34	1.02128	.10277	66	1.08909	.22355	98	1.24050	.41234
35	1.02260	.10604	67	1.09223	.22807	99	1.24753	.42034
36	1.02396	.10933	68	1.09546	.23266	100	1.25475	.42852
37	1.02537	.11265	69	1.09876	.23731			

D_c	$L_s = 150'$		200'		250'		300'		350'		400'		500'		600'		Δ = 6°
	T_s	E_s	T_s	E_s	T_s	E_s	T_s	E_s	T_s	E_s	T_s	E_s	T_s	E_s	T_s	E_s	
1-30	275.20	5.5	300.20	5.7	325.21	5.9	350.23	6.2	375.24	6.6	400.25	6.98					70 mph
2-00	225.15	4.3	250.16	4.5	275.18	4.8	300.19	5.23									60 mph
2-30	195.13	3.6	220.14	3.9													50 mph
3-00	175.11	3.1	200.13	3.49													40 mph
3-30	160.82	2.8															
4-00	150.10	2.62															30 mph

TABLE IV
T_s AND E_s

Δ = 6°

Table IV — T_s and E_s — $\Delta = 7°$

D_c	$L_s = 150'$ T_s	E_s	$200'$ T_s	E_s	$250'$ T_s	E_s	$300'$ T_s	E_s	$350'$ T_s	E_s	$400'$ T_s	E_s	$500'$ T_s	E_s	$600'$ T_s	E_s
1-30	308.64	7.4	333.65	7.6	358.66	7.8	383.68	8.1	408.69	8.5	433.71	8.9				
2-00	250.24	5.7	275.25	5.9	300.27	6.3	325.28	6.7	350.31	7.14						
2-30	215.20	4.7	240.21	5.0	265.23	5.4										
3-00	191.84	4.1	216.86	4.4												
3-30	175.15	3.6	200.18	4.08												
4-00	162.64	3.3														

70 mph 60 mph 50 mph 40 mph 30 mph

TABLE IV
Ts AND Es   Δ=8°

Dc	Ls = 150' Ts	Es	200' Ts	Es	250' Ts	Es	300' Ts	Es	350' Ts	Es	400' Ts	Es	500' Ts	Es	600' Ts	Es	Δ=8°
1-30	342.12	9.6	367.13	9.8	392.14	10.0	417.16	10.3	442.18	10.7	467.20	11.1	517.26	12.1			
2-00	275.35	7.3	300.36	7.6	325.38	7.9	350.40	8.3	375.43	8.8	400.46	9.32					70 mph
2-30	235.29	6.0	260.31	6.3	285.33	6.7	310.35	7.2									60 mph
3-00	208.58	5.2	233.60	5.5	258.63	6.0											50 mph
3-30	189.51	4.6	214.53	5.0													
4-00	175.20	4.2	200.23	4.66													40 mph
5	155.18	3.6															

30 mph

TABLE IV
T_s AND E_s

$\Delta = 9°$

D_c	$L_s = 150'$		$200'$		$250'$		$300'$		$350'$		$400'$		$500'$		$600'$	
	T_s	E_s	T_s	E_s	T_s	E_s	T_s	E_s	T_s	E_s	T_s	E_s	T_s	E_s	T_s	E_s
1-30	375.64	12.1	400.65	12.2	425.67	12.5	450.69	12.8	475.71	13.1	500.74	13.5	550.80	14.5	600.87	15.74
2-00	300.49	9.2	325.51	9.4	350.53	9.8	375.55	10.2	400.58	10.6	425.62	11.2				
2-30	255.40	7.5	280.42	7.8	305.45	8.2	330.48	8.7	355.51	9.3						
3-00	225.34	6.4	250.37	6.8	275.40	7.3	300.43	7.87								
3-30	203.88	5.6	228.90	6.1	253.94	6.7										
4-00	187.78	5.1	212.81	5.6												
5	165.24	4.4														
6	150.22	3.94														

70 mph, 60 mph, 50 mph, 40 mph, 30 mph

Δ = 10°

TABLE IV

T_s AND E_s

Δ = 10°

D_c	L_s = 150'		200'		250'		300'		350'		400'		500'		600'	
	T_s	E_s	T_s	E_s	T_s	E_s	T_s	E_s	T_s	E_s	T_s	E_s	T_s	E_s	T_s	E_s
1-30	409.20	14.8	434.22	15.0	459.24	15.3	484.26	15.6	509.29	15.9	534.31	16.3	584.39	17.3	634.47	18.5
2-00	325.66	11.3	350.68	11.5	375.71	11.9	400.74	12.3	425.77	12.7	450.81	13.3	500.89	14.59		
2-30	275.54	9.2	300.57	9.5	325.60	9.9	350.63	10.4	375.67	11.0	400.71	11.67				
3-00	242.13	7.8	267.16	8.2	292.19	8.7	317.23	9.3								
3-30	218.27	6.8	243.30	7.3	268.34	7.8										
4	200.37	6.1	225.40	6.6	250.45	7.30										
5	175.32	5.2	200.36	5.84												
6	158.62	4.6														

70 mph · 60 mph · 50 mph · 40 mph · 30 mph

D_c	$L_s=150'$ T_s	E_s	$200'$ T_s	E_s	$250'$ T_s	E_s	$300'$ T_s	E_s	$350'$ T_s	E_s	$400'$ T_s	E_s	$500'$ T_s	E_s	$600'$ T_s	E_s
1-30	442.82	17.9	467.84	18.1	492.86	18.4	517.88	18.7	542.91	19.0	567.94	19.4	618.02	20.4	668.12	21.6
2-00	350.88	13.6	375.90	13.8	400.93	14.2	425.96	14.6	451.00	15.1	476.04	15.6	526.13	16.9		
2-30	295.72	11.0	320.74	11.3	345.77	11.8	370.81	12.3	395.86	12.8	420.91	13.5				
3-00	258.94	9.3	283.97	9.7	309.01	10.2	334.06	10.8	359.11	11.5						
3-30	232.68	8.2	257.71	8.6	282.76	9.2	307.81	9.9								
4-00	211.98	7.3	238.02	7.8	263.07	8.5										
5	185.41	6.1	210.45	6.8												
6	167.03	5.4														
7	153.90	4.9														

70 mph
60 mph
50 mph
40 mph
30 mph

TABLE IV
T_s AND E_s

Δ=11°

72

Δ = 12°

D_c	L_s = 150' T_s	E_s	200' T_s	E_s	250' T_s	E_s	300' T_s	E_s	350' T_s	E_s	400' T_s	E_s	500' T_s	E_s	600' T_s	E_s
1-30	476.49	21.3	501.51	21.5	526.54	21.7	551.56	22.0	576.60	22.4	601.63	22.8	651.72	23.8	701.82	25.0
2-00	376.14	16.1	401.16	16.4	426.19	16.7	451.22	17.1	476.27	17.6	501.31	18.1	551.42	19.4	601.54	21.05
2-30	315.92	13.0	340.95	13.4	365.99	13.8	391.03	14.3	416.08	14.9	441.14	15.6				
3-00	275.78	11.0	300.82	11.4	325.86	11.9	350.91	12.5	375.97	13.2	401.03	14.03				
3-30	247.11	9.6	272.15	10.0	297.20	10.6	322.26	11.3								
4-00	225.61	8.5	250.66	9.1	275.71	9.7	300.77	10.52								
5	195.52	7.1	220.57	7.8												
6	175.46	6.2	200.51	7.02												
7	161.13	5.7														
8	150.39	5.26														

70 mph
60 mph
50 mph
40 mph
30 mph

TABLE IV
T_s AND E_s
Δ = 12°

Δ=13°

TABLE IV
T_s AND E_s

D_c	$L_s = 150'$		200'		250'		300'		350'		400'		500'		600'	
	T_s	E_s	T_s	E_s	T_s	E_s	T_s	E_s	T_s	E_s	T_s	E_s	T_s	E_s	T_s	E_s
1-30	510.23	25.0	535.25	25.2	560.28	25.4	585.31	25.7	610.34	26.1	635.38	26.5	685.48	27.5	735.59	28.7
2-00	401.44	18.9	426.46	19.1	451.50	19.4	476.54	19.8	501.58	20.3	526.63	20.9	576.75	22.2	626.89	23.8
2-30	336.17	15.2	361.20	15.6	386.24	16.0	411.29	16.5	436.34	17.1	461.40	17.8	511.54	19.4		19.4
3-00	292.65	12.9	317.69	13.2	342.74	13.7	367.79	14.3	392.86	15.0	417.93	15.9				
3-30	261.57	11.2	286.62	11.6	311.67	12.2	336.73	12.9	361.80	13.7						
4-00	238.27	9.9	263.32	10.4	288.38	11.1	313.45	11.9								
5	205.64	8.2	230.70	8.9	255.77	9.7										
6	183.90	7.2	208.96	7.9												
7	168.37	6.4														
8	156.72	6.0														

70 mph
60 mph
50 mph
40 mph
30 mph

Δ=13°

74

TABLE IV
T_s AND E_s Δ=14°

D_c	L_s = 150' T_s	E_s	200' T_s	E_s	250' T_s	E_s	300' T_s	E_s	350' T_s	E_s	400' T_s	E_s	500' T_s	E_s	600' T_s	E_s	
1-30	544.03	28.9	569.05	29.1	594.08	29.4	619.11	29.7	644.15	30.0	669.20	30.4	719.30	31.4	769.42	32.6	
2-00	426.79	21.8	451.82	22.1	476.86	22.4	501.90	22.8	526.95	23.3	552.01	23.9	602.13	25.2	652.29	26.8	
2-30	356.45	17.6	381.49	17.9	406.53	18.4	431.58	18.9	456.64	19.5	481.71	20.1	531.86	21.8			70 mph
3-00	309.56	14.8	334.60	15.2	359.65	15.7	384.71	16.3	409.78	17.0	434.86	17.9					60 mph
3-30	276.07	12.9	301.11	13.3	326.17	13.9	351.24	14.6	376.32	15.4	401.40	16.40					
4-00	250.95	11.4	276.00	11.9	301.07	12.6	326.14	13.4	351.23	14.35							50 mph
5	215.79	9.4	240.85	10.1	265.93	10.9											
6	192.36	8.2	217.43	8.9													
7	175.62	7.3	200.70	8.20												40 mph
8	163.07	6.7															
9	153.31	6.3															30 mph

75

TABLE IV
T_s AND E_s

$\Delta = 15°$

D_c	$L_s=150'$		$200'$		$250'$		$300'$		$350'$		$400'$		$500'$		$600'$		
	T_s	E_s	T_s	E_s	T_s	E_s	T_s	E_s	T_s	E_s	T_s	E_s	T_s	E_s	T_s	E_s	
1-30	577.91	33.2	602.93	33.4	627.96	33.7	653.00	34.0	678.04	34.3	703.09	34.7	753.20	35.7	803.33	36.9	70 mph
2-00	452.20	25.1	477.23	25.3	502.27	25.6	527.31	26.0	552.37	26.5	577.43	27.1	627.57	28.4	677.74	30.0	60 mph
2-30	376.78	20.2	401.82	20.5	426.86	20.9	451.92	21.4	476.98	22.0	502.06	22.7	552.23	24.4	602.41	26.38	
3-00	326.50	17.0	351.54	17.4	376.60	17.9	401.67	18.5	426.74	19.2	451.83	20.0	502.01	21.98			50 mph
3-30	290.59	14.7	315.64	15.2	340.70	15.7	365.78	16.4	390.86	17.3	415.95	18.2					
4-00	263.66	13.0	288.72	13.5	313.79	14.2	338.87	15.0	363.96	16.0							
5	225.96	10.7	251.03	11.4	276.11	12.2	301.21	13.19									40 mph
6	200.83	9.2	225.91	10.0	251.01	10.99											
7	182.89	8.2	207.98	9.1													
8	169.43	7.5															
9	158.97	7.0													30 mph		
10	150.60	6.60															

76

TABLE IV — T_s AND E_s — Δ=16°

D_c	$L_s=150'$ T_s	E_s	$200'$ T_s	E_s	$250'$ T_s	E_s	$300'$ T_s	E_s	$350'$ T_s	E_s	$400'$ T_s	E_s	$500'$ T_s	E_s	$600'$ T_s	E_s
1-30	611.86	37.8	636.89	38.0	661.92	38.2	686.96	38.5	712.00	38.9	737.05	39.3	787.17	40.3	837.32	41.5
2-00	477.67	28.5	502.70	28.7	527.74	29.1	552.79	29.5	577.85	30.0	602.91	30.5	653.07	31.8	703.25	33.4
2-30	397.15	22.9	422.19	23.3	447.24	23.7	472.30	24.2	497.37	24.8	522.45	25.5	572.64	27.1	622.84	29.1
3-00	343.48	19.3	368.53	19.7	393.59	20.1	418.66	20.8	443.74	21.5	468.83	22.3	519.04	24.3		
3-30	305.14	16.7	330.20	17.1	355.27	17.7	380.35	18.4	405.44	19.2	430.54	20.2				
4-00	276.40	14.7	301.46	15.3	326.53	15.9	351.62	16.7	376.72	17.7	401.83	18.78				
5	236.15	12.1	261.23	12.7	286.32	13.6	311.42	14.6								
6	209.33	10.4	234.42	11.1	259.52	12.1										
7	190.17	9.2	215.27	10.1												
8	175.81	8.4	200.92	9.39												
9	164.64	7.7														
10	155.71	7.3														

70 mph · 60 mph · 50 mph · 40 mph · 30 mph

77

D_c	$L_s = 150'$ T_s	E_s	$200'$ T_s	E_s	$250'$ T_s	E_s	$300'$ T_s	E_s	$350'$ T_s	E_s	$400'$ T_s	E_s	$500'$ T_s	E_s	$600'$ T_s	E_s
1-30	645.90	42.7	670.92	42.9	695.96	43.1	721.00	43.4	746.05	43.8	771.10	44.2	821.23	45.2	871.39	46.4
2-00	503.19	32.2	528.23	32.4	553.27	32.7	578.33	33.1	603.39	33.6	628.46	34.2	678.62	35.5	728.82	37.1
2-30	417.58	25.9	442.62	26.2	467.67	26.6	492.74	27.1	517.82	27.7	542.90	28.4	593.10	30.1	643.32	32.1
3-00	360.50	21.7	385.55	22.1	410.62	22.6	435.69	23.2	460.78	23.9	485.88	24.7	536.10	26.7		
3-30	319.73	18.8	344.79	19.2	369.87	19.8	394.96	20.5	420.05	21.3	445.16	22.3				
4-00	289.16	16.6	314.23	17.1	339.31	17.8	364.41	18.6	389.52	19.5	414.64	20.6				
5	246.37	13.6	271.45	14.2	296.55	15.0	321.66	16.0								
6	217.85	11.6	242.94	12.4	268.05	13.4										
7	197.48	10.3	222.58	11.2												
8	182.21	9.3	207.32	10.3												
9	170.23	8.6														
10	160.83	8.0														
11	153.06	7.6														

70 mph 60 mph 50 mph 40 mph 30 mph

TABLE IV
T_s AND E_s

Δ=17°

TABLE IV — Ts AND Es — Δ=18°

Dc	Ls=150' Ts	Es	200' Ts	Es	250' Ts	Es	300' Ts	Es	350' Ts	Es	400' Ts	Es	500' Ts	Es	600' Ts	Es
1-30	680.02	47.9	705.05	48.1	730.09	48.1	755.13	48.6	780.18	49.0	805.24	49.4	855.38	50.4	905.55	51.6
2-00	528.79	36.1	553.83	36.3	578.88	36.6	603.93	37.0	629.00	37.5	654.07	38.1	704.25	39.4	754.46	41.0
2-30	438.05	29.0	463.10	29.3	488.16	29.7	513.23	30.2	538.31	30.8	563.40	31.5	613.61	33.2	663.85	35.2
3-00	377.57	24.3	402.62	24.7	427.69	25.2	452.77	25.8	477.87	26.5	502.97	27.3	553.21	29.3	603.49	31.76
3-30	334.36	21.0	359.43	21.4	384.51	22.0	409.60	22.7	436.71	23.6	459.82	24.5	510.09	26.9		
4-00	301.97	18.5	327.04	19.0	352.13	19.7	377.23	20.5	402.35	21.5	427.47	22.6				
5	256.62	15.1	281.70	15.8	306.81	16.6	331.93	17.6	357.06	18.8						
6	226.39	12.9	251.49	13.7	276.61	14.7	301.75	15.88								
7	204.80	11.4	229.91	12.3	255.05	13.4										
8	188.62	10.3	213.74	11.3												
9	176.03	9.4	201.16	10.59												
10	165.96	8.8														
11	157.73	8.3														
12	150.87	7.94														

70 mph · 60 mph · 50 mph · 40 mph · 30 mph

D_c	$L_s=150'$		$200'$		$250'$		$300'$		$350'$		$400'$		$500'$		$600'$	
	T_s	E_s	T_s	E_s	T_s	E_s	T_s	E_s	T_s	E_s	T_s	E_s	T_s	E_s	T_s	E_s
1-30	714.24	53.4	739.27	53.6	764.31	53.8	789.36	54.1	814.41	54.5	839.47	54.9	889.62	55.9	939.80	57.1
2-00	554.46	40.2	579.50	40.4	604.55	40.8	629.61	41.2	654.68	41.7	679.76	42.2	729.95	43.5	780.17	45.2
2-30	458.59	32.3	483.64	32.6	508.70	33.0	533.77	33.5	558.86	34.1	583.96	34.8	634.18	36.5	684.44	38.5
3-00	394.68	27.1	419.74	27.4	444.81	27.9	469.90	28.6	495.00	29.3	520.11	30.1	570.37	32.1	620.67	34.5
3-30	349.03	23.4	374.10	23.8	399.19	24.4	424.29	25.1	449.40	25.9	474.53	26.9	524.81	29.2		
4-00	314.80	20.6	339.88	21.1	364.97	21.8	390.08	22.6	415.21	23.5	440.35	24.6				
5	266.89	16.8	291.98	17.4	317.09	18.2	342.22	19.3	367.37	20.5						
6	234.95	14.3	260.06	15.1	285.19	16.0	310.33	17.3								
7	212.14	12.5	237.26	13.5	262.41	14.6										
8	195.04	11.3	220.17	12.3												
9	181.75	10.3	206.89	11.5												
10	171.11	9.6														
11	162.41	9.1														
12	155.17	8.6														

70 mph 60 mph 50 mph 40 mph 30 mph

$\Delta = 19°$

TABLE IV
T_s AND E_s

$\Delta = 19°$

80

TABLE IV
T_s AND E_s Δ = 20°

D_c	$L_s=150'$ T_s	E_s	$200'$ T_s	E_s	$250'$ T_s	E_s	$300'$ T_s	E_s	$350'$ T_s	E_s	$400'$ T_s	E_s	$500'$ T_s	E_s	$600'$ T_s	E_s	
1-30	748.56	59.2	773.60	59.4	798.64	59.6	823.68	59.9	848.74	60.3	873.81	60.7	923.97	61.7	974.15	62.9	
2-00	580.20	44.5	605.24	44.8	630.29	45.1	655.36	45.5	680.43	46.0	705.52	46.6	755.72	47.9	805.95	49.5	
2-30	479.18	35.8	504.23	36.1	529.30	36.5	554.38	37.0	579.47	37.6	604.57	38.3	654.82	40.0	705.09	42.0	70 mph
3-00	411.84	30.0	436.90	30.3	461.98	30.9	487.08	31.5	512.18	32.2	537.30	33.0	587.58	35.0	637.90	37.4	
3-30	363.75	25.8	388.82	26.3	413.91	26.9	439.01	27.6	464.14	28.4	489.27	29.4	539.58	31.7			
4-00	327.68	22.8	352.76	23.3	377.86	23.9	402.98	24.8	428.11	25.7	453.26	26.8	503.60	29.48			
5	277.19	18.5	302.29	19.2	327.41	20.0	352.55	21.0	377.71	22.2	402.88	23.58					60 mph
6	243.54	15.7	268.65	16.5	293.79	17.5	318.95	18.7									
7	219.51	13.8	244.64	14.7	269.79	15.9											
8	201.49	12.4	226.63	13.4	251.80	14.74											50 mph
9	187.43	11.3	212.63	12.5													
10	176.27	10.5	201.44	11.79													
11	167.11	9.9															
12	159.48	9.4															40 mph
13	153.02	9.0															

30 mph

* if carried out to two places (decimal) – full spiral (E_s) is indicated

81

TABLE IV
T_s AND E_s

D_c	$L_s=150'$ T_s	E_s	$200'$ T_s	E_s	$250'$ T_s	E_s	$300'$ T_s	E_s	$350'$ T_s	E_s	$400'$ T_s	E_s	$500'$ T_s	E_s	$600'$ T_s	E_s
1-30	782.99	65.3	808.02	65.5	833.06	65.7	858.12	66.0	883.18	66.4	908.25	66.8	958.41	67.8	1008.61	69.0
2-00	606.02	49.1	631.06	49.4	656.12	49.7	681.18	50.1	706.27	50.6	731.36	51.2	781.57	52.5	831.82	54.1
2-30	499.84	39.4	524.89	39.8	549.96	40.2	575.05	40.7	600.14	41.3	625.25	42.0	675.51	43.7	725.81	45.7
3-00	429.06	33.0	454.12	33.4	479.21	33.9	504.31	34.5	529.42	35.2	554.55	36.1	604.84	38.1	655.18	40.5
3-30	378.50	28.5	403.58	28.9	428.68	29.5	453.79	30.2	478.92	31.0	504.06	32.0	554.39	34.3	604.77	37.19
4-00	340.59	25.1	365.68	25.6	390.78	26.2	415.91	27.1	441.05	28.0	466.21	29.1	516.57	31.8		
5	287.52	20.3	312.63	21.0	337.76	21.8	362.90	22.8	388.07	24.0	413.26	25.4				
6	252.15	17.3	277.27	18.0	302.42	19.0	327.59	20.3	352.78	21.69						
7	226.89	15.1	252.03	16.0	277.19	17.2	302.38	18.60								
8	207.96	13.5	233.10	14.6	258.29	15.9										
9	193.23	12.3	218.39	13.5												
10	181.45	11.4	206.63	12.7												
11	171.82	10.7														
12	163.80	10.1														
13	157.01	9.7														
14	151.19	9.30														

70 mph · 60 mph · 50 mph · 40 mph · 30 mph

TABLE IV — T_s AND E_s — $\Delta = 22°$

D_c	$L_s = 150'$ T_s	E_s	$200'$ T_s	E_s	$250'$ T_s	E_s	$300'$ T_s	E_s	$350'$ T_s	E_s	$400'$ T_s	E_s	$500'$ T_s	E_s	$600'$ T_s	E_s
1-30	817.53	71.8	842.56	72.0	867.61	72.2	892.66	72.5	917.72	72.9	942.80	73.3	992.97	74.3	1043.18	75.5
2-00	631.92	54.0	656.97	54.2	682.03	54.6	707.10	55.0	732.18	55.4	757.28	56.0	807.50	57.3	857.77	59.0
2-30	520.56	43.3	545.62	43.6	570.69	44.1	595.78	44.6	620.89	45.2	646.00	45.9	696.27	47.5	746.59	49.6
3-00	446.33	36.3	471.40	36.6	496.49	37.1	521.59	37.8	546.71	38.5	571.85	39.3	622.15	41.3	672.52	43.7
3-30	393.31	31.2	418.39	31.7	443.49	32.3	468.61	33.0	493.75	33.8	518.90	34.8	569.25	37.1	619.65	40.0
4-00	353.55	27.5	378.64	28.0	403.75	28.7	428.88	29.5	454.04	30.4	479.20	31.6	529.59	34.2		
5	297.89	22.3	323.00	22.9	348.14	23.8	373.29	24.8	398.47	26.0	423.67	27.4				
6	260.80	18.9	285.92	19.7	311.08	20.7	336.26	21.9	361.46	23.3						
7	234.30	16.5	259.45	17.4	284.62	18.6	309.82	20.0								
8	214.44	14.7	239.60	15.8	264.79	17.1										
9	199.00	13.4	224.17	14.6												
10	186.65	12.4	211.84	13.7												
11	176.55	11.6	201.75	13.01												
12	168.13	10.9														
13	161.01	10.4														
14	154.91	10.0														

70 mph
60 mph
50 mph
40 mph
30 mph

83

D_c	$L_s = 150'$		200'		250'		300'		350'		400'		500'		600'	
	T_s	E_s	T_s	E_s	T_s	E_s	T_s	E_s	T_s	E_s	T_s	E_s	T_s	E_s	T_s	E_s
1-30	852.18	78.5	877.22	78.7	902.27	79.0	927.32	79.3	952.39	79.6	977.47	80.0	1027.65	81.0	1077.87	82.3
2-00	657.91	59.0	682.96	59.3	708.03	59.6	733.10	60.0	758.19	60.5	783.29	61.1	833.52	62.4	883.80	64.0
2-30	541.36	47.4	566.42	47.7	591.50	48.1	616.59	48.6	641.70	49.2	666.82	49.9	717.11	51.6	767.44	53.6
3-00	463.66	39.6	488.73	40.0	513.83	40.5	538.93	41.1	564.06	41.9	589.20	42.7	639.53	44.7	689.92	47.1
3-30	408.17	34.1	433.25	34.6	458.36	35.2	483.48	35.9	508.62	36.7	533.78	37.7	584.16	40.0	634.58	42.9
4-00	366.55	30.0	391.64	30.5	416.76	31.2	441.90	32.0	467.06	33.0	492.24	34.1	542.65	36.8		
5	308.30	24.3	333.41	25.0	358.55	25.8	383.72	26.8	408.91	28.0	434.12	29.4				
6	269.47	20.6	294.60	21.3	319.77	22.4	344.96	23.6	370.17	25.0						
7	241.74	17.9	266.89	18.8	292.08	20.0	317.29	21.4								
8	220.95	16.0	246.12	17.0	271.32	18.3										
9	204.79	14.5	229.97	15.7	255.19	17.2										
10	191.86	13.4	217.06	14.7												
11	181.29	12.5	206.50	13.9												
12	172.48	11.8														
13	165.03	11.2														
14	158.65	10.7														
15	153.12	10.3														

70 mph
60 mph
50 mph
40 mph
30 mph

TABLE IV
T_s AND E_s

Δ=23°

84

TABLE IV
T_s AND E_s   **Δ=24°**

D_c	$L_s=150'$ T_s	E_s	200' T_s	E_s	250' T_s	E_s	300' T_s	E_s	350' T_s	E_s	400' T_s	E_s	500' T_s	E_s	600' T_s	E_s
1-30	886.96	85.6	912.00	85.8	937.05	86.0	962.11	86.3	987.18	86.7	1012.26	87.1	1062.45	88.1	1112.68	89.3
2-00	684.00	64.3	709.05	64.6	734.12	64.9	759.19	65.3	784.29	65.8	809.39	66.4	859.64	67.7	909.93	69.3
2-30	562.23	51.6	587.29	52.0	612.37	52.4	637.47	52.9	662.58	53.5	687.71	54.2	738.01	55.8	788.36	57.9
3-00	481.05	43.2	506.13	43.6	531.23	44.1	556.34	44.7	581.47	45.4	606.62	46.2	656.97	48.2	707.38	50.7
3-30	423.08	37.2	448.16	37.6	473.27	38.2	498.41	38.9	523.56	39.8	548.73	40.7	599.12	43.1	649.57	45.9
4-00	379.60	32.7	404.70	33.2	429.82	33.9	454.97	34.7	480.14	35.6	505.32	36.8	555.75	39.4	606.25	42.69
5	318.74	26.4	343.86	27.1	369.01	27.9	394.18	28.9	419.38	30.2	444.60	31.5				
6	278.17	22.3	303.31	23.1	328.49	24.1	353.69	25.3	378.92	26.8	404.17	28.46				
7	249.20	19.5	274.36	20.4	299.56	21.5	324.79	23.0								
8	227.48	17.3	252.66	18.4	277.88	19.7	303.13	21.35								
9	210.60	15.7	235.79	16.9	261.03	18.4										
10	197.09	14.5	222.30	15.8												
11	186.05	13.5	211.27	14.9												
12	176.84	12.7	202.08	14.23												
13	169.06	12.0														
14	162.39	11.5														
15	156.62	11.0														
16	151.56	10.67														

70 mph · 60 mph · 50 mph · 40 mph · 30 mph

Δ=25°

TABLE IV
T_s AND E_s

Δ=25°

Speeds noted: 70 mph, 60 mph, 50 mph, 40 mph, 30 mph

D_c	L_s=150' T_s	E_s	200' T_s	E_s	250' T_s	E_s	300' T_s	E_s	350' T_s	E_s	400' T_s	E_s	500' T_s	E_s	600' T_s	E_s
1-30	921.87	93.0	946.91	93.2	971.96	93.4	997.02	93.7	1022.09	94.1	1047.18	94.5	1097.38	95.5	1147.62	96.8
2-00	710.18	69.9	735.23	70.2	760.30	70.5	785.38	70.9	810.48	71.4	835.59	71.9	885.85	73.3	936.16	74.9
2-30	583.18	56.1	608.24	56.4	633.33	56.8	658.43	57.3	683.55	57.9	708.68	58.6	759.00	60.3	809.36	62.4
3-00	498.51	46.9	523.59	47.3	548.69	47.8	573.81	48.4	598.95	49.1	624.11	49.9	674.47	52.0	724.90	54.4
3-30	438.04	40.3	463.13	40.8	488.25	41.4	513.39	42.1	538.54	42.9	563.72	43.9	614.13	46.3	664.61	49.1
4-00	392.69	35.4	417.80	36.0	442.93	36.6	468.08	37.5	493.26	38.4	518.45	39.5	568.91	42.2	619.44	45.5
5	329.22	28.7	354.34	29.3	379.50	30.1	404.68	31.2	429.89	32.4	455.13	33.8	505.66	37.12		
6	286.91	24.2	312.05	25.0	337.24	26.0	362.45	27.2	387.69	28.7	412.96	30.3				
7	256.69	21.0	281.86	22.0	307.07	23.1	332.31	24.6	357.57	26.3						
8	234.04	18.7	259.23	19.8	284.46	21.1	309.72	22.7								
9	216.43	17.0	241.63	18.1	266.88	19.6										
10	202.34	15.6	227.56	16.9	252.83	18.56										
11	190.82	14.5	216.06	15.9												
12	181.23	13.6	206.48	15.2												
13	173.11	12.9														
14	166.15	12.3														
15	160.13	11.8														
16	154.86	11.4														

Δ = 26°

TABLE IV
T_s AND E_s Δ=26°

D_c	$L_s = 150'$ T_s	E_s	$200'$ T_s	E_s	$250'$ T_s	E_s	$300'$ T_s	E_s	$350'$ T_s	E_s	$400'$ T_s	E_s	$500'$ T_s	E_s	$600'$ T_s	E_s	
1-30	956.91	100.7	981.95	100.9	1007.00	101.2	1032.07	101.5	1057.15	101.9	1082.23	102.2	1132.45	103.3	1182.70	104.5	70 mph
2-00	736.46	75.7	761.52	75.9	786.59	76.3	811.68	76.7	836.78	77.2	861.89	77.7	912.16	79.1	962.49	80.7	
2-30	604.20	60.7	629.27	61.0	654.36	61.4	679.47	62.0	704.59	62.6	729.73	63.3	780.06	64.9	830.45	67.0	
3-00	516.04	50.7	541.12	51.1	566.22	51.6	591.35	52.2	616.49	53.0	641.66	53.8	692.04	55.8	742.49	58.3	60 mph
3-30	453.06	43.6	478.16	44.1	503.28	44.7	528.42	45.4	553.59	46.3	578.78	47.2	629.21	49.6	679.71	52.5	
4-00	405.84	38.3	430.95	38.9	456.08	39.5	481.24	40.4	506.43	41.3	531.64	42.4	582.12	45.1	632.67	48.4	
5	339.73	31.0	364.87	31.6	390.03	32.5	415.22	33.5	440.45	34.7	465.69	36.1	516.26	39.5			50 mph
6	295.67	26.1	320.83	26.9	346.02	27.9	371.25	29.1	396.50	30.6	421.78	32.3					
7	264.21	22.7	289.39	23.6	314.61	24.8	339.86	26.2	365.14	27.9							
8	240.62	20.2	265.82	21.2	291.06	22.6	316.34	24.2									
9	222.28	18.5	247.50	19.4	272.76	20.9											
10	207.61	16.7	232.85	18.1	258.13	19.7											40 mph
11	195.62	15.5	220.87	17.0													
12	185.62	14.6	210.89	16.1													
13	177.17	13.8	202.45	15.47													
14	169.93	13.1															
15	163.66	12.6															
16	158.17	12.1															
17	153.33	11.7															30 mph

87

TABLE IV
T_s AND E_s

Δ = 27°

D_c	L_s=150' T_s	E_s	200' T_s	E_s	250' T_s	E_s	300' T_s	E_s	350' T_s	E_s	400' T_s	E_s	500' T_s	E_s	600' T_s	E_s
1-30	992.09	108.8	1017.14	109.0	1042.19	109.3	1067.26	109.6	1092.34	109.9	1117.43	110.3	1167.65	111.4	1217.92	112.6
2-00	762.85	81.8	787.91	82.0	812.99	82.4	838.07	82.8	863.18	83.2	888.30	83.8	938.58	85.2	988.92	86.8
2-30	625.32	65.6	650.39	65.9	675.48	66.3	700.59	66.8	725.72	67.4	750.87	68.1	801.21	69.8	851.62	71.9
3-00	533.63	54.8	558.72	55.2	583.83	55.7	608.96	56.3	634.11	57.0	659.28	57.9	709.68	59.9	760.16	62.3
3-30	468.15	47.1	493.25	47.6	518.37	48.2	543.52	48.9	568.70	49.7	593.89	50.7	644.35	53.1	694.88	55.9
4-00	419.04	41.4	444.15	41.9	469.29	42.6	494.46	43.4	519.66	44.4	544.87	45.5	525.38	48.2	645.96	51.5
5	350.30	33.4	375.43	34.1	400.61	34.9	425.81	35.9	451.04	37.1	476.30	38.5	526.89	41.9		
6	304.48	28.1	329.64	28.9	354.84	29.9	380.08	31.2	405.35	32.6	430.64	34.3				
7	271.76	24.4	296.95	25.4	322.17	26.5	347.44	28.0	372.73	29.7						
8	247.23	21.7	272.44	22.7	297.69	24.1	322.98	25.7								
9	228.16	19.6	253.39	20.8	278.66	22.3	303.98	24.14								
10	212.91	18.0	238.15	19.3	263.45	21.0										
11	200.43	16.7	225.70	18.1												
12	190.04	15.6	215.32	17.2												
13	181.25	14.7	206.55	16.4												
14	173.72	14.0														
15	167.20	13.4														
16	161.49	12.9														
17	156.46	12.4														
18	151.99	12.07														

Design speed boundaries (staircase): 70 mph, 60 mph, 50 mph, 40 mph, 30 mph.

TABLE IV — T_s and E_s $\Delta = 28°$

D_c	$L_s=150'$ T_s	E_s	$200'$ T_s	E_s	$250'$ T_s	E_s	$300'$ T_s	E_s	$350'$ T_s	E_s	$400'$ T_s	E_s	$500'$ T_s	E_s	$600'$ T_s	E_s	
1-30	1027.42	117.2	1052.47	117.4	1077.53	117.6	1102.60	117.9	1127.68	118.3	1152.78	118.7	1203.01	119.7	1253.28	121.0	
2-00	789.35	88.0	814.41	88.3	839.49	88.3	864.58	89.0	889.69	89.5	914.82	90.1	965.11	91.4	1015.47	93.1	
2-30	646.52	70.6	671.59	70.9	696.69	71.3	721.80	71.8	746.94	72.4	772.09	73.2	822.45	74.8	872.88	76.9	70 mph
3-00	551.30	59.0	576.39	59.4	601.50	59.9	626.64	60.5	651.80	61.2	676.98	62.1	727.40	64.1	777.89	66.5	60 mph
3-30	483.29	50.7	508.40	51.2	533.53	51.7	558.69	52.5	583.87	53.3	609.07	54.3	659.55	56.7	710.10	59.5	
4-00	432.29	44.5	457.41	45.0	482.56	45.7	507.73	46.5	532.94	47.5	558.16	48.6	608.69	51.3	659.31	54.6	
5	360.90	35.9	386.05	36.6	411.23	37.4	436.44	38.5	461.68	39.7	486.95	41.1	537.58	44.4			50 mph
6	313.32	30.2	338.49	31.0	363.70	32.0	388.95	33.3	414.23	34.7	439.54	36.4					
7	279.34	26.2	304.54	27.2	329.77	28.3	355.05	29.8	380.36	31.5	405.71	33.43					
8	253.87	23.3	279.08	24.3	304.35	25.7	329.65	27.3	355.00	29.25							
9	234.06	21.0	259.30	22.2	284.59	23.7	309.92	25.5									
10	218.22	19.2	243.48	20.5	268.79	22.2											
11	205.26	17.8	230.54	19.2	255.87	21.1											40 mph
12	194.47	16.6	219.77	18.2													
13	185.35	15.7	210.66	17.4													
14	177.53	14.9	202.85	16.72													
15	170.75	14.2															
16	164.83	13.7															
17	159.60	13.2															
18	154.96	12.8															

30 mph

$\Delta = 28°$

89

TABLE IV — T_s AND E_s — Δ=29°

D_c	$L_s=150'$ T_s	E_s	$200'$ T_s	E_s	$250'$ T_s	E_s	$300'$ T_s	E_s	$350'$ T_s	E_s	$400'$ T_s	E_s	$500'$ T_s	E_s	$600'$ T_s	E_s
1-30	1062.91	125.9	1087.96	126.1	1113.02	126.4	1138.09	126.7	1163.18	127.0	1188.28	127.5	1238.52	128.5	1288.80	129.7
2-00	815.97	94.6	841.03	94.9	866.11	95.2	891.21	95.6	916.32	96.1	941.45	96.7	991.76	98.0	1042.13	99.7
2-30	667.81	75.8	692.89	76.2	717.99	76.6	743.11	77.1	768.25	77.7	793.41	78.4	843.79	80.1	894.23	82.2
3-00	569.05	63.3	594.14	63.7	619.26	64.2	644.40	64.9	669.57	65.6	694.75	66.4	745.19	68.5	795.71	70.9
3-30	498.50	54.4	523.61	54.9	548.75	55.5	573.91	56.2	599.10	57.1	624.32	58.1	674.81	60.4	725.40	63.3
4-00	445.60	47.8	470.73	48.3	495.88	49.0	521.07	49.8	546.28	50.8	571.51	51.9	622.07	54.6	672.71	57.9
5	371.56	38.5	396.70	39.2	421.89	40.0	447.11	41.1	472.37	42.3	497.65	43.7	548.31	47.1		
6	322.20	32.4	347.38	33.2	372.60	34.2	397.85	35.5	423.15	36.9	448.47	38.6				
7	286.96	28.1	312.16	29.0	337.41	30.2	362.70	31.7	388.02	33.4	413.39	35.3				
8	260.53	24.9	285.76	26.0	311.03	27.3	336.35	29.0	361.71	30.9						
9	239.99	22.5	265.24	23.6	290.54	25.2	315.89	27.0								
10	223.56	20.5	248.83	21.9	274.15	23.5										
11	210.12	19.0	235.41	20.4	260.76	22.3										
12	198.93	17.7	224.24	19.3												
13	189.46	16.7	214.79	18.4												
14	181.35	15.8	206.69	17.7												
15	174.32	15.1														
16	168.18	14.5														
17	162.76	14.0														
18	157.94	13.5														
19	153.64	13.1														

Speed annotations: 70 mph, 60 mph, 50 mph, 40 mph, 30 mph

D_c	$L_s = 150'$		$200'$		$250'$		$300'$		$350'$		$400'$		$500'$		$600'$		$\Delta = 30°$
	T_s	E_s	T_s	E_s	T_s	E_s	T_s	E_s	T_s	E_s	T_s	E_s	T_s	E_s	T_s	E_s	
1-30	1098.56	135.0	1123.61	135.2	1148.67	135.5	1173.75	135.8	1198.83	136.1	1223.94	136.1	1274.19	137.6	1324.48	138.8	
2-00	842.71	101.4	867.77	101.7	892.85	102.0	917.95	102.4	943.07	102.9	968.21	103.5	1018.53	104.8	1068.91	106.5	
2-30	689.20	81.3	714.28	81.6	739.39	82.0	764.51	82.5	789.66	83.2	814.82	83.9	865.22	85.6	915.67	87.6	70 mph
3-00	586.87	67.9	611.97	68.3	637.09	68.8	662.24	69.4	687.41	70.1	712.61	71.0	763.06	73.0	813.60	75.5	
3-30	513.79	58.3	538.90	58.8	564.04	59.4	589.21	60.1	614.41	61.0	639.63	62.0	690.15	64.3	740.76	67.2	
4-00	458.98	51.2	484.10	51.7	509.26	52.4	534.46	53.2	559.68	54.2	584.92	55.4	635.50	58.1	686.17	61.4	60 mph
5	382.26	41.3	407.41	41.9	432.61	42.8	457.84	43.8	483.10	45.0	508.40	46.4	559.08	49.8	609.86	53.95	
6	331.12	34.7	356.30	35.5	381.53	36.5	406.80	37.8	432.11	39.2	457.45	40.9	508.22	44.95			
7	294.61	30.1	319.82	31.0	345.07	32.2	370.38	33.6	395.72	35.3	421.10	37.3					50 mph
8	267.23	26.6	292.46	27.7	317.75	29.0	343.09	30.7	368.46	32.6							
9	245.94	24.0	271.20	25.2	296.52	26.7	321.88	28.5									
10	228.92	21.9	254.20	23.2	279.54	24.9	304.93	26.97									
11	215.00	20.2	240.30	21.7	265.67	23.5											
12	203.40	18.9	228.72	20.5	254.11	22.48											40 mph
13	193.59	17.8	218.93	19.5													
14	185.19	16.8	210.55	18.6													
15	177.91	16.0	203.29	17.98													
16	171.54	15.3															
17	165.93	14.8															
18	160.94	14.3															
19	156.48	13.9															
20	152.47	13.49															

Δ = 30°

TABLE IV
T_s AND E_s

30 mph

TABLE IV — Tₛ AND Eₛ — Δ=31°

D_c	$L_s=150'$ Tₛ	Eₛ	$200'$ Tₛ	Eₛ	$250'$ Tₛ	Eₛ	$300'$ Tₛ	Eₛ	$350'$ Tₛ	Eₛ	$400'$ Tₛ	Eₛ	$500'$ Tₛ	Eₛ	$600'$ Tₛ	Eₛ
1-30	1134.37	144.4	1159.42	144.6	1184.49	144.9	1209.57	145.2	1224.66	145.5	1259.76	146.0	1310.02	147.0	1360.33	148.2
2-00	869.57	108.5	894.63	108.7	919.72	109.1	944.82	109.5	969.95	110.0	995.09	110.5	1045.42	111.9	1095.82	113.5
2-30	710.69	86.9	735.78	87.2	760.88	87.7	786.01	88.2	811.16	88.8	836.34	89.5	886.74	91.2	937.22	93.3
3-00	604.78	72.6	629.88	73.0	655.01	73.5	680.17	74.1	705.34	74.9	730.55	75.7	781.02	77.7	831.58	80.2
3-30	529.14	62.4	554.26	62.8	579.40	63.4	604.58	64.2	629.79	65.0	655.02	66.0	705.56	68.4	756.19	71.3
4-00	472.41	54.7	497.54	55.3	522.71	55.9	547.91	56.8	573.14	57.8	598.40	58.9	649.00	61.6	699.70	64.9
5	393.01	44.1	418.17	44.8	443.37	45.6	468.61	46.6	493.89	47.9	519.20	49.3	569.91	52.7	620.73	56.8
6	340.08	37.1	365.27	37.8	390.51	38.9	415.79	40.1	441.11	41.6	466.47	43.3	517.27	47.3		
7	302.29	32.1	327.51	33.0	352.78	34.2	378.10	35.6	403.45	37.4	428.85	39.3				
8	273.96	28.4	299.20	29.4	324.50	30.8	349.85	32.5	375.25	34.4						
9	251.92	25.6	277.19	26.7	302.52	28.3	327.91	30.1								
10	234.31	23.3	259.60	24.6	284.96	26.3	310.36	28.4								
11	219.90	21.5	245.22	23.0	270.60	24.8										
12	207.90	20.1	233.23	21.6	258.64	23.7										
13	197.74	18.8	223.10	20.6												
14	189.05	17.8	214.43	19.7												
15	181.51	17.0	206.91	18.9												
16	174.93	16.2														
17	169.11	15.6														
18	163.95	15.1														
19	159.34	14.6														
20	155.18	14.2														

Speed zone labels (along stepped boundary): 70 mph, 60 mph, 50 mph, 40 mph, 30 mph

$\Delta=31°$

Table IV — T_s and E_s, $\Delta = 32°$

D_c	$L_s=150'$ T_s	E_s	$200'$ T_s	E_s	$250'$ T_s	E_s	$300'$ T_s	E_s	$350'$ T_s	E_s	$400'$ T_s	E_s	$500'$ T_s	E_s	$600'$ T_s	E_s
1-30	1170.36	154.2	1195.41	154.4	1220.48	154.6	1245.56	155.0	1270.66	155.3	1295.77	155.7	1346.03	156.8	1396.35	158.0
2-00	896.56	115.8	921.63	116.1	946.72	116.4	971.82	116.8	996.95	117.3	1022.10	117.9	1072.44	119.2	1122.86	120.9
2-30	732.29	92.8	757.37	93.1	782.48	93.5	807.62	94.1	832.78	94.7	857.95	95.4	908.38	97.1	958.88	99.2
3-00	622.78	77.5	647.88	77.9	673.02	78.4	698.18	79.0	723.36	79.7	748.57	80.6	799.06	82.6	849.65	85.1
3-30	544.57	66.6	569.69	67.0	594.84	67.6	620.02	68.4	645.24	69.2	670.48	70.2	721.04	72.6	771.70	75.5
4-00	485.91	58.4	511.05	58.9	536.22	59.6	561.43	60.4	586.67	61.4	611.93	62.6	662.56	65.3	713.29	68.6
5	403.81	47.0	428.98	47.7	454.19	48.5	479.44	49.6	504.73	50.8	530.05	52.2	580.79	55.6	631.65	59.8
6	349.09	39.5	374.29	40.3	399.53	41.3	424.82	42.6	450.16	44.0	475.53	45.7	526.37	49.8		
7	310.01	34.2	335.24	35.1	360.52	36.3	385.85	37.7	411.22	39.5	436.64	41.4				
8	280.71	30.2	305.97	31.3	331.28	32.6	356.65	34.3	382.06	36.3	407.51	38.52				
9	257.94	27.2	283.22	28.4	308.56	29.9	333.96	31.8	359.40	34.0						
10	239.72	24.8	265.02	26.1	290.40	27.8	315.82	29.9								
11	224.82	22.9	250.15	24.3	275.55	26.2										
12	212.41	21.3	237.76	22.9	263.19	24.9										
13	201.92	20.0	227.29	21.7												
14	192.93	18.9	218.32	20.7												
15	185.14	17.9	210.55	19.91												
16	178.32	17.2	203.75	19.26												
17	172.32	16.5														
18	166.98	15.9														
19	162.21	15.4														
20	157.91	14.9														
21	154.03	14.6														

Speed annotations along stepped boundary: 70 mph, 60 mph, 50 mph, 40 mph, 30 mph.

D_c	L_s=150'		200'		250'		300'		350'		400'		500'		600'	
	T_s	E_s	T_s	E_s	T_s	E_s	T_s	E_s	T_s	E_s	T_s	E_s	T_s	E_s	T_s	E_s
1-30	1206.52	164.3	1231.58	164.5	1256.65	164.8	1281.73	165.1	1306.83	165.4	1331.95	165.9	1382.22	166.9	1432.56	168.1
2-00	923.69	123.4	948.76	123.7	973.85	124.0	998.96	124.4	1024.10	124.9	1049.25	125.5	1099.60	126.8	1150.03	128.5
2-30	753.99	98.9	779.08	99.2	804.19	99.6	829.33	100.1	854.50	100.8	879.68	101.5	930.12	103.2	980.64	105.3
3-00	640.87	82.5	665.97	82.9	691.11	83.4	716.28	84.1	741.47	84.8	766.69	85.7	817.20	87.7	867.81	90.2
3-30	560.07	70.9	585.20	71.4	610.36	72.0	635.55	72.7	660.77	73.6	686.01	74.6	736.60	76.9	787.28	79.9
4-00	499.48	62.2	524.62	62.7	549.80	63.4	575.02	64.3	600.26	65.2	625.54	66.4	676.19	69.1	726.95	72.4
5	414.67	50.1	439.84	50.7	465.06	51.6	490.32	52.6	515.62	53.9	540.95	55.3	591.73	58.7	642.62	62.8
6	358.14	42.0	383.34	42.8	408.60	43.9	433.90	45.1	459.25	46.6	484.64	48.3	535.52	52.4		
7	317.77	36.3	343.01	37.3	368.30	38.5	393.64	39.9	419.03	41.6						
8	287.51	32.1	312.77	33.2	338.10	34.6	363.48	36.2	388.91	38.2	414.38	40.4				
9	263.98	28.9	289.27	30.1	314.63	31.6	340.04	33.5	365.50	35.7						
10	245.16	26.3	270.48	27.6	295.87	29.3	321.31	31.4								
11	229.77	24.2	255.11	25.7	280.53	27.6	306.00	29.86								
12	216.95	22.6	242.32	24.1	267.76	26.2										
13	206.11	21.1	231.50	22.9	256.96	25.1										
14	196.82	20.0	222.23	21.8												
15	188.78	19.0	214.21	20.9												
16	181.74	18.1	207.19	20.2												
17	175.53	17.4														
18	170.02	16.7														
19	165.09	16.2														
20	160.66	15.7														
21	156.64	15.3														
22	153.00	14.93														

Speed boundary markers: 70 mph, 60 mph, 50 mph, 40 mph, 30 mph

TABLE IV
T_s AND E_s

Δ=33°

TABLE IV — Tₛ and Eₛ, Δ=34°

D_c	$L_s=150'$ T_s	E_s	$200'$ T_s	E_s	$250'$ T_s	E_s	$300'$ T_s	E_s	$350'$ T_s	E_s	$400'$ T_s	E_s	$500'$ T_s	E_s	$600'$ T_s	E_s	
1-30	1242.88	174.8	1267.94	175.0	1293.01	175.2	1318.10	175.5	1343.20	175.9	1368.32	176.3	1418.60	177.4	1468.95	178.6	
2-00	950.95	131.2	976.03	131.5	1001.13	131.5	1026.24	132.3	1051.38	132.8	1076.53	133.3	1126.90	134.7	1177.35	136.4	
2-30	775.81	105.1	800.90	105.5	826.02	105.9	851.16	106.4	876.33	107.0	901.52	107.8	951.98	109.5	1002.51	111.6	
3-00	659.05	87.8	684.16	88.2	709.30	88.7	734.47	89.3	759.67	90.1	784.90	90.9	835.43	93.0	886.06	95.5	70 mph
3-30	575.66	75.4	600.79	75.9	625.95	76.5	651.15	77.2	676.38	78.1	701.63	79.1	752.24	81.4	802.95	84.4	
4-00	513.12	66.1	538.27	66.7	563.45	67.3	588.67	68.2	613.93	69.2	639.22	70.3	689.89	73.0	740.69	76.4	
5	425.58	53.2	450.76	53.9	475.99	54.7	501.26	55.8	526.57	57.0	551.92	58.4	602.72	61.8	653.65	66.0	60 mph
6	367.24	44.7	392.45	45.5	417.71	46.5	443.03	47.7	468.39	49.2	493.79	50.9	544.71	55.0			
7	325.57	38.6	350.82	39.5	376.12	40.7	401.48	42.2	426.88	43.9	452.33	45.9					50 mph
8	294.34	34.1	319.61	35.2	344.95	36.5	370.34	38.2	395.79	40.2	421.28	42.4					
9	270.05	30.6	295.35	31.8	320.72	33.4	346.16	35.2	371.64	37.4							
10	250.63	27.9	275.96	29.2	301.36	30.9	326.83	33.0									
11	234.74	25.7	260.10	27.1	285.53	29.0	311.03	31.3									40 mph
12	221.52	23.9	246.90	25.5	272.35	27.5											
13	210.32	22.4	235.73	24.1	261.21	26.3											
14	200.74	21.1	226.17	22.9													
15	192.43	20.0	217.88	22.0													
16	185.17	19.1	210.64	21.2													
17	178.77	18.3	204.26	20.55													
18	173.08	17.6															
19	167.99	17.0															
20	163.41	16.5															
21	159.27	16.0															
22	155.51	15.7															

30 mph

95

Δ=35°

TABLE IV — T_s AND E_s

D_c	L_s=150' T_s	E_s	200' T_s	E_s	250' T_s	E_s	300' T_s	E_s	350' T_s	E_s	400' T_s	E_s	500' T_s	E_s	600' T_s	E_s	mph
1-30	1279.43	185.6	1304.49	185.8	1329.56	186.1	1354.65	186.4	1379.76	186.8	1404.88	187.2	1455.18	188.2	1505.53	189.5	
2-00	978.37	139.4	1003.44	139.6	1028.54	140.0	1053.66	140.4	1078.80	140.7	1103.97	141.5	1154.35	142.8	1204.81	144.5	
2-30	797.74	111.7	822.83	112.0	847.96	112.4	873.11	112.9	898.28	113.6	923.48	114.3	973.95	116.0	1024.50'	118.1	
3-00	677.33	93.2	702.44	93.6	727.59	94.1	752.77	94.7	777.97	95.5	803.20	96.3	853.75	98.4	904.41	100.9	70 mph
3-30	591.33	80.0	616.46	80.5	641.63	81.1	666.83	81.8	692.07	82.7	717.34	83.7	767.96	86.1	818.70	89.0	
4-00	526.83	70.2	551.98	70.7	577.17	71.4	602.40	72.3	627.67	73.3	652.97	74.4	703.67	77.1	754.49	80.5	
5	436.55	56.5	461.74	57.1	486.97	58.0	512.25	59.0	537.57	60.3	562.93	61.7	613.77	65.1	664.74	69.3	60 mph
6	376.38	47.4	401.60	48.2	426.88	49.2	452.20	50.5	477.58	51.9	503.00	51.9	553.95	57.8			
7	333.42	40.9	358.67	41.9	383.98	43.1	409.35	44.5	434.77	46.3	460.24	46.3	511.30	53.02			
8	301.20	36.1	326.48	37.2	351.84	38.6	377.25	40.2	402.71	42.2	428.22	44.5					50 mph
9	276.16	32.4	301.47	33.6	326.85	35.2	352.30	37.1	377.81	39.3							
10	256.13	29.5	281.47	30.9	306.89	32.6	332.37	34.7	357.91	37.12							
11	239.75	27.2	265.12	28.6	290.56	30.5	316.08	32.8									
12	226.10	25.2	251.50	26.8	276.37	28.9											
13	214.56	23.6	239.98	25.3	265.49	27.6											
14	204.68	22.3	230.12	24.1	255.65	26.51											40 mph
15	196.11	21.1	221.58	23.1													
16	188.62	20.1	214.11	22.2													
17	182.02	19.3	207.53	21.5													
18	176.15	18.5															
19	170.91	17.9															
20	166.19	17.3															
21	161.92	16.8															
22	158.04	16.4															
23	154.50	16.0															30 mph

Δ=35°

Δ = 36°

TABLE IV
Tₛ AND Eₛ

Dc	Ls = 150' Tₛ	Eₛ	200' Tₛ	Eₛ	250' Tₛ	Eₛ	300' Tₛ	Eₛ	350' Tₛ	Eₛ	400' Tₛ	Eₛ	500' Tₛ	Eₛ	600' Tₛ	Eₛ	
1-30	1316.18	196.8	1341.24	197.0	1366.32	197.3	1391.41	197.6	1416.52	198.0	1441.65	198.4	1491.95	199.4	1542.32	200.7	
2-00	1005.93	147.8	1031.01	148.0	1056.11	148.4	1081.24	148.8	1106.38	149.3	1131.55	149.9	1181.94	151.2	1232.42	152.9	
2-30	819.79	118.4	844.89	118.7	870.02	119.1	895.17	119.7	920.35	120.3	945.55	121.0	996.04	122.7	1046.61	124.8	
3-00	695.71	98.8	720.82	99.2	745.98	99.7	771.16	100.3	796.37	101.1	821.61	101.9	872.18	104.0	922.86	106.5	70 mph
3-30	607.08	84.8	632.22	85.3	657.39	85.9	682.60	86.7	707.85	87.5	733.12	88.5	783.77	90.9	834.54	93.9	
4-00	540.62	74.4	565.78	74.9	590.97	75.6	616.21	76.5	641.48	77.5	666.79	78.6	717.52	81.4	768.37	84.7	
5	447.59	59.8	472.78	60.5	498.02	61.4	523.31	62.4	548.64	63.7	574.02	65.1	624.88	68.5	675.89	72.7	60 mph
6	385.58	50.2	410.81	51.0	436.09	52.0	461.43	53.2	486.82	54.8	512.25	56.5	563.24	60.6	614.38	65.59	
7	341.30	43.3	366.56	44.3	391.89	45.5	417.27	46.9	442.71	48.7	468.20	50.7	519.30	55.5			
8	308.11	38.2	333.40	39.3	358.76	40.7	384.19	42.4	409.67	44.3	435.20	46.6					50 mph
9	282.29	34.3	307.62	35.5	333.02	37.1	358.49	38.9	384.01	41.2	409.58	43.73					
10	261.65	31.2	287.01	32.5	312.44	34.3	337.94	36.3	363.51	38.8							
11	244.77	28.7	270.16	30.2	295.62	32.1	321.16	34.4									
12	230.71	26.6	256.12	28.2	281.62	30.3	307.19	32.80									
13	218.82	24.9	244.26	26.6	269.78	28.9											
14	208.64	23.5	234.10	25.3	259.65	27.7											40 mph
15	199.81	22.2	225.30	24.2													
16	192.09	21.2	217.60	23.3													
17	185.29	20.3	210.82	22.5													
18	179.24	19.5	204.79	21.87													
19	173.84	18.8															
20	168.97	18.2															
21	164.57	17.6															
22	160.58	17.2															
23	156.93	16.8															
24	153.59	16.40															

30 mph

Δ=37°

TABLE IV — T_s AND E_s

D_c	$L_s=150'$ T_s	E_s	$200'$ T_s	E_s	$250'$ T_s	E_s	$300'$ T_s	E_s	$350'$ T_s	E_s	$400'$ T_s	E_s	$500'$ T_s	E_s	$600'$ T_s	E_s
1-30	1353.14	208.4	1378.21	208.6	1403.28	208.9	1428.38	209.2	1453.49	209.5	1478.62	210.0	1528.94	211.0	1579.31	212.3
2-00	1033.65	156.4	1058.74	156.7	1083.84	157.1	1108.97	157.5	1134.12	158.0	1159.29	158.6	1209.70	159.9	1260.19	161.6
2-30	841.97	125.3	867.07	125.6	892.20	126.1	917.36	126.6	942.55	127.2	967.76	127.9	1018.26	129.7	1068.85	131.8
3-00	714.19	104.6	739.31	105.0	764.47	105.5	789.66	106.1	814.88	106.9	840.13	107.7	890.71	109.8	941.41	112.3
3-30	622.93	89.8	648.07	90.3	673.25	90.9	698.46	91.6	723.72	92.5	749.00	93.5	799.67	95.9	850.47	98.9
4-00	554.48	78.7	579.65	79.3	604.85	80.0	630.09	80.8	655.38	81.8	680.70	83.0	731.45	85.7	782.23	89.1
5	458.68	63.3	483.88	64.0	509.13	64.8	534.43	65.9	559.77	67.1	585.16	68.6	636.06	72.0	687.10	76.2
6	394.83	53.1	420.06	53.9	445.36	54.9	470.71	56.2	496.11	57.7	521.56	59.4	572.59	63.5	623.77	68.5
7	349.23	45.8	374.50	46.7	399.84	48.0	425.23	49.4	450.69	51.2	476.19	53.2	527.34	58.0		
8	315.05	40.4	340.35	41.5	365.73	42.9	391.17	44.5	416.67	46.5	442.22	48.8				
9	288.47	36.2	313.88	37.4	339.22	39.0	364.70	40.9	390.24	43.1	415.85	45.7				
10	267.21	32.9	292.58	34.3	318.03	36.0	343.55	38.1	369.14	40.6						
11	249.83	30.3	275.23	31.8	300.71	33.6	326.27	36.0								
12	235.35	28.1	260.78	29.7	286.29	31.8	311.88	34.3								
13	223.11	26.3	248.56	28.0	274.11	30.2										
14	212.62	24.7	238.10	26.6	263.67	29.0										
15	203.53	23.4	229.03	25.4												
16	195.58	22.3	221.11	24.4												
17	188.58	21.3	214.13	23.4												
18	182.35	20.4	207.92	22.8												
19	176.78	19.7														
20	171.78	19.1														
21	167.25	18.5														
22	163.14	18.0														
23	159.38	17.5														
24	155.94	17.1														

Design speed boundaries marked: 70 mph, 60 mph, 50 mph, 40 mph, 30 mph

Δ=37°

TABLE IV — T_s AND E_s ($\Delta = 38°$)

D_c	$L_s=150'$ T_s	E_s	$200'$ T_s	E_s	$250'$ T_s	E_s	$300'$ T_s	E_s	$350'$ T_s	E_s	$400'$ T_s	E_s	$500'$ T_s	E_s	$600'$ T_s	E_s	speed
1-30	1390.32	220.4	1415.38	220.6	1440.47	220.8	1465.56	221.1	1490.68	221.5	1515.81	221.9	1566.14	223.0	1616.53	224.2	
2-00	1061.54	165.4	1086.62	165.7	1111.73	166.0	1136.86	166.4	1162.02	167.0	1187.19	167.5	1237.61	168.9	1288.12	170.6	
2-30	864.28	132.5	889.39	132.8	914.52	133.3	939.68	133.8	964.87	134.4	990.09	135.1	1040.61	136.9	1091.22	139.0	
3-00	732.78	110.6	757.91	111.0	783.07	111.5	808.26	112.1	833.49	112.9	858.75	113.7	909.35	115.8	960.07	118.3	70 mph
3-30	638.86	94.9	664.01	95.4	689.20	96.0	711.42	96.7	739.68	97.6	764.97	98.6	815.67	101.1	866.49	104.0	
4-00	568.43	83.2	593.60	83.8	618.81	84.5	644.06	85.3	669.35	86.3	694.68	87.5	745.46	90.2	796.38	93.6	
5	469.84	66.9	495.05	67.6	520.30	68.4	545.61	69.5	570.97	70.7	596.37	72.2	647.30	75.6	698.38	79.8	60 mph
6	404.13	56.1	429.37	56.9	454.68	57.9	480.04	59.2	505.45	60.7	530.92	62.4	581.99	66.5	633.21	71.6	
7	357.21	48.4	382.49	49.3	407.83	50.5	433.24	52.0	458.71	53.7	484.24	55.8	535.43	60.6			
8	322.03	42.7	347.34	43.7	372.73	45.1	398.19	46.8	423.71	48.8	449.28	51.1					50 mph
9	294.68	38.2	320.03	39.4	345.45	41.0	370.95	42.9	396.52	45.1	422.14	47.7					
10	272.81	34.7	298.18	36.1	323.65	37.8	349.95	39.9	374.80	42.4							
11	254.92	31.9	280.33	33.4	305.83	35.4	331.41	37.6									
12	240.02	29.6	265.46	31.2	290.99	33.3	316.61	35.8									
13	227.42	27.6	252.89	29.4	278.45	31.6											
14	216.62	26.0	242.12	27.9	267.72	30.3											40 mph
15	207.27	24.6	232.79	26.6	258.42	29.2											
16	199.10	23.4	224.64	25.5													
17	191.88	22.4	217.46	24.6													
18	185.48	21.5	211.07	23.9													
19	179.75	20.7	205.36	23.20													
20	174.60	20.0															
21	169.94	19.3															
22	165.70	18.8															30 mph
23	161.84	18.3															
24	158.30	17.9															
25	155.05	17.5															

99

Δ=39°

TABLE IV
T_s AND E_s

Δ=39°

Speed reference lines: 70 mph, 60 mph, 50 mph, 40 mph, 30 mph

D_c	$L_s=150'$ T_s	E_s	200' T_s	E_s	250' T_s	E_s	300' T_s	E_s	350' T_s	E_s	400' T_s	E_s	500' T_s	E_s	600' T_s	E_s
1-30	1427.72	232.7	1452.79	232.9	1477.87	233.2	1502.97	233.5	1528.09	233.8	1553.23	234.3	1603.56	235.3	1653.96	236.6
2-00	1089.59	174.7	1114.68	174.9	1139.79	175.3	1164.92	175.7	1190.08	176.2	1215.27	176.8	1265.70	178.2	1316.22	179.9
2-30	886.72	139.9	911.83	140.2	936.97	140.7	962.14	141.2	987.33	141.8	1012.56	142.5	1063.09	144.3	1113.72	146.4
3-00	751.49	116.7	776.62	117.1	801.78	117.7	826.98	118.3	852.21	119.1	877.48	119.9	928.10	122.0	978.85	124.5
3-30	654.90	100.2	680.05	100.7	705.24	101.3	730.47	102.0	755.74	102.9	781.04	103.9	831.76	106.4	882.61	109.3
4-00	582.46	87.9	607.63	88.4	632.85	89.1	658.11	89.9	683.41	90.9	708.75	92.1	759.56	94.9	810.50	98.3
5	481.07	70.6	506.28	71.3	531.55	72.1	556.86	73.2	582.23	74.5	607.64	75.9	658.61	79.4	709.73	83.6
6	413.49	59.1	438.74	60.0	464.05	61.0	489.43	62.3	514.85	63.8	540.34	65.5	591.44	69.7	642.72	74.7
7	365.23	51.0	390.52	52.0	415.88	53.2	441.30	54.7	466.79	56.4	492.33	58.4	543.57	63.3		
8	329.06	45.0	354.38	46.0	379.78	47.4	405.25	49.1	430.79	51.1	456.39	53.4				
9	300.93	40.3	326.28	41.5	351.73	43.1	377.25	45.0	402.83	47.2	428.48	49.8				
10	278.43	36.6	303.82	37.9	329.31	39.7	354.87	41.8	380.50	44.3						
11	260.04	33.6	285.46	35.1	310.98	37.0	336.58	39.3	362.25	42.0						
12	244.71	31.1	270.17	32.8	295.72	34.8	321.36	37.4								
13	231.75	29.1	257.24	30.8	282.82	33.1	308.50	35.81								
14	220.65	27.3	246.44	29.2	271.78	31.6										
15	211.04	25.8	236.58	27.9	262.22	30.4										
16	202.63	24.6	228.19	26.7												
17	195.21	23.5	220.80	25.7												
18	188.62	22.5	214.24	24.9												
19	182.73	21.6	208.37	24.2												
20	177.43	20.9														
21	172.64	20.2														
22	168.29	19.7														
23	164.32	19.1														
24	160.68	18.7														
25	157.33	18.3														

Δ = 40°

D_c	$L_s = 150'$		200'		250'		300'		350'		400'		500'		600'	
	T_s	E_s	T_s	E_s	T_s	E_s	T_s	E_s	T_s	E_s	T_s	E_s	T_s	E_s	T_s	E_s
1-30	1465.35	245.4	1490.42	245.6	1515.51	245.9	1540.61	246.2	1565.74	246.6	1590.88	247.0	1641.22	248.0	1691.63	249.3
2-00	1117.82	184.2	1142.91	184.5	1168.02	184.8	1193.16	185.8	1218.32	185.8	1243.51	186.3	1293.96	187.7	1344.49	189.4
2-30	909.30	147.5	934.42	147.9	959.56	148.3	984.73	148.8	1009.93	149.5	1035.17	150.2	1085.72	151.9	1136.37	154.1
3-00	770.31	123.1	795.44	123.5	820.61	124.0	845.82	124.7	871.06	125.4	896.33	126.3	946.97	128.4	997.74	130.9
3-30	671.03	105.7	696.19	106.1	721.38	106.8	746.62	107.5	771.90	108.4	797.21	109.4	847.95	111.8	898.82	114.8
4-00	596.58	92.6	621.76	93.2	646.98	93.9	672.25	94.7	697.56	95.7	722.91	96.9	773.74	99.7	824.72	103.1
5	492.37	74.4	517.58	75.1	542.86	76.0	568.18	77.0	593.56	78.3	618.99	79.7	669.99	83.2	721.15	87.4
6	422.91	62.3	448.17	63.1	473.49	64.2	498.87	65.5	524.31	67.0	549.81	68.7	600.96	72.9	652.28	77.9
7	373.31	53.8	398.61	54.7	423.97	55.9	449.41	57.4	474.91	59.2	500.48	61.2	551.76	66.0		
8	336.12	47.4	361.46	48.4	386.87	49.8	412.36	51.5	437.92	53.5	463.53	55.8	514.94	61.38		
9	307.21	42.4	332.58	43.6	358.04	45.2	383.58	47.1	409.18	49.4	434.85	52.0				
10	284.09	38.5	309.50	39.9	334.99	41.6	360.57	43.7	386.23	46.2	411.95	49.10				
11	265.18	35.3	290.62	36.8	316.16	38.7	341.78	41.1	367.48	43.8						
12	249.44	32.7	274.91	34.4	300.48	36.4	326.14	39.0								
13	236.12	30.5	261.62	32.3	287.22	34.6	312.92	37.3								
14	224.71	28.7	250.24	30.6	275.88	33.0										
15	214.82	27.1	240.38	29.1	266.05	31.7										
16	206.18	25.8	231.77	27.9	257.47	30.69										
17	198.56	24.6	224.17	26.9												
18	191.79	23.6	217.43	26.0												
19	185.73	22.7	211.40	25.2												
20	180.29	21.9	205.97	24.55												
21	175.36	21.2														
22	170.89	20.5														
23	166.81	20.0														
24	163.07	19.5														
25	159.63	19.0														

Speed annotations: 70 mph, 60 mph, 50 mph, 40 mph, 30 mph

TABLE IV

T_s AND E_s

$\Delta = 40°$

Δ=41°

D_c	$L_s=150'$ T_s	E_s	$200'$ T_s	E_s	$250'$ T_s	E_s	$300'$ T_s	E_s	$350'$ T_s	E_s	$400'$ T_s	E_s	$500'$ T_s	E_s	$600'$ T_s	E_s
1-30	1503.23	258.5	1528.30	258.7	1553.39	259.0	1578.49	259.3	1603.62	259.7	1628.77	260.1	1679.12	261.2	1729.54	262.4
2-00	1146.22	194.0	1171.31	194.3	1196.43	194.7	1221.57	195.1	1246.75	195.6	1271.94	196.2	1332.40	197.6	1372.95	199.3
2-30	932.03	155.4	957.15	155.7	982.29	156.2	1007.47	156.7	1032.68	157.3	1057.92	158.1	1108.48	159.8	1159.15	161.9
3-00	789.25	129.7	814.38	130.1	839.56	130.6	864.77	131.2	890.02	132.0	915.30	132.8	965.96	134.9	1016.76	137.5
3-30	687.27	111.3	712.43	111.8	737.63	112.4	762.87	113.1	788.16	114.0	813.48	115.0	864.24	117.5	915.15	120.5
4-00	610.79	97.5	635.97	98.1	661.20	98.8	686.47	99.6	711.80	100.6	737.16	101.8	788.01	104.6	839.02	108.0
5	503.74	78.3	528.96	79.0	554.24	79.9	579.58	81.0	604.97	82.2	630.41	83.7	681.44	87.2	732.64	91.4
6	432.39	65.6	457.65	66.4	482.98	67.5	508.38	68.8	533.84	70.3	559.35	72.0	610.53	76.2	661.90	81.3
7	381.44	56.6	406.74	57.5	432.12	58.7	457.57	60.2	483.09	62.0	508.67	64.0	560.00	68.9		
8	343.24	49.8	368.58	50.9	394.01	52.3	419.51	54.0	445.09	56.0	470.73	58.3	522.18	63.9		
9	313.54	44.6	338.92	45.8	364.39	47.4	389.95	49.3	415.57	51.6	441.27	54.2				
10	289.79	40.5	315.21	41.8	340.72	43.6	366.32	45.7	392.00	48.2	417.74	51.1				
11	270.37	37.1	295.82	38.6	321.37	40.5	347.02	42.9	372.74	45.6						
12	254.19	34.4	279.67	36.0	305.27	38.1	330.95	40.6								
13	240.51	32.1	266.02	33.8	291.65	36.1	317.38	38.8								
14	228.79	30.1	254.34	32.0	280.00	34.4										
15	218.63	28.4	244.21	30.5	269.91	33.1										
16	209.76	27.0	235.36	29.2	261.09	31.9										
17	201.93	25.8	227.56	28.1												
18	194.97	24.7	220.63	27.1												
19	188.75	23.7	214.44	26.3												
20	183.16	22.9	208.87	25.6												
21	178.10	22.1														
22	173.51	21.4														
23	169.32	20.8														
24	165.48	20.3														
25	161.94	19.8														

Design speed annotations (stepped): 70 mph, 60 mph, 50 mph, 40 mph, 30 mph

TABLE IV
T_s AND E_s
Δ=41°

102

	$L_s = 150'$		$200'$		$250'$		$300'$		$350'$		$400'$		$500'$		$600'$		$\Delta = 42°$
D_c	T_s	E_s	T_s	E_s	T_s	E_s	T_s	E_s	T_s	E_s	T_s'	E_s	T_s	E_s	T_s	E_s	
1-30	1541.35	272.0	1566.42	272.2	1591.51	272.5	1616.62	272.8	1641.75	273.2	1666.90	273.6	1717.26	274.7	1767.70	275.9	
2-00	1174.82	204.2	1199.91	204.4	1225.03	204.8	1250.18	205.2	1275.35	205.7	1300.55	206.3	1351.02	207.7	1401.59	209.4	
2-30	954.91	163.5	980.02	163.8	1005.17	164.3	1030.36	164.8	1055.57	165.4	1080.82	166.2	1131.40	167.9	1182.09	170.1	
3-00	808.31	136.4	833.45	136.8	858.63	137.3	883.85	138.0	909.10	138.7	934.39	139.6	985.08	141.7	1035.89	144.3	70 mph
3-30	703.61	117.1	728.77	117.5	753.98	118.2	779.23	118.9	804.52	119.8	829.86	120.8	880.64	123.3	931.57	126.2	
4-00	625.09	102.6	650.28	103.1	675.51	103.8	700.80	104.7	726.13	105.7	751.50	106.9	802.38	109.7	853.42	113.1	
5	515.18	82.4	540.41	83.1	565.70	84.0	591.05	85.0	616.45	86.3	641.90	87.7	692.96	91.2	744.20	95.5	
6	441.93	69.0	467.20	69.8	492.54	70.9	517.95	72.1	543.42	73.7	568.95	75.4	620.17	79.6	671.59	84.7	60 mph
7	389.62	59.5	414.93	60.4	440.32	61.6	465.79	63.1	491.32	64.9	516.92	66.9	568.29	71.8	619.86	77.77	
8	350.40	52.4	375.75	53.4	401.19	54.8	426.71	56.6	452.31	58.6	477.97	60.9	529.47	66.5			50 mph
9	319.91	46.9	345.30	48.1	370.78	49.7	396.36	51.6	422.00	53.9	447.72	56.5					
10	295.52	42.5	320.95	43.9	346.48	45.6	372.10	47.8	397.81	50.3	423.58	53.2					
11	275.58	39.0	301.05	40.5	326.62	42.4	352.29	44.7	378.03	47.5							
12	258.97	36.1	284.47	37.7	310.09	39.8	335.79	42.3	361.59	45.36							
13	244.93	33.6	270.46	35.4	296.11	37.7	321.86	40.4									
14	232.89	31.6	258.46	33.5	284.15	35.9	309.93	38.88									40 mph
15	222.47	29.8	248.07	31.8	273.79	34.4											
16	213.36	28.3	238.98	30.4	264.74	33.2											
17	205.32	27.0	230.98	29.3													
18	198.18	25.8	223.86	28.2													
19	191.79	24.8	217.50	27.3													
20	186.05	23.9	211.79	26.6													
21	180.86	23.1	206.62	25.92													
22	176.14	22.4															
23	171.84	21.7															30 mph
24	167.90	21.2															
25	164.27	20.7															

TABLE IV
T_s AND E_s
$\Delta = 42°$

TABLE IV — T_s AND E_s ($\Delta = 43°$)

D_c	$L_s=150'$ T_s	E_s	$200'$ T_s	E_s	$250'$ T_s	E_s	$300'$ T_s	E_s	$350'$ T_s	E_s	$400'$ T_s	E_s	$500'$ T_s	E_s	$600'$ T_s	E_s
1-30	1579.72	285.9	1604.80	286.1	1629.89	286.4	1655.01	286.7	1680.14	287.1	1705.29	287.5	1755.67	288.6	1806.11	289.9
2-00	1203.60	214.6	1228.70	214.9	1253.82	215.2	1278.97	215.7	1304.15	216.2	1329.35	216.8	1379.84	218.1	1430.42	219.9
2-30	977.94	171.0	1003.06	172.2	1028.21	172.6	1053.40	173.2	1078.62	173.8	1103.87	174.5	1154.47	176.3	1205.18	178.4
3-00	827.50	143.4	852.65	143.8	877.83	144.3	903.06	144.9	928.32	145.7	953.62	146.6	1004.32	148.7	1055.16	151.1
3-30	720.06	123.0	745.23	123.5	770.44	124.1	795.70	124.9	821.00	125.8	846.34	126.8	897.15	129.3	948.11	132.3
4-00	639.49	107.8	664.68	108.4	689.92	109.1	715.21	109.9	740.55	111.0	765.94	112.1	816.84	114.9	867.92	118.4
5	526.70	86.6	551.94	87.3	577.23	88.1	602.59	89.2	628.01	90.5	653.47	92.0	704.57	95.5	755.85	99.7
6	451.53	72.5	476.81	73.3	502.16	74.4	527.58	75.6	553.07	77.2	578.61	78.9	629.87	83.1	681.34	88.2
7	397.85	62.4	423.17	63.4	448.58	64.6	474.06	66.1	499.61	67.9	525.23	70.0	576.64	74.9	628.27	80.8
8	357.61	55.0	382.97	56.1	408.42	57.5	433.96	59.2	459.57	61.2	485.25	63.5	536.81	69.1		
9	326.32	49.2	351.72	50.4	377.22	52.0	402.81	53.9	428.48	56.2	454.23	58.8				
10	301.30	44.6	326.74	46.0	352.29	47.7	377.92	49.9	403.65	52.4	429.45	55.3				
11	280.83	40.9	306.31	42.4	331.90	44.3	357.59	46.7	383.36	49.4						
12	263.79	37.8	289.31	39.5	314.94	41.6	340.67	44.1	366.49	47.1						
13	249.38	35.2	274.93	37.0	300.60	39.3	326.37	42.1								
14	237.03	33.1	262.61	35.0	288.32	37.4	314.13	40.4								
15	226.33	31.2	251.95	33.2	277.69	35.9										
16	216.98	29.6	242.63	31.8	268.41	34.6										
17	208.73	28.2	234.41	30.5	260.22	33.5										
18	201.41	27.0	227.11	29.4												
19	194.85	25.9	220.59	28.5												
20	188.96	24.9	214.73	27.7												
21	183.63	24.1	209.42	26.9												
22	178.80	23.3														
23	174.38	22.7														
24	170.53	22.1														
25	166.62	21.5														

Speed markers along the staircase boundary: 70 mph, 60 mph, 50 mph, 40 mph, 30 mph.

$\Delta = 43°$

104

TABLE IV
T_s AND E_s
Δ=44°

Speed markers (stair-step boundaries): 70 mph, 60 mph, 50 mph, 40 mph, 30 mph

D_c	$L_s=150'$ T_s	E_s	$200'$ T_s	E_s	$250'$ T_s	E_s	$300'$ T_s	E_s	$350'$ T_s	E_s	$400'$ T_s	E_s	$500'$ T_s	E_s	$600'$ T_s	E_s
1-30	1618.37	300.2	1643.44	300.4	1668.54	300.7	1693.65	301.0	1718.79	301.4	1743.95	301.8	1794.33	302.9	1844.79	304.2
2-00	1232.58	225.3	1257.68	225.6	1282.81	226.0	1307.96	226.4	1333.15	226.9	1358.36	227.5	1408.85	228.9	1459.46	230.6
2-30	1001.12	180.4	1026.25	180.8	1051.41	181.2	1076.60	181.7	1101.82	182.4	1127.08	183.1	1177.70	184.9	1228.43	187.0
3-00	846.83	150.5	871.98	150.9	897.17	151.4	922.40	152.1	947.66	152.9	972.97	153.7	1023.69	155.9	1074.56	158.4
3-30	736.62	129.2	761.80	129.2	787.02	130.3	812.28	131.0	837.52	131.9	862.95	132.9	913.77	135.4	964.76	138.4
4-00	653.98	113.2	679.18	113.7	704.43	114.4	729.73	115.3	755.08	116.3	780.47	117.5	831.41	120.3	882.51	123.8
5	538.30	90.9	563.54	91.6	588.85	92.4	611.22	93.5	639.64	94.8	665.12	96.3	716.25	99.8	767.57	104.1
6	461.20	76.0	486.49	76.9	511.85	77.9	537.28	79.2	562.78	80.8	588.34	82.5	639.64	86.7	691.16	91.9
7	406.14	65.5	431.47	66.5	456.89	67.7	482.38	69.2	507.95	71.0	533.59	73.0	585.05	78.0	636.73	84.0
8	364.86	57.7	390.24	58.8	415.70	60.2	441.26	61.9	466.89	63.9	492.59	66.3	544.20	71.9		
9	332.77	51.6	358.19	52.8	383.70	54.4	409.31	56.3	435.00	58.6	460.77	61.2				
10	307.11	46.8	332.56	48.1	358.13	49.9	383.79	52.0	409.54	54.6	435.36	57.5				
11	286.12	42.8	311.62	44.4	337.22	46.3	362.93	48.6	388.73	51.4	414.61	54.64				
12	268.64	39.6	294.17	41.3	319.82	43.4	345.58	45.9	371.43	49.0						
13	253.86	36.9	279.42	38.7	305.11	41.0	330.92	43.7								
14	241.19	34.6	266.79	36.5	292.53	39.0	318.37	42.0								
15	230.22	32.6	255.86	34.7	281.63	37.3										
16	220.63	30.9	246.30	33.1	272.10	35.9										
17	212.17	29.5	237.87	31.8	263.71	34.8										
18	204.66	28.2	230.39	30.6												
19	197.94	27.0	223.70	29.6												
20	191.89	26.0	217.68	28.7												
21	186.43	25.1	212.24	28.0												
22	181.47	24.3	207.31	27.32												
23	176.94	23.6														
24	172.79	23.0														
25	168.98	22.4														

TABLE IV — T_s AND E_s Δ=45°

D_c	$L_s=150'$ T_s	E_s	$200'$ T_s	E_s	$250'$ T_s	E_s	$300'$ T_s	E_s	$350'$ T_s	E_s	$400'$ T_s	E_s	$500'$ T_s	E_s	$600'$ T_s	E_s
1-30	1657.28	315.0	1682.36	315.2	1707.46	315.4	1732.58	315.8	1757.72	316.2	1782.88	316.6	1833.27	317.7	1883.75	319.0
2-00	1261.77	236.4	1286.87	236.7	1312.00	237.0	1337.16	237.4	1362.35	238.0	1387.57	238.5	1438.08	240.0	1488.69	241.7
2-30	1024.47	189.3	1049.60	189.6	1074.76	190.1	1099.96	190.6	1125.20	191.2	1150.46	192.0	1201.09	193.7	1251.85	195.9
3-00	866.29	157.9	891.44	158.3	916.64	158.8	941.87	159.5	967.15	160.2	992.46	161.1	1043.20	163.3	1094.09	165.8
3-30	753.31	135.5	778.49	136.0	803.71	136.6	828.98	137.4	854.30	138.2	879.66	139.3	930.52	141.8	981.53	144.8
4-00	668.58	118.7	693.78	119.3	719.04	120.0	744.35	120.8	769.71	121.9	795.11	123.1	846.07	125.9	897.21	129.3
5	549.98	95.3	575.23	96.0	600.55	96.9	625.92	98.0	651.36	99.2	676.86	100.7	728.02	104.2	779.38	108.5
6	470.94	79.7	496.23	80.6	521.60	81.6	547.05	82.9	572.56	84.5	598.14	86.2	649.48	90.5	701.04	95.6
7	414.49	68.7	439.83	69.6	465.26	70.9	490.77	72.4	516.35	74.2	542.01	76.2	593.52	81.2	645.26	87.2
8	372.17	60.4	397.56	61.5	423.04	62.9	448.61	64.7	474.26	66.7	499.98	69.1	551.65	74.7		
9	339.27	54.0	364.70	55.3	390.23	56.9	415.86	58.8	441.57	61.1	467.36	63.7	519.16	70.06		
10	312.96	49.0	338.43	50.4	364.01	52.1	389.69	54.3	415.46	56.8	441.32	59.7				
11	291.45	44.9	316.95	46.4	342.58	48.3	368.31	50.7	394.14	53.5	420.05	56.7				
12	273.52	41.5	299.07	43.1	324.74	45.2	350.52	47.8	376.40	50.9						
13	258.37	38.6	283.95	40.4	309.66	42.7	335.49	45.5								
14	245.38	36.2	271.01	38.1	296.76	40.6	322.63	43.6								
15	234.14	34.1	259.79	36.2	285.59	38.8	311.50	42.04								
16	224.30	32.3	249.99	34.5	275.82	37.3										
17	215.63	30.8	241.35	33.1	267.22	36.1										
18	207.93	29.4	233.68	31.9	259.58	35.03										
19	201.04	28.2	226.82	30.8												
20	194.84	27.1	220.66	29.9												
21	189.24	26.2	215.09	29.1												
22	184.16	25.3	210.02	28.3												
23	179.51	24.6														
24	175.26	23.9														
25	171.35	23.3														

Speed bands (stepped through the table): 70 mph, 60 mph, 50 mph, 40 mph, 30 mph

TABLE IV
T_s AND E_s $\Delta = 46°$

D_c	$L_s=150'$ T_s	E_s	$200'$ T_s	E_s	$250'$ T_s	E_s	$300'$ T_s	E_s	$350'$ T_s	E_s	$400'$ T_s	E_s	$500'$ T_s	E_s	$600'$ T_s	E_s
1-30	1291.17	247.8	1316.27	248.0	1341.41	248.4	1366.57	248.8	1391.76	249.3	1416.99	249.9	1467.51	251.4	1518.14	253.1
2-00	1048.00	198.4	1073.13	198.7	1098.29	199.2	1123.50	199.7	1148.74	200.3	1174.01	201.1	1224.66	202.9	1275.43	205.0
2-30																
3-00	885.89	165.5	911.05	165.9	936.25	166.4	961.49	167.1	986.77	167.8	1012.10	168.7	1062.86	170.9	1113.77	173.5
3-30	770.11	142.0	795.29	142.5	820.53	143.1	845.81	143.9	871.13	144.8	896.50	145.8	947.38	148.3	998.43	151.3
4-00	683.29	124.4	708.49	125.0	733.75	125.7	759.07	126.5	784.44	127.6	809.86	128.8	860.84	131.6	912.02	135.1
5	561.75	99.8	587.00	100.5	612.33	101.4	637.72	102.5	663.17	103.8	688.68	105.3	739.87	108.8	791.27	113.1
6	480.75	83.5	506.05	84.4	531.43	85.4	556.89	86.7	582.42	88.3	608.01	90.0	659.39	94.3	711.00	99.5
7	422.90	71.9	448.25	72.9	473.69	74.1	499.21	75.7	524.81	77.5	550.49	79.5	602.05	84.5	653.84	90.5
8	379.54	63.3	404.93	64.4	430.42	65.8	456.01	67.5	481.68	69.6	507.43	71.9	559.14	77.6		
9	345.82	56.6	371.26	57.8	396.80	59.4	422.45	61.4	448.18	63.7	474.00	66.3	525.86	72.7		
10	318.86	51.3	344.34	52.6	369.94	54.4	395.64	56.6	421.43	59.1	447.32	62.1				
11	296.81	46.9	322.33	48.5	347.98	50.4	373.73	52.8	399.58	55.6	425.52	58.8				
12	278.44	43.4	304.01	45.0	329.70	47.1	355.50	49.7	381.41	52.8						
13	262.91	40.4	288.51	42.2	314.25	44.5	340.10	47.3	366.06	50.6						
14	249.61	37.8	275.25	39.8	301.02	42.2	326.92	45.3								
15	238.08	35.7	263.76	37.7	289.58	40.4	315.52	43.6								
16	228.01	33.8	253.71	36.0	279.57	38.8										
17	219.12	32.1	244.86	34.5	270.76	37.5										
18	211.23	30.7	237.00	33.2	262.93	36.3										
19	204.17	29.4	229.97	32.0												
20	197.82	28.3	223.66	31.0												
21	192.08	27.3	217.95	30.2												
22	186.87	26.4	212.76	29.4												
23	182.11	25.6	208.03	28.74												
24	177.75	24.9														
25	173.75	24.2														

70 mph 60 mph 50 mph 40 mph 30 mph

$\Delta = 46°$

107

D_c	L_s = 150' T_s	150' E_s	200' T_s	200' E_s	250' T_s	250' E_s	300' T_s	300' E_s	350' T_s	350' E_s	400' T_s	400' E_s	500' T_s	500' E_s	600' T_s	600' E_s	Speed
1-30																	
2-00	1320.79	259.5	1345.90	259.7	1371.03	260.1	1396.20	260.5	1421.40	261.0	1446.62	261.6	1497.16	263.1	1547.81	264.8	
2-30	1071.69	207.7	1096.83	208.1	1122.00	208.5	1147.21	209.1	1172.45	209.7	1197.73	210.4	1248.40	212.2	1299.19	214.4	
3-00	905.64	173.3	930.80	173.7	956.01	174.2	981.25	174.9	1006.54	175.6	1031.88	176.5	1082.66	178.7	1133.60	181.3	
3-30	787.04	148.7	812.23	149.2	837.46	149.8	862.75	150.6	888.09	151.5	913.47	152.5	964.37	155.0	1015.44	158.0	
4-00	698.10	130.3	723.31	130.8	748.58	131.5	773.91	132.4	799.29	133.4	824.71	134.6	875.73	137.5	926.93	141.0	70 mph
5	573.60	104.5	598.87	105.2	624.20	106.1	643.60	107.2	675.06	108.5	700.58	110.0	751.81	113.5	803.25	117.9	
6	490.63	87.4	515.94	88.3	541.33	89.3	566.80	90.6	592.34	92.2	617.96	94.0	669.38	98.2	721.04	103.4	
7	431.38	75.3	456.73	76.2	482.19	77.5	507.72	79.0	533.34	80.8	559.04	82.9	610.64	87.9	662.49	93.9	60 mph
8	386.95	66.2	412.36	67.3	437.86	68.7	463.47	70.5	489.16	72.5	514.93	74.9	566.70	80.6			
9	352.42	59.2	377.87	60.4	403.43	62.0	429.09	64.0	454.85	66.3	480.69	69.0	532.61	75.3			50 mph
10	324.80	53.6	350.29	55.0	375.91	56.8	401.63	58.9	427.45	61.5	453.36	64.5					
11	302.21	49.1	327.75	50.6	353.41	52.5	379.19	54.9	405.07	57.7	431.04	61.0					
12	283.40	45.3	308.98	47.0	334.69	49.1	360.52	51.7	386.45	54.8							
13	267.49	42.2	293.11	44.0	318.86	46.3	344.75	49.1	370.73	52.4							
14	253.86	39.5	279.52	41.4	305.32	43.9	331.25	47.0									40 mph
15	242.06	37.2	267.75	39.3	293.59	42.0	319.57	45.2									
16	231.73	35.2	257.46	37.4	283.35	.40.3											
17	222.63	33.5	248.40	35.9	274.32	38.9											
18	214.55	32.0	240.35	34.5	266.31	37.7											
19	207.32	30.7	233.15	33.3													
20	200.81	29.5	226.68	32.2													
21	194.93	28.4	220.83	31.3													
22	189.59	27.5	215.52	30.5													
23	184.72	26.6	210.68	29.8													
24	180.26	25.9															
25	176.16	25.2															30 mph

$\Delta = 47°$

TABLE IV
T_s AND E_s

$\Delta = 47°$

TABLE IV — T_s AND E_s — $\Delta = 48°$

D_c	$L_s=150'$ T_s	E_s	$200'$ T_s	E_s	$250'$ T_s	E_s	$300'$ T_s	E_s	$350'$ T_s	E_s	$400'$ T_s	E_s	$500'$ T_s	E_s	$600'$ T_s	E_s
1-30	1350.63	271.5	1375.74	271.8	1400.88	272.1	1426.05	272.6	1451.26	273.1	1476.49	273.7	1527.04	275.1	1577.71	276.9
2-00	1095.57	217.5	1120.71	217.7	1145.88	218.1	1171.10	218.7	1196.35	219.3	1221.63	220.1	1272.32	221.9	1323.13	224.1
2-30																
3-00	925.54	181.3	950.70	181.7	975.91	182.2	1001.17	182.9	1026.47	183.3	1051.81	184.6	1102.61	186.7	1153.57	189.3
3-30	804.10	155.6	829.22	156.0	854.53	156.7	879.83	157.4	905.62	158.3	930.56	159.4	981.49	161.9	1032.59	165.0
4-00	713.03	136.3	738.24	136.8	763.52	137.6	788.85	138.4	814.24	139.5	839.68	140.7	890.72	143.5	941.96	147.0
5	585.55	109.3	610.82	110.0	636.16	110.9	661.57	112.0	687.04	113.3	712.58	114.8	763.84	118.4	815.32	122.7
6	500.58	91.4	525.90	92.3	551.31	93.4	576.79	94.7	602.34	96.2	627.97	98.0	679.44	102.3	731.15	107.5
7	439.91	78.7	465.28	79.7	490.74	80.9	516.30	82.5	541.93	84.3	567.65	86.4	619.30	91.3	671.21	97.4
8	394.43	69.2	419.84	70.3	445.36	71.8	470.98	73.5	496.69	75.6	522.48	77.9	574.31	83.6	626.39	90.57
9	359.06	61.9	384.52	63.1	410.10	64.7	435.78	66.7	461.56	69.0	487.43	71.7	539.41	78.1		
10	330.78	56.0	356.29	57.4	381.92	59.2	407.66	61.4	433.51	63.9	459.45	66.9				
11	307.66	51.3	333.21	52.8	358.89	54.8	384.69	57.2	410.59	60.0	436.60	63.2				
12	288.39	47.3	313.99	49.0	339.72	51.1	365.57	53.8	391.54	56.8	417.60	60.38				
13	272.10	44.0	297.74	45.8	323.52	48.2	349.43	51.0	375.44	54.3						
14	258.15	41.2	283.82	43.2	309.65	45.7	335.60	48.7								
15	246.06	38.8	271.78	40.9	297.64	43.6	323.65	46.8								
16	235.49	36.8	261.24	39.0	287.15	41.8	313.20	45.28								
17	226.17	34.9	251.96	37.3	277.91	40.3										
18	217.89	33.3	243.72	35.8	269.71	39.0										
19	210.49	31.9	236.35	34.6	262.37	37.9										
20	203.83	30.7	229.72	33.5												
21	197.81	29.6	223.74	32.5												
22	192.35	28.6	218.30	31.6												
23	187.36	27.7	213.34	30.9												
24	182.79	26.9	208.80	30.19												
25	178.59	26.1														

Design-speed annotations (right margin): 70 mph, 60 mph, 50 mph, 40 mph, 30 mph

109

TABLE IV
T_s AND E_s

Δ=49°

D_c	$L_s=150'$ T_s	E_s	$200'$ T_s	E_s	$250'$ T_s	E_s	$300'$ T_s	E_s	$350'$ T_s	E_s	$400'$ T_s	E_s	$500'$ T_s	E_s	$600'$ T_s	E_s
1-30	1380.71	283.8	1405.82	284.1	1430.97	284.5	1456.14	284.9	1481.35	285.4	1506.59	286.0	1557.15	287.5	1607.84	289.2
2-00	1119.63	227.2	1144.77	227.6	1169.95	228.0	1195.17	228.6	1220.43	229.2	1245.72	230.0	1296.42	231.8	1347.26	234.0
2-30																
3-00	945.59	189.5	970.76	189.5	995.98	190.5	1021.24	191.1	1046.54	191.9	1071.89	192.8	1122.71	195.0	1173.70	197.6
3-30	821.29	162.6	846.49	163.1	871.73	163.7	897.04	164.5	922.39	165.4	947.79	166.5	998.74	169.0	1049.87	172.0
4-00	728.07	142.5	753.29	143.0	778.58	143.7	803.92	144.6	829.32	145.7	854.77	146.8	905.84	149.7	957.11	153.2
5	597.59	114.3	622.86	115.0	648.21	115.9	673.63	117.0	699.12	118.3	724.67	119.8	775.97	123.4	827.49	127.7
6	510.62	95.6	535.95	96.4	561.36	97.5	586.85	98.8	612.43	100.4	638.07	102.2	689.58	106.4	741.33	111.7
7	448.52	82.3	473.90	83.2	499.37	84.5	524.94	86.0	550.59	87.8	576.33	89.9	628.02	94.9	679.99	101.0
8	401.96	72.3	427.38	73.4	452.92	74.9	478.55	76.6	504.29	78.7	530.10	81.1	581.98	86.8	634.13	93.7
9	365.76	64.6	391.24	65.9	416.83	67.5	442.53	69.5	468.33	71.8	494.22	74.5	546.26	80.9		
10	336.82	58.5	362.33	59.9	387.98	61.7	413.75	63.9	439.62	66.5	465.58	69.4				
11	313.14	53.5	338.71	55.1	364.41	57.0	390.23	59.4	416.16	62.3	442.20	65.5				
12	293.43	49.4	319.04	51.1	344.79	53.2	370.67	55.5	396.66	58.9	422.75	62.5				
13	276.75	45.9	302.64	47.8	328.21	50.1	354.14	52.9	380.19	56.3						
14	262.47	43.0	288.16	45.0	314.01	47.5	340.00	50.5	366.10	54.1						
15	250.10	40.5	275.83	42.6	301.72	45.3	327.76	48.5								
16	239.28	38.3	265.05	40.5	290.99	43.4	317.07	46.9								
17	229.74	36.4	255.55	38.8	281.53	41.8										
18	221.26	34.7	247.11	37.2	273.13	40.4										
19	213.69	33.2	239.57	35.9	265.63	39.3										
20	206.87	31.9	232.79	34.7												
21	200.71	30.8	226.66	33.7												
22	195.12	29.7	221.10	32.8												
23	190.01	28.8	216.02	32.0												
24	185.33	27.9	211.38	31.2												
25	181.03	27.2														

Speed annotations: 70 mph, 60 mph, 50 mph, 40 mph, 30 mph

110

D_c	$L_s=150'$ T_s	E_s	$200'$ T_s	E_s	$250'$ T_s	E_s	$300'$ T_s	E_s	$350'$ T_s	E_s	$400'$ T_s	E_s	$500'$ T_s	E_s	$600'$ T_s	E_s
1-30																
2-00	1411.03	296.5	1436.14	296.5	1461.29	297.2	1486.47	297.6	1511.68	298.1	1536.93	298.7	1587.50	300.2	1638.21	301.9
2-30	1143.89	237.4	1169.03	237.4	1194.21	238.2	1219.44	238.7	1244.70	239.4	1270.00	240.1	1320.72	241.9	1371.58	244.2
3-00	965.81	198.0	990.98	198.0	1016.20	198.9	1041.47	199.6	1066.78	200.4	1092.14	201.3	1142.98	203.5	1194.00	206.1
3-30	838.62	169.9	863.82	170.4	889.07	171.0	914.38	171.8	939.74	172.7	965.16	173.7	1016.13	176.3	1067.29	179.3
4-00	743.23	148.8	768.46	149.4	793.75	150.1	819.10	151.0	844.51	152.0	869.97	153.2	921.07	156.1	972.38	159.6
5	609.72	119.4	635.00	120.1	660.36	121.0	685.79	122.1	711.29	123.4	736.86	124.9	788.19	128.5	839.75	132.9
6	520.73	99.8	546.07	100.6	571.49	101.7	597.00	103.1	622.59	104.6	648.25	106.4	699.80	110.7	751.60	116.0
7	457.19	85.9	482.58	86.9	508.06	88.1	533.65	89.7	559.31	91.5	585.07	93.6	636.82	98.6	688.85	104.7
8	409.55	75.5	434.99	76.6	460.54	78.0	486.19	79.8	511.94	81.9	537.78	84.3	589.71	90.0	641.93	97.0
9	372.51	67.4	398.00	68.7	423.61	70.3	449.33	72.3	475.15	74.6	501.07	77.3	553.17	83.8		
10	342.90	61.0	368.43	62.4	394.09	64.2	419.88	66.4	445.77	69.0	471.77	72.0	524.01	79.15		
11	318.67	55.8	344.25	57.4	369.97	59.4	395.82	61.8	421.78	64.6	447.84	67.9				
12	298.50	51.5	324.13	53.2	349.90	55.4	375.80	58.0	401.83	61.1	427.95	64.7				
13	281.44	47.9	307.11	49.7	332.93	52.1	358.89	54.9	384.98	58.3						
14	266.82	44.8	292.54	46.8	318.41	49.3	344.42	52.4	370.56	56.0						
15	254.16	42.2	279.92	44.3	305.84	47.0	331.90	50.3								
16	243.10	39.9	268.89	42.1	294.86	45.0	320.96	48.5								
17	233.33	37.9	259.17	40.3	285.18	43.3										
18	224.66	36.2	250.54	38.7	276.59	41.9										
19	216.91	34.6	242.82	37.2	268.91	40.6										
20	209.94	33.2	235.88	36.0	262.01	39.58										
21	203.64	32.0	229.62	34.9												
22	197.91	30.9	223.92	33.9												
23	192.69	29.9	218.73	33.1												
24	187.90	29.0	213.98	32.3												
25	183.50	28.2	209.61	31.66												

70 mph
60 mph
50 mph
40 mph
30 mph

TABLE IV
T_s AND E_s
Δ=50°

111

Δ = 51°

TABLE IV
T_s AND E_s

Δ = 51°

Speed annotations (staircase boundaries): 70 mph, 60 mph, 50 mph, 40 mph, 30 mph

D_c	L_s=150' T_s	E_s	200' T_s	E_s	250' T_s	E_s	300' T_s	E_s	350' T_s	E_s	400' T_s	E_s	500' T_s	E_s	600' T_s	E_s
1-30																
2-00	1441.59	309.6	1466.71	309.6	1491.86	310.2	1517.04	310.6	1542.26	311.1	1567.51	311.8	1618.10	313.2	1668.82	315.0
2-30	1168.34	247.8	1193.49	248.2	1218.68	248.6	1243.91	249.2	1269.17	249.8	1294.48	250.6	1345.22	252.4	1396.10	254.6
3-00	986.19	206.7	1011.36	207.1	1036.59	207.6	1061.86	208.3	1087.18	209.1	1112.55	210.0	1163.41	212.2	1214.45	214.8
3-30	856.09	177.3	881.29	177.8	906.55	178.4	931.87	179.2	957.24	180.1	982.66	181.2	1033.66	183.7	1084.85	186.8
4-00	758.52	155.3	783.76	155.9	809.05	156.6	834.41	157.5	859.83	158.5	885.30	159.8	936.43	162.6	987.77	166.2
5	621.95	124.6	647.24	125.3	672.61	126.3	698.05	127.3	723.56	128.6	749.14	130.1	800.51	133.7	852.12	138.1
6	530.93	104.2	556.27	105.0	581.71	106.1	607.23	107.4	632.83	109.0	658.51	110.8	710.10	115.1	761.96	120.4
7	465.94	89.6	491.33	90.6	516.83	91.9	542.43	93.4	568.11	95.2	593.89	97.3	645.69	102.4	697.77	108.6
8	417.21	78.7	442.65	79.9	468.21	81.3	493.88	83.1	519.66	85.2	545.52	87.6	597.51	93.3	649.79	100.4
9	379.32	70.3	404.82	71.6	430.44	73.2	456.18	75.2	482.02	77.6	507.97	80.3	560.14	86.7		
10	349.03	63.7	374.57	65.1	400.25	66.9	426.06	69.1	451.98	71.7	478.00	74.7	530.32	81.8		
11	324.25	58.2	349.85	59.8	375.58	61.7	401.45	64.2	427.44	67.0	453.54	70.3				
12	303.61	53.7	329.26	55.4	355.05	57.6	380.98	60.2	407.03	63.3	433.19	66.9				
13	286.16	49.9	311.85	51.8	337.70	54.1	363.69	57.0	389.80	60.3						
14	271.21	46.7	296.95	48.7	322.84	51.2	348.89	54.3	375.06	57.9						
15	258.27	43.9	284.04	46.0	309.99	48.7	336.08	52.0								
16	246.94	41.5	272.76	43.8	298.75	46.7	324.90	50.2								
17	236.96	39.5	262.82	41.8	288.85	44.9	315.04	48.62								
18	228.09	37.6	253.99	40.1	280.07	43.4										
19	220.16	36.0	246.10	38.6	272.22	42.1										
20	213.03	34.5	239.00	37.3	265.16	40.9										
21	206.58	33.3	232.59	36.2												
22	200.73	32.1	226.77	35.2												
23	195.38	31.0	221.46	34.3												
24	190.49	30.1	216.60	33.5												
25	185.99	29.2	212.13	32.7												

30 mph

TABLE IV — T_s AND E_s — $\Delta = 52°$

D_c	$L_s=150'$ T_s	E_s	$200'$ T_s	E_s	$250'$ T_s	E_s	$300'$ T_s	E_s	$350'$ T_s	E_s	$400'$ T_s	E_s	$500'$ T_s	E_s	$600'$ T_s	E_s
1-30	1472.41	322.9	1497.53	323.2	1522.69	323.6	1547.87	324.0	1573.10	324.6	1598.35	325.2	1648.96	326.6	1699.70	328.4
2-00	1193.00	258.5	1218.15	258.9	1243.34	259.3	1268.58	259.9	1293.85	260.5	1319.17	261.1	1369.92	263.1	1420.82	265.3
2-30																
3-00	1006.74	215.6	1031.92	216.0	1057.15	216.6	1082.43	217.2	1107.76	218.0	1133.13	218.9	1184.02	221.1	1235.08	223.8
3-30	873.70	185.0	898.91	185.5	924.18	186.1	949.50	186.9	974.88	187.8	1000.32	188.9	1051.34	191.4	1102.56	194.5
4-00	773.94	162.0	799.18	162.6	824.48	163.3	849.85	164.2	875.28	165.3	900.76	166.5	951.91	169.4	1003.29	172.9
5	634.29	129.9	659.58	130.6	684.96	131.6	710.41	132.7	735.94	134.0	761.53	135.5	812.93	139.1	864.58	143.6
6	541.21	108.6	566.57	109.5	592.01	110.6	617.54	111.9	643.16	113.5	668.86	115.3	720.49	119.6	772.40	124.9
7	474.75	93.4	500.16	94.4	525.67	95.7	551.28	97.3	576.98	99.1	602.78	101.2	654.63	106.3	706.77	112.5
8	424.92	82.1	450.38	83.2	475.96	84.7	501.64	86.5	527.44	88.6	553.32	91.0	605.37	96.8	657.72	103.8
9	386.18	73.3	411.69	74.6	437.33	76.2	463.09	78.2	488.96	80.6	514.93	83.3	567.16	89.8		
10	355.21	66.3	380.77	67.7	406.47	69.6	432.29	71.8	458.24	74.4	484.29	77.4	536.68	84.6		
11	329.87	60.7	355.48	62.2	381.24	64.2	407.13	66.6	433.15	69.5	459.28	72.8				
12	308.77	55.9	334.43	57.6	360.24	59.8	386.20	62.5	412.29	65.6	438.48	69.2				
13	290.93	52.0	316.63	53.8	342.50	56.2	368.52	59.1	394.67	62.4	420.92	66.33				
14	275.64	48.6	301.39	50.6	327.31	53.1	353.39	56.2	379.59	59.9						
15	262.40	45.7	288.20	47.9	314.17	50.6	340.30	53.9								
16	250.82	43.2	276.66	45.5	302.68	48.4	328.86	51.9								
17	240.61	41.0	266.50	43.4	292.56	46.5	318.78	50.2								
18	231.55	39.1	257.47	41.6	283.58	44.9										
19	223.44	37.4	249.40	40.1	275.55	43.5										
20	216.15	35.9	242.15	38.7	268.34	42.3										
21	209.55	34.5	235.59	37.5												
22	203.57	33.3	229.64	36.4												
23	198.10	32.2	224.21	35.5												
24	193.10	31.2	219.24	34.6												
25	188.50	30.3	214.67	33.8												

Design speed boundaries marked diagonally across the table: 70 mph, 60 mph, 50 mph, 40 mph, 30 mph.

Δ=53°

TABLE IV — T_s AND E_s — Δ=53°

D_c	$L_s=150'$ T_s	E_s	$200'$ T_s	E_s	$250'$ T_s	E_s	$300'$ T_s	E_s	$350'$ T_s	E_s	$400'$ T_s	E_s	$500'$ T_s	E_s	$600'$ T_s	E_s
1-30	1503.49	336.7	1528.62	337.0	1553.78	337.3	1578.97	337.8	1604.20	338.3	1629.46	338.9	1680.08	340.4	1730.83	342.2
2-00	1217.87	269.5	1243.02	269.9	1268.22	270.3	1293.46	270.9	1318.74	271.5	1344.06	272.3	1394.83	274.1	1445.75	276.4
2-30																
3-00	1027.46	224.8	1052.64	225.2	1077.88	225.7	1103.17	226.4	1128.50	227.2	1153.89	228.1	1204.80	230.3	1255.89	233.0
3-30	891.47	192.8	916.68	193.2	941.96	194.1	967.29	194.7	992.68	195.7	1018.12	196.7	1069.17	199.3	1120.42	202.4
4-00	789.48	168.9	814.73	169.5	840.04	170.2	865.42	171.1	890.86	172.1	916.35	173.4	967.53	176.3	1018.94	179.8
5	646.73	135.4	672.03	136.2	697.42	137.1	722.88	138.2	748.42	139.5	774.03	141.0	825.46	144.7	877.16	149.1
6	551.59	113.2	576.94	114.1	602.40	115.2	627.94	116.5	653.58	118.1	679.30	119.9	730.97	124.3	782.93	129.6
7	483.64	97.4	509.06	98.4	534.58	99.6	560.21	101.2	585.93	103.1	611.75	105.2	663.64	110.3	715.85	116.5
8	432.71	85.5	458.18	86.7	483.77	88.1	509.47	89.9	535.28	92.0	561.19	94.5	613.29	100.3	665.71	107.3
9	393.11	76.4	418.63	77.7	444.28	79.3	470.06	81.3	495.95	83.7	521.95	86.4	574.24	92.9		
10	361.44	69.1	387.01	70.5	412.73	72.3	438.58	74.6	464.55	77.2	490.63	80.2	543.09	87.4		
11	335.54	63.2	361.17	64.7	386.95	66.7	412.86	69.2	438.90	72.1	465.07	75.4				
12	313.93	58.2	339.65	60.0	365.48	62.1	391.46	64.8	417.58	67.9	443.81	71.6				
13	295.73	54.1	321.45	56.0	347.35	58.3	373.39	61.2	399.57	64.6	425.86	68.5				
14	280.11	50.6	305.88	52.6	331.82	55.1	357.93	58.2	384.17	61.9						
15	266.57	47.6	292.39	49.7	318.39	52.4	344.55	55.8	370.84	59.7						
16	254.74	45.0	280.60	47.2	306.65	50.1	332.86	53.7								
17	244.30	42.7	270.21	45.1	296.30	48.2	322.56	51.9								
18	235.03	40.7	260.98	43.2	287.12	46.5										
19	226.74	38.9	252.73	41.6	278.92	45.0										
20	219.29	37.3	245.32	40.1	271.54	43.7										
21	212.55	35.9	238.62	38.8	264.89	42.6										
22	206.43	34.6	232.53	37.7												
23	200.85	33.4	226.99	36.7												
24	195.73	32.4	221.91	35.8												
25	191.03	31.5	217.24	35.0												

Speed annotations (diagonal markers): 70 mph, 60 mph, 50 mph, 40 mph, 30 mph

114

TABLE IV
Ts AND Es
Δ = 54°

Dc	Ls=150' Ts	Es	200' Ts	Es	250' Ts	Es	300' Ts	Es	350' Ts	Es	400' Ts	Es	500' Ts	Es	600' Ts	Es
1-30	1532.85	350.8	1559.98	351.1	1585.14	351.1	1610.33	351.9	1635.57	352.4	1660.84	353.1	1711.47	354.5	1762.24	356.3
2-00	1242.95	280.8	1268.11	281.2	1293.31	281.6	1318.56	282.2	1343.85	282.9	1369.18	283.5	1419.96	285.5	1470.91	287.7
2-30																
3-00	1048.37	234.2	1073.56	234.6	1098.80	235.2	1124.09	235.8	1149.43	236.6	1174.83	237.5	1225.76	239.8	1276.87	242.4
3-30	909.39	200.9	934.61	201.4	959.89	202.0	985.23	202.8	1010.63	203.8	1036.08	204.8	1087.15	207.4	1138.43	210.5
4-00	805.17	176.0	830.42	176.5	855.74	177.3	881.12	178.2	906.57	179.2	932.08	180.4	983.29	183.4	1034.73	187.0
5	659.28	141.1	684.59	141.8	709.98	142.7	735.45	143.9	761.01	145.2	786.63	146.7	838.10	150.4	889.84	154.8
6	562.05	117.9	587.41	118.8	612.88	119.9	638.44	121.2	664.09	122.6	689.82	124.6	741.54	129.0	793.55	134.4
7	492.62	101.4	518.04	102.4	543.58	103.7	569.22	105.3	594.96	107.1	620.80	109.3	672.74	114.4	725.01	120.6
8	440.56	89.1	466.04	90.2	491.65	91.7	517.37	93.5	543.20	95.6	569.13	98.0	621.29	103.9	673.78	111.0
9	400.09	79.5	425.63	80.8	451.30	82.5	477.09	84.5	503.01	86.9	529.03	89.6	581.39	96.1	634.08	104.11
10	367.73	71.9	393.32	73.4	419.05	75.2	444.92	77.4	470.92	80.1	497.03	83.1	549.56	90.4		
11	341.26	65.7	366.90	67.3	392.70	69.3	418.64	71.8	444.71	74.7	470.90	78.0				
12	319.22	60.6	344.91	62.3	370.77	64.5	396.78	67.2	422.92	70.4	449.19	74.0				
13	300.58	56.3	326.32	58.2	352.23	60.5	378.31	63.4	404.52	66.8	430.85	70.8				
14	284.61	52.6	310.40	54.6	336.37	57.2	362.50	60.3	388.78	64.0						
15	270.78	49.5	296.61	51.6	322.64	54.3	348.83	57.7	375.16	61.6						
16	258.68	46.7	284.57	49.0	310.65	51.9	336.89	55.5								
17	248.02	44.3	273.95	46.8	300.07	49.9	326.37	53.6								
18	238.55	42.2	264.52	44.8	290.70	48.1	317.04	52.06								
19	230.08	40.4	256.09	43.1	282.31	46.5										
20	222.46	38.7	248.52	41.5	274.78	45.2										
21	215.57	37.2	241.67	40.2	267.97	44.0										
22	209.32	35.9	235.45	39.0												
23	203.62	34.7	229.78	37.9												
24	198.39	33.6	224.59	37.0												
25	193.58	32.6	219.82	36.1												

Speed reference markings (right margin): 70 mph, 60 mph, 50 mph, 40 mph, 30 mph

Δ = 55°

TABLE IV — T_s and E_s (Δ = 55°)

D_c	$L_s=150'$ T_s	E_s	$200'$ T_s	E_s	$250'$ T_s	E_s	$300'$ T_s	E_s	$350'$ T_s	E_s	$400'$ T_s	E_s	$500'$ T_s	E_s	$600'$ T_s	E_s
1-30	1566.49	365.1	1591.61	365.6	1616.78	365.6	1641.98	366.4	1667.22	366.9	1692.49	367.5	1743.14	369.0	1793.93	370.8
2-00	1268.26	292.1	1293.42	292.8	1318.63	293.2	1343.88	293.8	1369.18	294.4	1394.51	295.2	1445.32	297.1	1496.29	299.3
2-30																
3-00	1069.46	343.8	1094.65	244.3	1119.90	244.8	1145.20	245.5	1170.55	246.3	1195.95	247.2	1246.90	249.4	1298.05	252.1
3-30	927.47	209.2	952.70	209.7	977.98	210.3	1003.33	211.1	1028.74	212.0	1054.20	213.1	1105.30	215.7	1156.61	218.8
4-00	820.99	183.2	846.25	183.8	871.57	184.5	896.97	185.4	922.43	186.5	947.95	187.7	999.18	190.6	1050.66	194.2
5	671.94	146.9	697.26	147.6	722.66	148.5	748.14	149.7	773.71	151.0	799.35	152.5	850.86	156.2	902.64	160.7
6	572.60	122.7	597.98	123.6	623.45	124.7	649.03	126.1	674.69	127.7	700.44	129.5	752.20	133.9	804.27	139.3
7	501.67	105.6	527.10	106.6	552.65	107.8	578.31	109.4	604.06	111.3	629.93	113.4	681.92	118.6	734.25	124.8
8	448.48	92.7	473.97	93.9	499.59	95.3	525.33	97.1	551.19	99.2	577.14	101.7	629.36	107.6	681.92	114.7
9	407.14	82.8	432.68	84.0	458.37	85.7	484.19	87.7	510.12	90.1	536.18	92.9	588.60	99.4	641.36	107.4
10	374.07	74.8	399.67	76.3	425.43	78.1	451.32	80.3	477.34	83.0	503.49	86.0	556.08	93.3		
11	347.03	68.4	372.69	70.0	398.51	72.0	424.47	74.4	450.57	77.4	476.80	80.7	529.56	88.71		
12	324.51	63.0	350.22	64.8	376.10	67.0	402.13	69.6	428.31	72.8	454.61	76.5				
13	305.47	58.5	331.23	60.4	357.17	62.8	383.27	65.7	409.52	69.1	435.88	73.1				
14	289.15	54.7	314.96	56.7	340.96	59.3	367.12	62.4	393.44	66.1						
15	275.02	51.4	300.88	53.6	326.93	56.3	353.16	59.7	379.53	63.6						
16	262.67	48.6	288.57	50.8	314.68	53.8	340.96	57.3								
17	251.77	46.1	277.72	48.5	303.88	51.6	330.21	55.4								
18	242.09	43.9	268.09	46.4	294.30	49.7	320.68	53.7								
19	233.44	41.9	259.48	44.6	285.74	48.1										
20	225.66	40.2	251.74	43.0	278.04	46.7										
21	218.62	38.6	244.75	41.6	271.09	45.4										
22	212.24	37.2	238.40	40.4	264.78	44.36										
23	206.41	36.0	232.61	39.2												
24	201.37	34.8	227.31	38.2												
25	196.16	33.8	222.43	37.3												

Design-speed boundaries (step lines across the table): 70 mph, 60 mph, 50 mph, 40 mph, 30 mph.

Table IV — T_s AND E_s, Δ = 56°

D_c	L_s=150' T_s	E_s	200' T_s	E_s	250' T_s	E_s	300' T_s	E_s	350' T_s	E_s	400' T_s	E_s	500' T_s	E_s	600' T_s	E_s
1-30																
2-00																
2-30	1293.80	304.3	1318.97	304.7	1344.18	305.1	1369.44	305.7	1394.74	306.3	1420.08	307.1	1470.91	309.0	1521.90	311.2
3-00	1090.75	253.7	1115.94	254.2	1141.20	254.7	1166.50	255.4	1191.86	256.2	1217.27	257.1	1268.25	259.4	1319.42	262.1
3-30	945.72	217.7	970.95	218.2	996.24	218.8	1021.60	219.6	1047.01	220.6	1072.49	221.6	1123.61	224.2	1174.95	227.4
4-00	836.96	190.7	862.22	191.2	887.55	192.0	912.95	192.9	938.43	193.9	963.96	195.2	1015.23	198.1	1066.74	201.7
5	684.72	152.8	710.04	153.6	735.45	154.5	760.95	155.6	786.53	157.0	812.18	158.5	863.73	162.2	915.55	166.7
6	583.25	127.7	608.64	128.6	634.12	129.7	659.71	131.0	685.29	132.6	711.16	134.5	762.96	138.9	815.08	144.3
7	510.80	109.8	536.24	110.8	561.80	112.1	587.48	113.7	613.25	115.6	639.14	117.7	691.18	122.9	743.57	129.2
8	456.48	96.4	481.98	97.6	507.61	99.1	533.37	100.9	559.24	103.0	585.22	105.5	637.50	111.3	690.13	118.5
9	414.25	86.1	439.81	87.4	465.51	89.0	491.35	91.1	517.31	93.5	543.39	96.2	595.87	102.8	648.72	110.9
10	380.48	77.8	406.09	79.2	431.86	81.1	457.78	83.4	483.83	86.0	510.00	89.1	562.67	96.4		
11	352.86	71.1	378.53	72.7	404.37	74.7	430.36	77.2	456.48	80.1	482.74	83.5	535.59	91.5		
12	329.86	65.5	355.58	67.2	381.48	69.5	407.54	72.2	433.75	75.3	460.09	79.0				
13	310.40	60.8	336.18	62.7	362.14	65.1	388.27	68.0	414.55	71.5	440.96	75.4				
14	293.74	56.8	319.57	58.9	345.59	61.4	371.79	64.6	398.13	68.3	424.61	72.5				
15	279.31	53.3	305.18	55.6	331.26	58.1	357.52	61.7	383.93	65.7						
16	266.69	50.4	292.61	52.7	318.75	55.7	345.07	59.3	371.54	63.4						
17	255.56	47.8	281.53	50.3	307.72	53.4	334.09	57.2								
18	245.67	45.5	271.69	48.1	297.94	51.4	324.36	55.4								
19	236.84	43.5	262.90	46.2	289.19	49.7										
20	228.89	41.7	255.00	44.5	281.33	48.2										
21	221.70	40.1	247.86	43.1	274.24	46.9										
22	215.18	38.6	241.37	41.7	267.79	45.8										
23	209.22	37.3	235.46	40.6												
24	203.77	36.1	230.04	39.5												
25	198.76	35.0	225.07	38.6												

Design-speed annotations (along the stepped boundary): 70 mph, 60 mph, 50 mph, 40 mph, 30 mph.

117

D_c	$L_s=150'$ T_s	E_s	$200'$ T_s	E_s	$250'$ T_s	E_s	$300'$ T_s	E_s	$350'$ T_s	E_s	$400'$ T_s	E_s	$500'$ T_s	E_s	$600'$ T_s	E_s
1-30																
2-00																
2-30	1319.58	316.5	1344.75	316.8	1369.97	317.3	1395.23	317.9	1420.54	318.6	1445.89	319.3	1496.73	321.2	1547.74	323.5
3-00	1112.23	263.9	1137.43	264.3	1162.69	264.9	1188.00	265.6	1213.37	266.4	1238.79	267.3	1289.79	269.6	1340.98	272.3
3-30	964.13	226.4	989.37	226.9	1014.67	227.5	1040.03	228.3	1065.46	229.3	1090.94	230.4	1142.09	233.0	1193.47	236.1
4-00	853.07	198.3	878.34	198.8	900.68	199.6	929.09	200.5	954.57	201.6	980.12	202.8	1031.42	205.8	1082.97	209.4
5	697.62	158.9	722.95	159.7	748.37	160.6	773.87	161.7	799.46	163.1	825.13	164.6	876.71	168.3	928.59	172.9
6	594.80	132.8	619.40	133.7	644.89	134.8	670.49	136.1	696.19	137.8	721.98	139.6	773.82	144.1	826.00	149.5
7	520.02	114.2	545.47	115.2	571.05	116.5	596.73	118.1	622.53	120.0	648.43	122.1	700.53	127.3	752.98	133.6
8	464.55	100.2	490.06	101.4	515.71	102.9	541.48	104.7	567.38	106.8	593.38	109.3	645.72	115.2	698.42	122.4
9	421.42	89.5	447.00	90.8	472.72	92.4	498.57	94.5	524.56	96.9	550.67	99.7	603.22	106.3	656.14	114.4
10	386.94	80.9	412.57	82.3	438.36	84.2	464.29	86.4	490.37	89.1	516.57	92.2	569.31	99.6		
11	358.74	73.9	384.42	75.5	410.28	77.5	436.29	80.0	462.45	82.9	488.74	86.3	541.67	94.4		
12	335.25	68.1	360.99	69.8	386.91	72.0	413.00	74.7	439.24	77.9	465.61	81.6				
13	315.38	63.2	341.18	65.1	367.16	67.5	393.33	70.4	419.64	73.9	446.08	77.9				
14	298.37	59.0	324.22	61.1	350.27	63.7	376.49	66.8	402.88	70.5	429.40	74.8				
15	283.63	55.5	309.53	57.6	335.64	60.4	361.93	63.8	388.38	67.8						
16	270.74	52.4	296.69	54.7	322.86	57.6	349.21	61.2	375.72	65.5						
17	259.38	49.6	285.38	52.1	311.60	55.2	338.01	59.0								
18	249.29	47.2	275.33	49.8	301.61	53.1	328.07	57.2								
19	240.26	45.1	266.36	47.8	292.68	51.3	319.19	55.6								
20	232.15	43.2	258.29	46.1	284.66	49.8										
21	224.81	41.5	250.99	44.5	277.41	48.4										
22	218.15	40.0	244.37	43.2	270.84	47.2										
23	212.07	38.6	238.34	41.9												
24	206.50	37.4	232.81	40.8												
25	201.38	36.2	227.73	39.8												

Speed boundary markers: 70 mph, 60 mph, 50 mph, 40 mph, 30 mph

TABLE IV
T_s AND E_s

Δ = 57°

118

TABLE IV — T_s AND E_s — Δ = 58°

D_c	$L_s=150'$ T_s	E_s	$200'$ T_s	E_s	$250'$ T_s	E_s	$300'$ T_s	E_s	$350'$ T_s	E_s	$400'$ T_s	E_s	$500'$ T_s	E_s	$600'$ T_s	E_s
1-30																
2-00																
2-30	1345.61	329.0	1370.78	329.4	1396.00	329.8	1421.27	330.4	1446.58	331.1	1471.94	331.9	1522.80	333.7	1573.84	336.0
3-00	1133.92	274.3	1159.12	274.8	1184.39	275.3	1209.71	276.0	1235.08	276.8	1260.51	277.8	1311.53	280.0	1362.76	282.8
3-30	982.73	235.5	1007.97	235.9	1033.29	236.5	1058.64	237.3	1084.08	238.2	1109.57	239.3	1160.75	241.9	1212.16	245.1
4-00	869.34	206.1	894.62	206.7	919.96	207.4	945.39	208.3	970.88	209.4	996.44	210.7	1047.76	213.6	1099.35	217.3
5	710.64	165.2	735.97	165.9	761.40	166.9	786.92	168.0	812.52	169.4	838.21	170.9	889.83	174.6	941.75	179.2
6	604.86	138.0	630.26	138.9	655.77	140.0	681.38	141.4	707.09	143.0	732.90	144.9	784.79	149.3	837.02	154.8
7	529.32	118.6	554.79	119.7	580.37	121.0	606.08	122.6	631.89	124.5	657.82	126.6	709.97	131.8	762.48	138.2
8	472.69	104.2	498.22	105.3	523.88	106.8	549.67	108.6	575.59	110.8	601.62	113.3	654.01	119.2	706.79	126.5
9	428.57	92.9	454.25	94.3	479.99	95.9	505.87	98.0	531.87	100.4	558.01	103.2	610.63	109.9	663.63	118.0
10	393.46	84.0	419.11	85.5	444.91	87.3	470.87	89.6	496.98	92.3	523.21	95.4	576.02	102.8		
11	364.67	76.7	390.37	78.3	416.25	80.4	442.29	82.9	468.47	85.8	494.80	89.2	547.81	97.3		
12	340.69	70.7	366.45	72.4	392.39	74.7	418.51	77.4	444.78	80.6	471.19	84.3				
13	320.41	65.6	346.22	67.5	372.24	69.9	398.43	72.9	424.77	76.3	451.26	80.3				
14	303.04	61.3	328.91	63.3	354.98	65.9	381.24	69.1	407.66	72.8	434.23	77.1				
15	287.99	57.6	313.92	59.7	340.05	62.5	366.38	65.9	392.86	69.9						
16	274.84	54.3	300.81	56.6	327.01	59.6	353.39	63.2	379.95	67.5						
17	263.24	51.5	289.26	54.0	315.51	57.1	341.96	60.9								
18	252.93	49.0	279.01	51.6	305.31	54.9	331.82	59.0								
19	243.72	46.8	269.84	49.5	296.20	53.0	322.76	57.3								
20	235.44	44.8	261.60	47.7	288.01	51.4										
21	227.95	43.0	254.16	46.1	280.62	49.9										
22	221.14	41.4	247.40	44.6	273.90	48.7										
23	214.94	40.0	241.24	43.3	267.79	47.6										
24	209.25	38.7	235.60	42.2												
25	204.03	37.5	230.41	41.1												

Speed annotations: 70 mph, 60 mph, 50 mph, 40 mph, 30 mph.

119

Δ = 59°

TABLE IV — T_s AND E_s Δ = 59°

D_c	$L_s=150'$ T_s	E_s	$200'$ T_s	E_s	$250'$ T_s	E_s	$300'$ T_s	E_s	$350'$ T_s	E_s	$400'$ T_s	E_s	$500'$ T_s	E_s	$600'$ T_s	E_s
1-30 2-00 2-30	1371.89	341.9	1397.06	342.2	1422.28	342.7	1447.56	343.3	1472.88	343.9	1498.25	344.7	1549.13	346.6	1600.19	348.9
3-00	1155.82	285.1	1181.03	285.5	1206.30	286.1	1231.63	286.7	1257.01	287.6	1282.45	288.5	1333.49	290.8	1384.74	293.5
3-30	1001.50	244.5	1026.75	245.0	1052.06	245.5	1077.44	246.5	1102.88	247.4	1128.39	248.5	1179.96	251.2	1231.03	254.4
4-00	885.77	214.1	911.05	214.7	936.41	215.5	961.84	216.4	987.34	217.5	1012.91	218.7	1064.27	221.7	1115.89	225.4
5	723.78	171.6	749.13	172.4	774.56	173.3	800.07	174.5	825.71	175.8	851.41	177.4	903.07	181.1	955.03	185.7
6	615.81	143.4	641.22	144.3	666.75	145.4	692.37	146.8	718.10	148.4	743.93	150.3	795.86	154.7	848.14	160.2
7	538.72	123.2	564.19	124.3	589.79	125.6	615.51	127.2	641.35	129.1	667.29	131.3	719.49	136.5	772.07	142.9
8	480.92	108.2	506.46	109.4	532.13	110.9	557.94	112.7	583.88	114.9	609.94	117.3	662.39	123.3	715.24	130.6
9	435.98	96.5	461.58	97.8	487.33	99.5	513.23	101.6	539.26	104.0	565.43	106.8	618.11	113.5	671.20	121.7
10	400.05	87.2	425.71	88.7	451.54	90.6	477.52	92.8	503.65	95.6	529.91	98.7	582.80	106.1		
11	370.66	79.7	396.38	81.3	422.28	83.3	448.34	85.8	474.56	88.8	500.92	92.2	554.01	100.4		
12	346.19	73.4	371.96	75.1	397.93	77.4	424.07	80.1	450.38	83.3	476.82	87.1				
13	325.49	68.1	351.32	70.0	377.36	72.4	403.57	75.4	429.96	78.9	456.48	82.9				
14	307.76	63.6	333.65	65.6	359.75	68.3	386.04	71.4	412.50	75.2	439.10	79.5				
15	292.40	59.7	318.34	61.9	344.51	64.7	370.87	68.1	397.40	72.1						
16	278.97	56.3	304.97	58.7	331.19	61.7	357.62	65.3	384.22	69.6						
17	267.13	53.4	293.18	55.9	319.46	59.0	345.95	62.9								
18	256.62	50.8	282.71	53.4	309.06	56.8	335.60	60.8								
19	247.21	48.5	273.36	51.2	299.76	54.8	326.36	59.1								
20	238.76	46.4	264.96	49.3	291.40	53.0										
21	231.11	44.6	257.36	47.6	283.85	51.5										
22	224.17	42.9	250.46	46.1	277.00	50.2										
23	217.84	41.4	244.17	44.8	270.76	49.0										
24	212.04	40.1	238.41	43.5												
25	206.70	38.8	233.12	42.4												

Speed zone annotations: 70 mph, 60 mph, 50 mph, 40 mph, 30 mph.

TABLE IV — T_s AND E_s — Δ = 60°

D_c	$L_s=150'$ T_s	E_s	$200'$ T_s	E_s	$250'$ T_s	E_s	$300'$ T_s	E_s	$350'$ T_s	E_s	$400'$ T_s	E_s	$500'$ T_s	E_s	$600'$ T_s	E_s
1-30																
2-00																
2-30	1398.42	355.0	1423.60	355.4	1448.83	355.9	1474.11	356.4	1499.44	357.1	1524.82	357.9	1575.72	359.8	1626.80	362.1
3-00	1177.94	296.0	1203.15	296.5	1228.43	297.0	1253.76	297.7	1279.15	298.5	1304.60	299.5	1355.66	301.8	1406.94	304.5
3-30	1020.46	253.9	1045.71	254.4	1071.03	255.1	1096.42	255.9	1121.87	256.8	1147.39	257.9	1198.61	260.6	1250.09	263.8
4-00	902.36	222.3	927.65	222.9	953.01	223.7	978.45	224.6	1003.96	225.7	1029.55	227.0	1080.93	230.0	1132.59	233.7
5	737.06	178.2	762.41	179.0	787.86	179.9	813.40	181.1	839.03	182.4	864.75	184.0	916.44	187.8	968.45	192.3
6	626.88	148.9	652.30	149.7	677.83	150.9	703.47	152.3	729.22	153.9	755.06	155.8	807.04	160.3	859.38	165.8
7	548.21	127.9	573.69	129.0	599.31	130.3	625.04	131.9	650.90	133.8	676.86	136.0	729.12	141.3	781.76	147.7
8	489.23	112.3	514.77	113.5	540.47	115.0	566.30	116.8	592.26	119.0	618.33	121.5	670.85	127.5	723.77	134.8
9	443.37	100.2	468.98	101.5	494.75	103.2	520.67	105.3	546.73	107.7	572.92	110.5	625.67	117.2	678.84	125.5
10	406.70	90.5	432.37	92.0	458.22	93.9	484.22	96.2	510.38	98.9	536.68	102.0	589.64	109.5	643.04	118.57
11	376.71	82.7	402.45	84.3	428.37	86.3	454.46	88.9	480.70	91.8	507.10	95.3	560.27	103.5		
12	351.74	76.1	377.53	77.9	403.52	80.1	429.69	82.9	456.03	86.2	482.51	89.9	535.87	98.81		
13	330.61	70.6	356.47	72.5	382.53	75.0	408.78	78.0	435.20	81.5	461.76	85.5				
14	312.52	66.0	338.43	68.0	364.56	70.6	390.88	73.8	417.38	77.6	444.03	82.0				
15	296.85	61.9	322.82	64.1	349.01	66.9	375.40	70.4	401.97	74.4	428.70	79.05				
16	283.15	58.4	309.17	60.8	335.42	63.8	361.88	67.4	388.53	71.7						
17	271.07	55.3	297.14	57.8	323.46	61.0	349.98	64.9	376.68	69.5						
18	260.34	52.6	286.46	55.3	312.84	58.6	339.42	62.7								
19	250.74	50.2	276.92	53.0	303.35	56.6	329.99	60.9								
20	242.11	48.1	268.34	51.0	294.82	54.7	321.52	59.29								
21	234.31	46.2	260.59	49.2	287.12	53.1										
22	227.23	44.4	253.55	47.6	280.13	51.7										
23	220.77	42.9	247.13	46.2	273.76	50.5										
24	214.85	41.4	241.26	44.9	267.93	49.41										
25	209.40	40.2	235.86	43.8												

Design speed zones: 70 mph, 60 mph, 50 mph, 40 mph, 30 mph

△ = 61°

TABLE IV — T_s AND E_s

D_c	L_s=150' T_s	E_s	200' T_s	E_s	250' T_s	E_s	300' T_s	E_s	350' T_s	E_s	400' T_s	E_s	500' T_s	E_s	600' T_s	E_s
1-30																
2-00																
2-30	1425.23	368.5	1450.41	368.5	1475.65	368.9	1500.93	369.4	1526.27	370.6	1551.65	371.4	1602.57	373.3	1653.67	375.6
3-00	1200.28	307.1	1225.50	307.7	1250.78	308.3	1276.12	309.0	1301.52	309.8	1326.98	310.8	1378.06	313.0	1429.37	315.8
3-30	1039.61	263.6	1064.87	264.0	1090.19	264.7	1115.59	265.5	1141.05	266.5	1166.58	267.6	1217.83	270.7	1269.34	273.5
4-00	919.12	230.8	944.41	231.4	969.78	232.1	995.23	233.1	1020.76	234.2	1046.35	235.4	1097.77	238.5	1149.47	242.2
5	750.47	185.0	775.83	185.7	801.29	186.7	826.84	187.8	852.48	189.2	878.22	190.8	929.95	194.6	982.00	199.2
6	638.06	154.5	663.49	155.4	689.03	156.5	714.69	157.9	740.45	159.6	766.31	161.6	818.34	166.0	870.73	171.5
7	557.79	132.8	583.29	133.8	608.92	135.1	634.67	136.8	660.54	138.7	686.53	140.9	738.84	146.2	791.55	152.6
8	497.62	116.5	523.18	117.7	548.89	119.2	574.73	121.1	600.72	123.3	626.82	125.8	679.39	131.8	732.39	139.2
9	450.83	103.9	476.46	105.3	502.25	107.0	528.12	109.1	554.27	111.5	580.49	114.3	633.31	121.1	686.56	129.4
10	413.42	93.9	439.11	95.4	464.97	97.3	491.00	99.6	517.19	102.3	543.51	105.1	596.55	113.0	650.05	122.1
11	382.82	85.7	408.58	87.4	434.52	89.4	460.63	92.0	486.91	95.0	513.34	98.4	566.59	106.7		
12	351.34	79.0	383.16	80.7	409.17	83.0	435.37	85.8	461.74	89.0	488.26	92.8	541.71	101.8		
13	335.79	73.2	361.67	75.2	387.75	77.6	414.03	80.6	440.48	84.1	467.09	88.2				
14	317.34	68.4	343.27	70.4	369.42	73.1	395.77	76.3	422.31	80.1	449.00	84.5				
15	301.35	64.2	327.33	66.4	353.55	69.2	379.98	72.7	406.59	76.7	433.36	81.4				
16	287.37	60.5	313.41	62.9	339.70	65.9	366.19	69.6	392.88	73.9						
17	275.04	57.3	301.14	59.1	327.49	63.0	354.05	66.9	380.80	71.5						
18	264.09	54.5	290.24	57.1	316.65	60.6	343.28	64.7								
19	254.30	52.0	280.51	54.8	306.97	58.4	333.66	62.7								
20	245.50	49.8	271.76	52.7	298.28	56.5	325.02	61.1								
21	237.54	47.8	263.85	50.9	290.42	54.8										
22	230.32	46.0	256.67	49.2	283.30	53.3										
23	223.72	44.4	250.12	47.7	276.80	52.0										
24	217.68	42.9	244.13	46.4	270.85	50.9										
25	212.13	41.5	238.62	45.2												

Speed bands: 70 mph, 60 mph, 50 mph, 40 mph, 30 mph

△ = 61°

122

Δ = 62°

Table IV — T_s and E_s

D_c	$L_s=150'$ T_s	E_s	$200'$ T_s	E_s	$250'$ T_s	E_s	$300'$ T_s	E_s	$350'$ T_s	E_s	$400'$ T_s	E_s	$500'$ T_s	E_s	$600'$ T_s	E_s	
1-30																	
2-00																	
2-30	1452.31	382.4	1477.50	382.7	1502.74	383.2	1528.03	383.8	1553.37	384.5	1573.77	385.3	1629.70	387.2	1680.83	389.5	
3-00	1222.85	318.8	1248.07	319.3	1273.36	319.8	1298.71	320.5	1324.12	321.4	1349.58	322.3	1400.69	324.6	1452.03	327.4	
3-30	1058.96	273.4	1084.22	274.0	1109.55	274.6	1134.96	275.5	1160.43	276.4	1185.97	277.5	1237.25	280.2	1288.79	283.5	
4-00	936.05	239.4	961.35	240.0	986.73	240.8	1012.19	241.7	1037.72	242.8	1063.33	244.1	1114.78	247.2	1166.52	250.9	
5	764.02	191.9	789.38	192.6	814.85	193.6	840.42	194.8	866.08	196.1	891.82	197.7	943.59	201.5	995.70	206.2	70 mph
6	649.35	160.3	674.79	161.2	700.35	162.3	726.02	163.7	751.79	165.4	777.68	167.3	829.75	171.8	882.20	177.4	60 mph
7	567.48	137.7	592.98	138.8	618.63	140.1	644.39	141.7	670.29	143.7	696.30	145.9	748.66	151.2	801.43	157.7	
8	506.09	120.9	531.67	122.1	557.39	123.6	583.26	125.4	609.26	127.6	635.39	130.2	688.03	136.2	741.10	143.6	
9	458.37	107.8	484.01	109.1	509.82	110.8	535.78	112.9	561.88	115.4	588.13	118.3	641.02	125.1	694.36	133.4	50 mph
10	420.21	97.4	445.91	98.9	471.80	100.8	497.85	103.1	524.06	105.8	550.42	109.0	603.54	116.5	657.12	125.7	
11	389.00	88.9	414.77	90.5	440.73	92.6	466.87	95.2	493.18	98.2	519.64	101.6	572.98	109.9			
12	363.01	81.8	388.84	83.6	414.87	85.9	441.10	88.7	467.50	92.0	494.06	95.7	547.60	104.8			
13	341.03	75.9	366.92	77.8	393.03	80.3	419.34	83.3	445.83	86.9	472.47	91.0					
14	322.20	70.9	348.15	72.9	374.33	75.6	400.72	78.8	427.29	82.6	454.03	87.0					40 mph
15	305.89	66.5	331.90	68.7	358.15	71.6	384.61	75.0	411.26	79.1	438.08	83.8					
16	291.63	62.7	317.70	65.1	344.01	68.1	370.55	71.8	397.28	76.2							
17	279.06	59.4	305.18	61.9	331.56	65.1	358.16	69.1	384.96	73.7							
18	267.89	56.5	294.07	59.1	320.51	62.5	347.18	66.7									
19	257.90	53.9	284.14	56.7	310.64	60.3	337.37	64.6									
20	248.92	51.5	275.21	54.5	301.77	58.3	328.56	62.9									
21	240.81	49.5	267.14	52.6	293.76	56.5											
22	233.44	47.6	259.82	50.8	286.49	55.0											
23	226.71	45.9	253.15	49.3	279.86	53.6											
24	220.55	44.3	247.03	47.9	273.80	52.4											
25	214.89	42.9	241.41	46.6													30 mph

123

TABLE IV — T_s AND E_s | Δ = 63°

D_c	$L_s=150'$ T_s	E_s	$200'$ T_s	E_s	$250'$ T_s	E_s	$300'$ T_s	E_s	$350'$ T_s	E_s	$400'$ T_s	E_s	$500'$ T_s	E_s	$600'$ T_s	E_s
1-30 / 2-00 / 2-30	1479.68	396.6	1504.88	396.9	1530.12	397.4	1555.42	398.0	1580.77	398.7	1606.17	399.5	1657.12	401.4	1708.27	403.8
3-00	1245.66	330.7	1270.89	331.1	1296.18	331.7	1321.54	332.4	1346.95	333.2	1372.43	334.2	1423.56	336.5	1474.93	339.3
3-30	1078.51	283.6	1103.78	284.1	1129.12	284.8	1154.53	285.6	1180.01	286.6	1205.56	287.7	1256.87	290.4	1308.44	293.7
4-00	953.17	248.3	978.47	248.9	1003.85	249.7	1029.32	250.6	1054.87	251.7	1080.49	253.0	1131.97	256.1	1183.74	259.8
5	777.71	199.0	803.08	199.8	828.56	200.7	854.14	201.9	879.81	203.3	905.58	204.9	957.38	208.7	1009.54	213.4
6	660.77	166.2	686.22	167.1	711.78	168.2	737.46	169.6	763.26	171.2	789.16	173.2	841.28	177.8	893.79	183.4
7	577.27	142.8	602.78	143.9	628.44	145.2	654.22	146.8	680.13	148.8	706.17	151.0	758.58	156.3	811.42	162.9
8	514.66	125.3	540.25	126.5	565.99	128.0	591.87	129.9	617.90	132.1	644.05	134.7	696.75	140.8	749.90	148.2
9	465.99	111.8	491.64	113.1	517.47	114.8	543.45	116.9	569.58	119.4	595.86	122.3	648.82	129.1	702.24	137.4
10	427.07	100.9	452.79	102.4	478.69	104.3	504.77	106.7	531.01	109.4	557.40	112.6	610.59	120.2	664.27	129.4
11	395.24	92.1	421.03	93.8	447.01	95.9	473.14	98.4	499.51	101.5	526.01	105.0	579.44	113.3		
12	368.72	84.8	394.58	86.6	420.64	88.9	446.89	91.7	473.33	95.0	499.93	98.8	553.56	107.9		
13	346.31	78.7	372.23	80.6	398.36	83.1	424.70	86.1	451.23	89.7	477.92	93.8				
14	327.11	73.4	353.09	75.5	379.29	78.2	405.71	81.4	432.33	85.3	459.11	89.7				
15	310.48	68.9	336.51	71.1	362.79	74.0	389.29	77.5	415.98	81.6	442.85	86.3				
16	295.94	65.0	322.03	67.3	348.38	70.4	374.95	74.1	401.72	78.5						
17	283.11	61.5	309.26	64.0	335.68	67.3	362.32	71.2	389.16	75.8						
18	271.72	58.5	297.93	61.1	324.41	64.6	351.12	68.7	378.03	73.62						
19	261.54	55.8	287.80	58.6	314.34	62.2	341.12	66.6								
20	252.38	53.3	278.70	56.3	305.30	60.1	332.14	64.7								
21	244.11	51.2	270.48	54.3	297.13	58.3	324.03	63.10								
22	236.59	49.2	263.01	52.5	289.72	56.6										
23	229.73	47.5	256.20	50.9	282.96	55.2										
24	223.45	45.8	249.97	49.4	276.78	53.9										
25	217.67	44.4	244.44	48.1	271.10	52.8										

Speed annotations (stepped boundaries): 70 mph, 60 mph, 50 mph, 40 mph, 30 mph

Δ = 63°

124

D_c	$L_s = 150'$ T_s	E_s	$200'$ T_s	E_s	$250'$ T_s	E_s	$300'$ T_s	E_s	$350'$ T_s	E_s	$400'$ T_s	E_s	$500'$ T_s	E_s	$600'$ T_s	E_s
1-30																
2-00																
2-30	1507.35	411.1	1532.54	411.5	1557.79	412.0	1583.10	412.6	1608.45	413.3	1633.86	414.1	1684.84	416.0	1736.01	418.4
3-00	1268.72	342.8	1293.95	343.2	1319.25	343.8	1344.61	344.5	1370.03	345.4	1395.52	346.3	1446.68	348.6	1498.07	351.5
3-30	1098.28	294.0	1123.55	294.4	1148.89	295.2	1174.32	296.0	1199.81	297.0	1225.37	298.1	1276.70	300.8	1328.31	304.1
4-00	970.46	257.4	995.77	258.0	1021.16	258.8	1046.64	259.7	1072.20	260.9	1097.83	262.1	1149.34	265.2	1201.16	269.0
5	791.55	206.3	816.93	207.0	842.42	208.0	868.01	209.2	893.69	210.6	919.48	212.2	971.32	216.0	1023.52	220.7
6	672.31	172.3	697.76	173.2	723.34	174.3	749.04	175.7	774.85	177.4	800.77	179.3	852.94	183.9	905.50	189.6
7	587.16	148.0	612.69	149.1	638.35	150.4	664.16	152.1	690.09	154.0	716.15	156.2	768.61	161.6	821.52	168.2
8	523.32	129.9	548.92	131.1	574.67	132.6	600.58	134.5	626.63	136.7	652.81	139.3	705.57	145.4	758.79	152.9
9	473.69	115.8	499.36	117.2	525.20	118.9	551.20	121.0	577.36	123.5	603.67	126.4	656.70	133.3	710.20	141.6
10	434.00	104.6	459.74	106.1	485.66	108.0	511.76	110.4	538.03	113.1	564.45	116.3	617.73	124.0	671.50	133.2
11	401.55	95.5	427.35	97.1	453.36	99.2	479.55	101.8	505.92	104.8	532.45	108.3	585.96	116.7		
12	374.52	87.9	400.39	89.7	426.47	92.0	452.75	94.8	479.22	98.1	505.86	101.9	559.58	111.0		
13	351.66	81.5	377.59	83.4	403.75	85.9	430.12	89.0	456.69	92.6	483.42	96.7				
14	332.08	76.0	358.07	78.1	384.31	80.8	410.76	84.1	437.41	87.9	464.24	92.4				
15	315.12	71.3	341.17	73.6	367.48	76.4	394.02	80.0	420.75	84.1	447.67	88.8				
16	300.29	67.2	326.41	69.6	352.78	72.7	379.40	76.4	406.21	80.8	433.20	85.87				
17	287.21	63.7	313.39	66.2	339.84	69.5	366.52	73.4	393.41	78.1						
18	275.60	60.5	301.83	63.2	328.35	66.6	355.10	70.8	382.06	75.7						
19	265.22	57.7	291.51	60.5	318.09	64.2	344.91	68.6								
20	255.88	55.2	282.23	58.2	308.86	62.0	335.75	66.6								
21	247.44	52.9	273.84	56.1	300.54	60.1	327.48	64.9								
22	239.77	50.9	266.23	54.2	292.98	58.4										
23	232.78	49.1	259.29	52.5	286.09	56.9										
24	226.38	47.4	252.93	51.0	279.79	55.5										
25	220.49	45.9	247.09	49.6	274.01	54.3										

70 mph
60 mph
50 mph
40 mph
30 mph

TABLE IV
T_s AND E_s
Δ = 64°

125

D_c	L_s=150'		200'		250'		300'		350'		400'		500'		600'		
	T_s	E_s	T_s	E_s	T_s	E_s	T_s	E_s	T_s	E_s	T_s	E_s	T_s	E_s	T_s	E_s	
1-30																	
2-30																	
2-30	1535.32	426.1	1560.51	426.4	1585.77	426.9	1611.08	427.5	1636.44	428.2	1661.86	429.0	1712.86	431.0	1764.05	433.3	70 mph
3-00	1292.02	355.2	1317.26	355.7	1342.56	356.3	1367.93	357.0	1393.37	357.8	1418.87	358.8	1470.05	361.1	1521.47	363.9	
3-30	1118.26	304.7	1143.53	305.2	1168.89	305.9	1194.32	306.7	1219.82	307.7	1245.39	308.8	1296.76	311.5	1348.40	314.8	60 mph
4-00	987.95	266.8	1013.26	267.4	1038.66	268.1	1064.15	269.1	1089.72	270.2	1115.37	271.5	1166.91	274.6	1218.76	278.4	
5	805.54	213.8	830.93	214.5	856.43	215.5	882.03	216.7	907.73	218.1	933.53	219.7	985.42	223.5	1037.66	228.3	
6	683.97	178.5	709.43	179.4	735.04	180.6	760.73	182.0	786.56	183.7	812.51	185.6	864.72	190.2	917.34	195.9	50 mph
7	597.16	153.3	622.70	154.4	648.38	155.8	674.20	157.4	700.15	159.4	726.23	161.6	778.76	167.0	831.73	173.6	
8	532.07	134.5	557.68	135.7	583.46	137.3	609.38	139.2	635.45	141.4	661.66	144.0	714.48	150.2	767.78	157.7	
9	481.47	120.0	507.16	121.3	533.02	123.1	559.04	125.2	585.22	127.7	611.56	130.6	664.66	137.5	718.26	145.9	
10	441.01	108.3	466.76	109.8	492.71	111.8	518.83	114.1	545.13	116.9	571.59	120.1	624.94	127.8	678.81	137.1	
11	407.93	98.9	433.75	100.5	459.77	102.6	485.99	105.2	512.39	108.3	538.96	111.8	592.56	120.2			40 mph
12	380.37	91.0	406.25	92.8	432.36	95.1	458.67	97.9	485.18	101.3	511.86	105.1	565.67	114.3			
13	357.06	84.4	383.01	86.3	409.20	88.8	435.60	91.9	462.20	95.5	488.98	99.6	543.01	109.54			
14	337.10	78.7	363.12	80.8	389.38	83.5	415.87	86.8	442.56	90.7	469.43	95.1					
15	319.81	73.8	345.89	76.1	372.24	79.0	398.80	82.5	425.57	86.7	452.54	91.4					
16	304.69	69.6	330.83	72.0	357.24	75.1	383.89	78.8	410.75	83.2	437.80	88.3					
17	291.36	65.9	317.56	68.4	344.04	71.7	370.77	75.7	397.71	80.4							
18	279.52	62.6	305.78	65.3	332.33	68.8	359.13	73.0	386.14	77.9							
19	268.94	59.7	295.25	62.5	321.87	66.2	348.73	70.6									30 mph
20	259.42	57.1	285.79	60.1	312.47	63.9	339.40	68.6									
21	250.81	54.7	277.24	57.9	303.98	61.9	330.98	66.8									
22	243.00	52.6	269.48	55.9	296.28	60.1											
23	235.87	50.7	262.41	54.1	289.26	58.5											
24	229.34	49.0	255.93	52.6	282.84	57.1											
25	223.33	47.4	249.98	51.1	276.94	55.9											

TABLE IV
T_s AND E_s

△ = 65°

126

TABLE IV — Ts AND Es   Δ = 66°

Dc	Ls=150' Ts	Es	200' Ts	Es	250' Ts	Es	300' Ts	Es	350' Ts	Es	400' Ts	Es	500' Ts	Es	600' Ts	Es
1-30																
2-00																
2-30	1563.60	441.3	1588.80	441.7	1614.06	442.2	1639.37	442.8	1664.74	443.5	1690.17	444.3	1741.19	446.3	1792.41	448.7
3-00	1315.59	368.0	1340.83	368.4	1366.14	369.0	1391.52	369.7	1416.96	370.6	1442.47	371.5	1493.67	373.9	1545.13	376.7
3-30	1138.46	315.6	1163.74	316.1	1189.10	316.8	1214.54	317.6	1240.05	318.6	1265.64	319.8	1317.03	322.5	1368.71	325.8
4-00	1005.63	276.3	1030.95	276.9	1056.36	277.7	1081.85	278.7	1107.43	279.8	1133.10	281.1	1184.67	284.2	1236.56	288.0
5	819.69	221.4	845.09	222.2	870.59	223.1	896.21	224.3	921.92	225.7	947.74	227.4	999.67	231.2	1051.96	236.0
6	695.76	184.9	721.24	185.8	746.84	186.9	772.56	188.4	798.41	190.1	824.37	192.0	876.63	196.7	929.32	202.3
7	607.27	158.8	632.82	159.9	658.52	161.2	684.35	162.9	710.32	164.9	736.43	167.1	789.01	172.6	842.05	179.2
8	540.93	139.3	566.55	140.5	592.34	142.1	618.28	144.0	644.38	146.2	670.61	148.8	723.50	155.0	776.88	162.6
9	489.35	124.2	515.04	125.6	540.92	127.3	566.97	129.5	593.18	132.0	619.54	134.9	672.72	141.9	726.40	150.3
10	448.10	112.2	473.87	113.7	499.83	115.6	525.98	118.0	552.31	120.8	578.80	124.0	632.23	131.7	686.20	141.1
11	414.37	102.3	440.21	104.0	466.26	106.1	492.51	108.8	518.94	111.8	545.55	115.4	599.23	123.8	653.45	134.13
12	386.28	94.2	412.19	96.0	438.32	98.3	464.66	101.2	491.20	104.5	517.92	108.4	571.83	117.6		
13	362.53	87.3	388.50	89.3	414.71	91.8	441.14	94.9	467.78	98.5	494.60	102.7	548.74	112.6		
14	342.18	81.5	368.22	83.6	394.51	86.3	421.03	89.6	447.76	93.5	474.68	98.0				
15	324.55	76.4	350.65	78.7	377.02	81.6	403.63	85.1	430.45	89.3	457.46	94.1				
16	309.14	72.0	335.31	74.4	361.75	77.5	388.44	81.3	415.35	85.7	442.44	90.8				
17	295.55	68.1	321.78	70.7	348.30	74.0	375.06	78.0	402.05	82.7						
18	283.48	64.7	309.77	67.4	336.36	70.9	363.20	75.2	390.26	80.1						
19	272.69	61.7	299.04	64.6	325.70	68.2	352.61	72.7								
20	262.99	59.0	289.40	62.0	316.11	65.9	343.10	70.6								
21	254.22	56.6	280.69	59.7	307.46	63.8	334.51	68.7								
22	246.25	54.4	272.77	57.7	299.61	61.9	326.73	67.06								
23	238.99	52.4	265.56	55.9	292.46	60.3										
24	232.33	50.6	258.96	54.2	285.92	58.8										
25	226.21	48.9	252.89	52.7	279.90	57.5										

Speed annotations: 70 mph, 60 mph, 50 mph, 40 mph, 30 mph

Table IV — T_s and E_s ($\Delta = 67°$)

D_c	600′ T_s	600′ E_s	500′ T_s	500′ E_s	400′ T_s	400′ E_s	350′ T_s	350′ E_s	300′ T_s	300′ E_s	250′ T_s	250′ E_s	200′ T_s	200′ E_s	150′ T_s	150′ E_s
1-30																
2-00																
2-30	1821.09	464.4	1769.84	462.0	1718.80	460.0	1693.37	459.2	1667.99	458.5	1642.67	457.9	1617.40	457.4	1592.20	457.0
3-00	1569.06	389.9	1517.57	387.0	1466.35	384.6	1440.83	383.6	1415.38	382.8	1389.99	382.1	1364.67	381.5	1339.43	381.0
3-30	1389.25	337.1	1337.54	333.7	1286.12	331.0	1260.52	329.8	1235.00	328.8	1209.55	328.0	1184.18	327.3	1158.89	326.8
4-00	1254.56	297.9	1202.64	294.0	1151.03	290.9	1125.35	289.6	1099.76	288.5	1074.25	287.5	1048.83	286.7	1023.51	286.1
5	1066.42	243.0	1014.08	239.1	962.11	235.2	936.28	233.6	910.55	232.2	884.92	231.0	859.40	229.2	834.00	229.2
6	941.43	209.0	888.69	203.3	836.38	198.6	810.39	196.6	784.53	194.9	758.79	193.5	733.17	191.4	707.69	191.4
7	852.50	184.9	799.38	178.3	746.74	172.8	720.61	170.5	694.62	168.5	668.77	166.9	643.06	164.4	617.50	164.4
8	786.07	167.6	732.62	160.0	679.66	153.8	653.40	151.2	627.28	148.9	601.32	147.0	575.51	144.2	549.88	144.2
9	734.63	154.8	680.86	146.3	627.62	139.3	601.22	136.4	574.99	133.9	548.91	131.7	523.02	130.0	497.31	128.6
10	693.67	145.2	639.60	135.8	586.09	128.0	559.57	124.8	533.21	122.0	507.04	119.6	481.05	117.6	455.27	116.1
11	660.31	137.9	605.98	127.5	552.20	119.0	525.56	115.5	499.10	112.4	472.82	109.7	446.75	107.6	420.90	105.9
12			578.06	121.0	524.05	111.8	497.29	107.9	470.71	104.5	444.34	101.6	418.19	99.3	392.27	97.5
13			554.53	115.8	500.29	105.8	473.43	101.6	446.75	98.0	420.28	94.9	394.04	92.3	368.05	90.3
14					479.99	100.9	453.02	96.4	426.25	92.5	399.69	89.1	373.37	86.4	347.31	84.3
15					462.45	96.4	435.38	92.0	408.52	87.8	381.87	84.2	355.47	81.3	329.35	79.0
16					447.14	93.4	419.99	88.3	393.04	83.8	366.31	80.0	339.83	76.9	313.64	74.5
17							406.44	85.1	379.40	80.4	352.60	76.4	326.05	73.0	299.79	70.5
18							394.43	82.4	367.67	77.4	340.43	73.2	313.81	69.7	287.49	66.9
19							383.72	80.1	356.52	74.8	329.57	70.4	302.87	66.7	276.50	63.8
20									346.83	72.6	319.80	67.9	293.05	64.0	266.61	61.0
21									338.09	70.7	310.99	65.7	284.17	61.6	257.67	58.5
22									330.15	68.9	302.99	63.8	276.10	59.5	249.55	56.2
23											295.70	62.0	268.75	57.5	242.14	54.1
24											289.03	60.5	262.02	55.9	235.36	52.2
25											282.91	59.1	255.84	54.3	229.12	50.5

Design-speed annotations (right margin): 70 mph, 60 mph, 50 mph, 40 mph, 30 mph.

$\Delta = 67°$

128

TABLE IV — T_s AND E_s Δ = 68°

D_c	$L_s=150'$ T_s	E_s	$200'$ T_s	E_s	$250'$ T_s	E_s	$300'$ T_s	E_s	$350'$ T_s	E_s	$400'$ T_s	E_s	$500'$ T_s	E_s	$600'$ T_s	E_s
1-30																
2-00																
2-30																
3-00	1363.54	394.4	1388.79	394.9	1414.12	395.5	1439.51	396.2	1464.97	397.1	1490.50	398.1	1541.75	400.4	1593.26	403.3
3-30	1179.56	338.3	1204.86	338.8	1230.23	339.5	1255.69	340.4	1281.22	341.3	1306.83	342.5	1358.28	345.3	1410.03	348.6
4-00	1041.60	296.2	1066.93	296.8	1092.36	297.6	1117.87	298.5	1143.48	299.7	1169.17	301.0	1220.81	304.2	1272.78	308.0
5	848.47	237.3	873.89	238.1	899.41	239.1	925.05	240.3	950.80	241.7	976.65	243.3	1028.66	247.3	1081.05	252.1
6	719.76	198.1	745.25	199.0	770.88	200.2	796.63	201.7	822.52	203.4	848.52	205.3	900.88	210.0	953.68	215.8
7	627.84	170.2	653.42	171.2	679.14	172.6	705.01	174.3	731.03	176.3	757.18	178.6	809.87	184.1	863.06	190.8
8	558.94	149.3	584.58	150.5	610.40	152.1	636.39	154.0	662.53	156.3	688.82	158.9	741.84	165.2	795.37	172.8
9	505.36	133.1	531.09	134.4	557.00	136.2	583.10	138.4	609.36	140.9	635.79	143.9	689.11	150.9	742.97	159.5
10	462.53	120.1	488.32	121.7	514.33	123.6	540.53	126.0	566.91	128.9	593.47	132.1	647.06	139.9	701.23	149.4
11	427.49	109.6	453.37	111.3	479.46	113.4	505.76	116.1	532.26	119.2	558.94	122.8	612.80	131.3	667.24	141.7
12	398.32	100.8	424.26	102.7	450.44	105.0	476.84	107.9	503.45	111.3	530.25	115.2	584.36	124.5		
13	373.64	93.5	399.65	95.4	425.92	98.0	452.42	101.1	479.14	104.8	506.04	109.0	560.39	119.1		
14	352.51	87.2	378.59	89.3	404.94	92.0	431.53	95.4	458.34	99.3	485.36	103.9				
15	334.20	81.7	360.35	84.0	386.78	87.0	413.46	90.5	440.37	94.8	467.49	99.6				
16	318.20	77.0	344.41	79.4	370.92	82.6	397.69	86.4	424.69	90.9	451.89	96.1				
17	304.08	72.9	330.37	75.5	356.95	78.8	383.80	82.8	410.89	87.6	438.18	93.06				
18	291.55	69.2	317.89	71.9	344.55	75.5	371.48	79.7	398.65	84.8						
19	280.34	65.9	306.75	68.8	333.48	72.5	360.49	77.1	387.74	82.4						
20	270.26	63.0	296.74	66.1	323.53	70.0	350.61	74.7								
21	261.15	60.4	287.69	63.6	314.55	67.7	341.70	72.7								
22	252.88	58.0	279.47	61.4	306.40	65.7	333.62	70.9								
23	245.33	55.9	271.98	59.4	298.97	63.9										
24	238.42	54.0	265.13	57.6	292.18	62.3										
25	232.07	52.2	258.83	56.0	285.94	60.8										

Speed annotations along stepped boundary: 70 mph, 60 mph, 50 mph, 40 mph, 30 mph.

129

Δ = 69°

TABLE IV — T_s AND E_s

D_c	150' T_s	150' E_s	200' T_s	200' E_s	250' T_s	250' E_s	300' T_s	300' E_s	350' T_s	350' E_s	400' T_s	400' E_s	500' T_s	500' E_s	600' T_s	600' E_s
1-30																
2-00																
2-30																
3-00	1387.94	408.2	1413.20	408.6	1438.53	409.2	1463.93	410.0	1489.40	410.8	1514.94	411.8	1566.21	414.2	1617.76	417.1
3-30	1200.48	350.1	1225.78	350.6	1251.16	351.3	1276.63	352.1	1302.17	353.1	1327.79	354.3	1379.27	357.1	1431.05	360.5
4-00	1059.90	306.5	1085.24	307.1	1110.67	307.9	1136.20	308.9	1161.82	310.0	1187.52	311.3	1239.20	314.5	1291.21	318.4
5	863.12	245.5	888.54	246.3	914.08	247.3	939.73	248.5	965.49	250.0	991.36	251.6	1043.41	255.6	1095.86	260.4
6	731.96	205.0	757.47	205.9	783.11	207.1	808.88	208.6	834.78	210.3	860.81	212.3	913.21	217.0	966.08	222.8
7	638.31	176.1	663.90	177.1	689.64	178.5	715.53	180.2	741.56	182.2	767.74	184.5	820.49	190.1	873.75	196.8
8	568.10	154.4	593.76	155.7	619.60	157.3	645.60	159.2	671.77	161.5	698.09	164.1	751.17	170.4	804.79	178.1
9	513.51	137.6	539.25	139.0	565.19	140.8	591.30	143.0	617.59	145.6	644.05	148.5	697.44	155.6	751.40	164.2
10	469.87	124.3	495.68	125.8	521.71	127.8	547.93	130.2	574.34	133.1	600.94	136.3	654.61	144.2	708.88	153.7
11	434.17	113.3	460.06	115.0	486.18	117.2	512.51	119.9	539.03	123.0	565.76	126.6	619.71	135.2	674.26	145.7
12	404.44	104.3	430.40	106.1	456.61	108.5	483.04	111.4	509.69	114.8	536.53	118.7	590.73	128.1		
13	379.30	96.6	405.33	98.6	431.62	101.2	458.16	104.3	484.91	108.0	511.86	112.3	566.31	122.4		
14	357.76	90.1	383.87	92.3	410.25	95.0	436.87	98.4	463.73	102.4	490.79	106.9				
15	339.11	84.5	365.29	86.8	391.74	89.8	418.47	93.4	445.42	97.6	472.59	102.5				
16	322.80	79.6	349.04	82.1	375.59	85.2	402.39	89.1	429.44	93.6	456.70	98.8				
17	308.42	75.3	334.73	77.9	361.35	81.3	388.24	85.3	415.38	90.1	442.74	95.6				
18	295.65	71.5	322.03	74.3	348.72	77.8	375.70	82.1	402.92	87.2						
19	284.23	68.1	310.67	71.0	337.44	74.8	364.49	79.3	391.80	84.6						
20	273.96	65.1	300.47	68.2	327.31	72.1	354.44	76.9								
21	264.68	62.4	291.25	65.6	318.16	69.7	345.36	74.7								
22	256.25	59.9	282.88	63.3	309.85	67.6	337.13	72.8								
23	248.56	57.7	275.25	61.2	302.29	65.7	329.63	71.19								
24	241.52	55.7	263.26	59.4	295.37	64.1										
25	235.05	53.9	261.85	57.7	289.01	62.6										

Speed designations (right margin): 70 mph, 60 mph, 50 mph, 40 mph, 30 mph

Δ = 69°

130

D_c	$L_s = 150'$		$200'$		$250'$		$300'$		$350'$		$400'$		$500'$		$600'$	
	T_s	E_s	T_s	E_s	T_s	E_s	T_s	E_s	T_s	E_s	T_s	E_s	T_s	E_s	T_s	E_s
1-30																
2-00																
2-30																
3-00	1412.64	422.2	1437.90	422.7	1463.23	423.3	1488.64	424.0	1514.12	424.9	1539.67	425.9	1590.97	428.3	1642.55	431.2
3-30	1221.65	362.1	1246.95	362.6	1272.34	363.3	1297.82	364.2	1323.37	365.2	1349.01	366.4	1400.51	369.2	1452.33	372.6
4-00	1078.42	317.0	1103.77	317.6	1129.21	318.4	1154.75	319.4	1180.38	320.6	1206.10	321.9	1257.81	325.1	1309.86	329.0
5	877.94	254.0	903.37	254.8	928.92	255.8	954.58	257.0	980.36	258.4	1006.25	260.1	1058.34	264.1	1110.84	268.9
6	744.32	212.0	769.83	212.9	795.49	214.2	821.27	215.6	847.19	217.3	873.24	219.3	925.70	224.1	978.62	229.9
7	648.91	182.1	674.50	183.2	700.26	184.6	726.17	186.3	752.22	188.3	778.42	190.6	831.24	196.2	884.56	203.0
8	577.38	159.7	603.05	161.0	628.90	162.6	654.93	164.5	681.12	166.8	707.46	169.4	760.62	175.8	814.32	183.5
9	521.76	142.3	547.52	143.7	573.47	145.5	599.61	147.7	625.92	150.3	652.42	153.2	705.88	160.4	759.92	169.1
10	477.29	128.5	503.12	130.0	529.17	132.0	555.42	134.5	581.87	137.3	608.49	140.6	662.25	148.5	716.62	158.1
11	440.93	117.2	466.83	118.9	492.97	121.1	519.33	123.8	545.89	126.9	572.65	130.5	626.70	139.2	681.36	149.7
12	410.64	107.8	436.62	109.7	462.85	112.1	489.31	115.0	516.00	118.4	542.88	122.3	597.18	131.8		
13	385.02	99.9	411.08	101.9	437.40	104.5	463.96	107.6	490.76	111.4	517.75	115.6	572.31	125.8		
14	363.08	93.1	389.21	95.3	415.62	98.1	442.28	101.5	469.18	105.5	496.29	110.1	551.08	121.01		
15	344.08	87.3	370.28	89.6	396.77	92.6	423.53	96.2	450.53	100.5	477.75	105.4				
16	327.47	82.3	353.73	84.7	380.31	87.9	407.16	91.8	434.26	96.3	461.57	101.5				
17	312.81	77.	339.15	80.4	365.81	83.8	392.74	87.9	419.93	92.7	447.35	98.3				
18	299.80	73.	326.21	76.6	352.94	80.2	379.96	84.5	407.24	89.6						
19	288.17	70.4	314.64	73.3	341.45	77.1	368.55	81.6	395.91	87.0						
20	277.71	67.2	304.25	70.3	331.13	74.3	358.31	79.1	385.75	84.71						
21	268.25	64.4	294.85	67.7	321.81	71.8	349.06	76.8								
22	259.67	61.9	286.33	65.3	313.35	69.6	340.68	74.9								
23	251.83	59.6	278.55	63.1	305.64	67.6	333.04	73.1								
24	244.66	57.5	271.44	61.2	298.59	65.9										
25	238.06	55.6	264.90	59.4	292.12	64.3										

Speed annotations (diagonal): 70 mph, 60 mph, 50 mph, 40 mph, 30 mph

TABLE IV
T_s AND E_s
Δ = 70°

131

Δ = 71°

TABLE IV — T_s AND E_s, Δ = 71°

Speed markers (stepped along the table): 70 mph, 60 mph, 50 mph, 40 mph, 30 mph

D_c	$L_s=150'$ T_s	E_s	$200'$ T_s	E_s	$250'$ T_s	E_s	$300'$ T_s	E_s	$350'$ T_s	E_s	$400'$ T_s	E_s	$500'$ T_s	E_s	$600'$ T_s	E_s
1-30																
2-00																
2-30																
3-00	1437.64	436.7	1462.90	437.1	1488.24	437.8	1513.66	438.5	1539.15	439.4	1564.71	440.4	1616.04	442.8	1667.64	445.7
3-30	1243.08	374.5	1268.39	375.0	1293.79	375.7	1319.27	376.6	1344.83	377.6	1370.48	378.8	1422.02	381.6	1473.87	385.0
4-00	1097.18	327.9	1122.53	328.5	1147.98	329.3	1173.53	330.3	1199.17	331.4	1224.90	332.8	1276.64	336.0	1328.74	339.9
5	892.95	262.7	918.39	263.4	943.95	264.4	969.62	265.7	995.41	267.1	1021.32	268.8	1073.45	272.8	1126.00	277.7
6	756.83	219.2	782.35	220.2	808.02	221.4	833.82	222.9	859.76	224.6	885.83	226.6	938.34	231.4	991.32	237.3
7	659.63	188.3	685.24	189.4	711.01	190.8	736.94	192.5	763.01	194.5	789.24	196.9	842.11	202.5	895.51	209.3
8	586.76	165.1	612.45	166.4	638.32	168.0	664.37	170.0	690.59	172.3	716.96	174.9	770.18	181.3	823.96	189.1
9	530.11	147.2	555.88	148.6	581.85	150.4	608.02	152.6	634.36	155.2	660.88	158.2	714.43	165.3	768.56	174.1
10	484.81	132.8	510.66	134.4	536.73	136.4	563.00	138.8	589.48	141.7	616.14	145.1	669.99	153.0	724.46	162.7
11	447.77	121.1	473.69	122.9	499.85	125.1	526.24	127.7	552.84	130.9	579.64	134.6	633.77	143.3	688.55	153.9
12	416.91	111.4	442.91	113.3	469.17	115.7	495.66	118.6	522.38	122.1	549.31	126.1	603.71	135.6		
13	390.82	103.2	416.90	105.3	443.24	107.9	469.84	111.0	496.68	114.8	523.72	119.1	578.39	129.3		
14	368.47	96.3	394.62	98.4	421.06	101.2	447.76	104.6	474.70	108.7	501.86	113.3	556.76	124.3		
15	349.11	90.2	375.33	92.6	401.86	95.6	428.66	99.2	455.70	103.5	482.97	108.4				
16	332.19	85.0	358.48	87.5	385.09	90.7	411.98	94.5	439.13	99.1	466.50	104.4				
17	317.26	80.4	343.63	83.0	370.32	86.4	397.30	90.5	424.54	95.4	452.01	100.9				
18	304.01	76.3	330.44	79.1	357.21	82.7	384.28	87.0	411.61	92.2						
19	292.16	72.7	318.66	75.6	345.51	79.4	372.66	84.0	400.08	89.4						
20	281.50	69.4	308.07	72.5	334.99	76.5	362.23	81.3	389.73	87.0						
21	271.87	66.5	298.50	69.8	325.50	73.9	352.81	79.0								
22	263.12	63.9	289.82	67.3	316.89	71.6	344.27	76.9								
23	255.14	61.5	281.90	65.1	309.04	69.6	336.49	75.1								
24	247.83	59.3	274.65	63.0	301.86	67.8										
25	241.11	57.3	267.99	61.2	295.26	66.1										

Δ = 71°

TABLE IV — T_s AND E_s — $\triangle = 72°$

D_c	$L_s=150'$ T_s	E_s	$200'$ T_s	E_s	$250'$ T_s	E_s	$300'$ T_s	E_s	$350'$ T_s	E_s	$400'$ T_s	E_s	$500'$ T_s	E_s	$600'$ T_s	E_s	mph
1-30																	
2-00																	
2-30																	
3-00	1462.95	451.5	1488.22	451.9	1513.57	452.5	1538.99	453.3	1564.49	454.2	1590.06	455.2	1641.41	457.6	1693.05	460.6	70 mph
3-30	1266.78	387.2	1290.09	387.6	1315.50	388.4	1340.99	389.3	1366.52	390.3	1392.23	391.5	1443.79	394.3	1495.68	397.8	
4-00	1116.16	339.0	1141.52	339.6	1166.98	340.4	1192.54	341.4	1218.20	342.5	1243.94	343.9	1295.72	347.1	1347.86	351.1	
5	908.14	271.5	933.59	272.3	959.16	273.3	984.85	274.6	1010.66	276.0	1036.58	277.7	1088.76	281.7	1141.36	286.7	60 mph
6	769.50	226.6	795.03	227.6	820.71	228.8	846.53	230.3	872.48	232.0	898.57	234.0	951.13	238.9	1004.18	244.8	
7	670.50	194.6	696.11	195.7	721.90	197.2	747.84	198.9	773.94	200.9	800.19	203.3	853.12	208.9	906.60	215.8	
8	596.27	170.7	621.97	171.9	647.86	173.6	673.93	175.5	700.17	177.9	726.57	180.5	779.86	187.0	833.72	194.8	50 mph
9	538.57	152.1	564.35	153.5	590.34	155.3	616.53	157.6	642.90	160.2	669.46	163.2	723.08	170.4	777.31	179.2	
10	492.43	137.3	518.29	138.9	544.38	140.9	570.68	143.3	597.19	146.2	623.89	149.6	677.82	157.6	732.39	167.3	
11	454.69	125.2	480.64	126.9	506.82	129.1	533.23	131.8	559.87	135.0	586.71	138.7	640.94	147.5	695.82	158.1	
12	423.26	115.1	449.29	117.0	475.57	119.4	502.09	122.4	528.85	125.9	555.82	129.9	610.33	139.4	665.50	151.01	
13	396.69	106.7	422.78	108.7	449.16	111.3	475.79	114.5	502.67	118.2	529.75	122.6	584.54	132.9			
14	373.92	99.4	400.10	101.6	426.56	104.5	453.30	107.9	480.28	111.9	507.49	116.6	562.51	127.7			40 mph
15	354.20	93.2	380.45	95.6	407.01	98.6	433.85	102.2	460.94	106.6	488.26	111.5					
16	336.97	87.8	363.29	90.3	389.93	93.5	416.86	97.4	444.06	102.0	471.48	107.3					
17	321.76	83.0	348.16	85.7	374.89	89.1	401.91	93.2	429.20	98.1	456.74	103.7					
18	308.26	78.8	334.73	81.6	361.54	85.2	388.65	89.6	416.04	94.8	443.67	100.67					
19	296.19	75.0	322.72	78.0	349.62	81.8	376.82	86.4	404.30	91.9							
20	285.34	71.7	311.94	74.8	338.91	78.8	366.20	83.7	393.76	89.4							
21	275.53	68.6	302.20	71.9	329.24	76.1	356.61	81.2									
22	266.62	65.9	293.35	69.4	320.47	73.7	347.91	79.1									
23	258.49	63.4	285.29	67.0	312.48	71.5	339.99	77.2									
24	251.05	61.2	277.91	64.9	305.16	69.7	332.75	75.50									30 mph
25	244.20	59.1	271.13	63.0	298.45	68.0											

TABLE IV — T_s AND E_s — Δ = 73°

$L_s = 150'$

D_c	T_s (150')	E_s (150')	T_s (200')	E_s (200')	T_s (250')	E_s (250')	T_s (300')	E_s (300')	T_s (350')	E_s (350')	T_s (400')	E_s (400')	T_s (500')	E_s (500')	T_s (600')	E_s (600')
1-30																
2-00																
2-30																
3-00	1488.58	466.6	1513.86	467.1	1539.21	467.7	1564.64	468.4	1590.15	469.3	1615.73	470.3	1667.11	472.8	1718.78	475.8
3-30	1286.75	400.1	1312.07	400.7	1337.48	401.4	1362.99	402.1	1388.57	403.2	1414.25	404.5	1465.84	407.3	1517.77	410.8
4-00	1135.39	350.3	1160.76	351.0	1186.23	351.8	1211.80	352.8	1237.47	353.9	1263.23	355.3	1315.04	358.5	1367.22	362.5
5	923.53	280.6	948.98	281.4	974.57	282.4	1000.27	283.7	1026.09	285.1	1052.03	286.8	1104.25	290.9	1156.91	295.8
6	782.32	234.2	807.87	235.2	833.56	236.4	859.39	237.9	885.37	239.6	911.48	241.7	964.09	246.5	1017.21	252.5
7	681.49	201.1	707.12	202.2	732.92	203.7	758.89	205.4	785.01	207.5	811.29	209.8	864.28	215.5	917.83	222.4
8	605.90	176.4	631.61	177.6	657.52	179.3	683.61	181.3	709.88	183.6	736.31	186.3	789.66	192.8	843.61	200.6
9	547.13	157.2	572.93	158.6	598.94	160.4	625.15	162.7	651.55	165.3	678.14	168.3	731.84	175.6	786.16	184.4
10	500.14	141.8	526.02	143.4	552.13	145.4	578.46	147.9	605.00	150.8	631.73	154.2	685.75	162.3	740.43	172.1
11	461.70	129.3	487.67	131.1	513.88	133.3	540.32	136.0	566.99	139.2	593.87	142.9	648.19	151.8	703.19	162.5
12	429.70	118.9	455.74	120.8	482.05	123.0	508.60	126.2	535.40	129.7	562.41	133.8	617.02	143.4	672.32	155.0
13	402.63	110.2	428.75	112.2	455.15	114.9	481.82	118.1	508.74	121.9	535.87	126.2	590.76	136.6		
14	379.44	102.7	405.64	104.9	432.14	107.7	458.91	111.2	485.94	115.3	513.20	119.9	568.34	131.1		
15	359.36	96.3	385.64	98.6	412.22	101.6	439.10	105.3	466.24	109.7	493.62	114.7				
16	341.81	90.6	368.15	93.1	394.83	96.4	421.81	100.3	449.05	105.0	476.54	110.3				
17	326.32	85.7	352.75	88.4	379.51	91.8	406.58	96.0	433.93	100.9	461.52	106.5				
18	312.58	81.3	339.07	84.2	365.92	87.8	393.08	92.2	420.52	97.4	448.22	103.4				
19	300.28	77.4	326.85	80.4	353.78	84.3	381.03	88.9	408.57	94.4						
20	289.23	74.0	315.87	77.1	342.87	81.1	370.24	86.0	397.84	91.8						
21	279.24	70.8	305.94	74.1	333.03	78.4	360.45	83.5								
22	270.16	68.0	296.93	71.5	324.10	75.9	351.60	81.2								
23	261.88	65.4	288.72	69.1	315.96	73.7	343.53	79.3								
24	254.30	63.1	281.20	66.9	308.51	71.7	336.16	77.5								
25	247.33	61.0	274.30	64.9	301.68	69.9										

Design speed markers: 70 mph, 60 mph, 50 mph, 40 mph, 30 mph.

$\Delta = 74°$

TABLE IV T_s AND E_s $\Delta = 74°$

D_c	$L_s=150'$ T_s	E_s	$200'$ T_s	E_s	$250'$ T_s	E_s	$300'$ T_s	E_s	$350'$ T_s	E_s	$400'$ T_s	E_s	$500'$ T_s	E_s	$600'$ T_s	E_s
1–30																
2–00																
2–30																
3–00	1514.55	482.2	1539.83	482.6	1565.19	483.3	1590.63	484.0	1616.15	484.9	1641.74	485.9	1693.15	488.4	1744.85	491.4
3–30	1309.01	413.5	1334.34	414.0	1359.76	414.7	1385.27	415.6	1410.87	416.7	1436.55	417.9	1488.18	420.7	1540.15	424.2
4–00	1154.87	362.0	1180.25	362.6	1205.52	363.4	1231.30	364.4	1256.98	365.6	1282.76	367.0	1334.61	370.2	1386.83	374.3
5	939.12	290.0	964.58	290.8	990.17	291.8	1015.89	293.0	1041.73	294.5	1067.69	296.2	1119.95	300.3	1172.66	305.3
6	795.32	242.0	820.87	243.0	846.58	244.2	872.43	245.7	898.42	247.5	924.55	249.5	977.22	254.4	1030.40	260.4
7	692.63	207.8	718.28	208.9	744.09	210.4	770.07	212.1	796.22	214.2	822.52	216.6	875.58	222.3	929.20	229.3
8	615.65	182.2	641.38	183.5	667.30	185.1	693.42	187.1	719.71	189.5	746.17	192.2	799.60	198.7	853.63	206.6
9	555.80	162.4	581.62	163.8	607.65	165.6	633.88	167.9	660.31	170.5	686.93	173.6	740.71	180.9	795.14	189.8
10	507.95	146.5	533.84	148.1	559.98	150.1	586.33	152.6	612.90	155.6	639.68	159.0	693.78	167.1	748.57	176.9
11	468.81	133.6	494.79	135.3	521.03	137.6	547.50	140.3	574.20	143.6	601.12	147.3	655.54	156.2	710.66	167.0
12	436.21	122.8	462.28	124.8	488.61	127.2	515.24	130.2	542.03	133.7	569.09	137.8	623.81	147.4	679.23	159.2
13	408.65	113.8	434.87	115.9	461.22	118.5	487.93	121.7	514.88	125.5	542.06	129.9	597.07	140.4		
14	385.04	106.1	411.26	108.3	437.79	111.1	464.60	114.6	491.67	118.7	518.99	123.4	574.25	134.6		
15	364.59	99.4	390.89	101.8	417.51	104.8	444.43	108.5	471.61	112.9	499.05	118.0				
16	346.71	93.6	373.08	96.1	399.80	99.4	426.82	103.3	454.11	108.0	481.65	113.3				
17	330.94	88.5	357.40	91.2	384.20	94.6	411.31	98.8	438.71	103.3	466.37	109.4				
18	316.94	83.9	343.47	86.8	370.36	90.4	397.57	94.9	425.07	100.1	452.82	106.1				
19	304.42	79.9	331.02	82.9	358.00	86.8	385.30	91.5	412.39	97.0						
20	293.17	76.3	319.84	79.5	346.89	83.5	374.28	88.5	401.97	94.2						
21	282.99	73.1	309.73	76.4	336.87	80.7	364.34	85.8	392.12	91.9						
22	273.75	70.2	300.56	73.6	327.77	78.1	355.33	83.5								
23	265.32	67.5	292.20	71.1	319.48	75.8	347.12	81.4								
24	257.60	65.1	284.54	68.9	311.90	73.7	339.62	79.6								
25	250.51	62.9	277.51	66.8	304.94	71.9										

Speed annotations: 70 mph, 60 mph, 50 mph, 40 mph, 30 mph

135

Δ = 75°

TABLE IV
T_s AND E_s

Δ = 75°

Speed boundaries across the table: 70 mph, 60 mph, 50 mph, 40 mph, 30 mph.

D_c	$L_s = 150'$ T_s	E_s	$200'$ T_s	E_s	$250'$ T_s	E_s	$300'$ T_s	E_s	$350'$ T_s	E_s	$400'$ T_s	E_s	$500'$ T_s	E_s	$600'$ T_s	E_s
1-30																
2-00																
2-30																
3-00	1540.86	498.1	1566.14	498.6	1591.51	499.2	1616.96	499.9	1642.49	500.8	1668.09	501.9	1719.53	504.3	1771.26	507.4
3-30	1331.56	427.1	1356.90	427.7	1382.33	428.4	1407.85	429.3	1433.46	430.3	1459.16	431.5	1510.82	434.4	1562.82	437.9
4-00	1174.61	373.9	1199.99	374.1	1225.48	375.4	1251.07	376.4	1276.76	377.6	1302.55	379.0	1354.43	382.3	1406.70	386.3
5	954.91	299.5	980.38	300.3	1005.99	301.3	1031.72	302.6	1057.57	304.1	1083.55	305.8	1135.86	309.9	1188.63	314.9
6	808.48	250.0	834.05	250.9	859.77	252.2	885.63	253.7	911.65	255.5	937.80	257.5	990.52	262.4	1043.77	268.5
7	703.92	214.6	729.58	215.8	755.41	217.2	781.41	219.0	807.58	221.0	833.91	223.4	887.02	229.2	940.72	236.2
8	625.53	188.2	651.28	189.5	677.22	191.1	703.35	193.1	729.67	195.5	756.16	198.2	809.66	204.8	863.78	212.8
9	564.59	167.7	590.42	169.1	616.47	171.0	642.73	173.2	669.19	175.9	695.84	179.0	749.71	186.3	804.23	195.3
10	515.86	151.3	541.77	152.9	567.93	155.0	594.31	157.5	620.92	160.4	647.73	163.8	701.92	172.0	756.82	181.9
11	476.01	137.9	502.01	139.7	528.27	142.0	554.77	144.7	581.51	148.0	608.47	151.7	662.99	160.7	718.23	171.5
12	442.82	126.8	468.90	128.8	495.26	131.2	521.88	134.2	548.76	137.8	575.36	141.9	630.68	151.6	686.24	163.4
13	414.75	117.5	440.91	119.6	467.38	122.2	494.11	125.5	521.11	129.3	548.34	133.7	603.46	144.3		
14	390.71	109.5	416.95	111.7	443.16	114.6	470.36	118.1	497.48	122.2	524.84	127.0	580.23	138.3		
15	369.08	102.6	396.21	105.0	422.86	108.1	449.82	111.8	477.06	116.2	504.54	121.3	560.18	133.34		
16	351.68	96.6	378.03	99.1	404.83	102.4	431.89	106.4	459.24	111.1	486.84	116.5				
17	335.62	91.3	362.11	94.0	388.94	97.5	416.11	101.7	443.56	106.7	471.28	112.4				
18	321.37	86.6	347.92	89.5	374.85	93.2	402.11	97.6	429.67	102.9	457.49	108.9				
19	308.62	82.5	335.25	85.5	362.27	89.4	389.62	94.1	417.28	99.6						
20	297.16	78.7	323.86	81.9	350.96	86.0	378.41	91.0	406.16	96.8						
21	286.80	75.4	313.58	78.7	340.75	83.0	368.29	88.2	396.13	94.3						
22	277.39	72.4	304.23	75.9	331.49	80.3	359.11	85.8								
23	268.80	69.6	295.72	73.3	323.06	77.9	350.76	83.6								
24	260.94	67.1	287.93	70.9	315.34	75.8	343.12	81.7								
25	253.72	64.8	280.77	68.8	308.26	73.9	336.11	80.01								

TABLE IV — Ts AND Es — Δ=76°

D_c	$L_s=150'$ T_s	E_s	$200'$ T_s	E_s	$250'$ T_s	E_s	$300'$ T_s	E_s	$350'$ T_s	E_s	$400'$ T_s	E_s	$500'$ T_s	E_s	$600'$ T_s	E_s
1-30																
2-00																
2-30																
3-00	1567.53	514.3	1592.86	514.9	1618.19	515.5	1643.65	516.3	1669.18	517.2	1694.80	518.2	1746.26	520.7	1798.03	523.8
3-30	1354.42	441.1	1379.78	441.7	1405.20	442.4	1430.73	443.3	1456.35	444.3	1482.06	445.6	1533.76	448.5	1585.80	452.0
4-00	1194.61	386.0	1220.00	386.8	1245.50	387.6	1271.10	388.7	1296.81	389.9	1322.61	391.2	1374.53	394.6	1426.84	398.6
5	970.92	309.3	996.40	310.1	1022.01	311.1	1047.76	312.4	1073.63	313.9	1099.63	315.7	1151.98	319.8	1204.80	324.8
6	821.82	258.1	847.40	259.1	873.13	260.4	899.02	261.9	925.05	263.7	951.23	265.7	1004.00	270.7	1057.32	276.8
7	715.36	221.6	741.03	222.8	766.88	224.2	792.90	226.0	819.09	228.1	845.45	230.5	898.63	236.3	952.40	243.3
8	635.55	194.3	661.31	195.6	687.27	197.3	713.42	199.3	739.77	201.7	766.29	204.4	819.86	211.0	874.07	219.1
9	573.59	173.1	599.34	174.6	625.41	176.4	651.70	178.7	678.19	181.4	704.88	184.5	758.82	191.9	813.44	200.9
10	523.88	156.2	549.81	157.8	575.99	159.9	602.40	162.4	629.04	165.4	655.89	168.8	710.17	177.0	765.18	187.0
11	483.30	142.4	509.32	144.2	535.61	146.5	562.14	149.2	588.92	152.5	615.92	156.3	670.54	165.3	725.90	176.2
12	449.51	130.9	475.61	132.9	502.00	135.4	528.66	138.4	555.57	142.0	582.71	146.1	637.65	155.9	693.33	167.8
13	420.93	121.3	447.12	123.4	473.61	126.0	500.39	129.3	527.43	133.2	554.70	137.6	609.94	148.2		
14	396.45	113.0	422.72	115.3	449.32	118.1	476.20	121.7	503.37	125.8	530.78	130.6	586.29	142.0		
15	375.25	105.9	401.60	108.3	428.29	111.4	455.29	115.1	482.57	119.6	510.12	124.7	565.89	136.8		
16	356.71	99.7	383.14	102.2	409.93	105.5	437.04	109.5	464.44	114.3	492.10	119.7				
17	340.37	94.2	366.88	96.9	393.76	100.4	420.97	104.7	448.48	109.7	476.26	115.5				
18	325.85	89.4	352.44	92.3	379.41	96.0	406.72	100.5	434.33	105.8	462.22	111.8				
19	312.87	85.1	339.54	88.1	366.60	92.0	394.00	96.8	421.72	102.3	449.71	108.74				
20	301.20	81.2	327.94	84.4	355.09	88.5	382.59	93.5	410.41	99.4						
21	290.65	77.7	317.47	81.1	344.70	85.4	372.29	90.7	400.19	96.8						
22	281.07	74.6	307.96	78.1	335.27	82.6	362.95	88.1								
23	272.33	71.8	299.29	75.5	326.68	80.2	354.44	85.9								
24	264.33	69.2	291.36	73.0	318.82	77.9	346.67	83.9								
25	256.97	66.8	284.07	70.8	311.61	75.9	339.53	82.1								

Design-speed step boundaries: 70 mph, 60 mph, 50 mph, 40 mph, 30 mph.

TABLE IV
Ts AND Es

Δ = 77°

Dc	Ls=150' Ts	Es	200' Ts	Es	250' Ts	Es	300' Ts	Es	350' Ts	Es	400' Ts	Es	500' Ts	Es	600' Ts	Es
1-30																
2-00																
2-30																
3-00	1594.56	531.1	1619.85	531.6	1645.24	532.3	1670.70	533.0	1696.25	533.9	1721.87	535.0	1773.37	537.5	1825.17	540.5
3-30	1377.36	455.5	1402.94	456.0	1428.39	456.8	1453.93	457.7	1479.56	458.7	1505.29	459.9	1557.01	462.9	1609.09	466.4
4-00	1214.89	398.7	1240.29	399.4	1265.79	400.4	1291.40	401.2	1317.13	402.4	1342.95	403.8	1394.90	407.2	1447.26	411.3
5	987.14	319.4	1012.63	320.2	1038.26	321.2	1064.02	322.5	1089.91	324.0	1115.92	325.7	1168.33	329.9	1221.20	335.0
6	835.35	266.5	860.94	267.5	886.68	268.7	912.58	270.0	938.64	272.1	964.84	274.2	1017.06	279.2	1071.05	285.3
7	726.96	228.8	752.64	230.0	778.51	231.4	804.55	233.2	830.76	235.3	857.14	237.0	910.39	243.6	964.24	250.7
8	645.70	200.6	671.47	201.9	697.45	203.6	723.63	205.6	750.00	208.0	776.55	210.8	830.20	217.4	884.50	225.5
9	582.53	178.7	608.39	180.2	634.48	182.1	660.79	184.4	687.31	187.1	714.03	190.2	768.06	197.1	822.78	206.7
10	532.01	161.2	557.96	162.9	584.16	165.0	610.60	167.5	637.27	170.5	664.16	174.0	718.53	182.2	773.65	192.3
11	490.70	147.0	516.74	148.8	543.05	151.1	569.62	153.9	596.42	157.2	623.47	161.0	678.19	170.0	733.67	181.1
12	456.29	135.1	482.42	137.1	508.84	139.6	535.52	142.6	562.48	146.2	589.67	150.4	644.71	160.2	700.53	172.2
13	427.20	125.1	453.41	127.3	479.93	130.0	506.74	133.3	533.82	137.1	561.15	141.6	616.51	152.3		
14	402.27	116.6	428.57	118.9	455.20	121.8	482.12	125.0	509.18	129.5	536.80	134.3	592.44	145.8		
15	380.69	109.2	407.07	111.7	433.79	114.8	460.83	118.6	488.17	123.1	515.77	128.2	571.67	140.4		
16	361.82	102.8	388.28	105.4	415.10	108.7	442.25	112.8	469.70	117.5	497.42	123.0				
17	345.17	97.2	371.72	99.9	398.63	103.4	425.89	107.7	453.46	112.8	481.30	118.6				
18	330.40	92.2	357.02	95.1	384.03	98.8	411.39	103.4	439.06	108.7	467.02	114.8				
19	317.18	87.7	343.88	90.8	370.98	94.7	398.44	99.5	426.22	105.1	454.29	111.6				
20	305.30	83.7	332.08	87.0	359.27	91.1	386.83	96.1	414.71	102.0						
21	294.56	80.2	321.42	83.6	348.69	87.9	376.34	93.2	404.31	99.3						
22	284.81	76.9	311.73	80.5	339.09	85.0	366.83	90.5	394.90	96.99						
23	275.91	74.0	302.91	77.7	330.35	82.4	358.18	88.2								
24	267.76	71.3	294.83	75.2	322.35	80.1	350.26	86.1								
25	260.27	68.9	287.41	72.9	315.01	78.0	343.00	84.3								

Speed reference lines: 70 mph, 60 mph, 50 mph, 40 mph, 30 mph

TABLE IV
T_s AND E_s   Δ = 78°

D_c	$L_s=150'$ T_s	E_s	200' T_s	E_s	250' T_s	E_s	300' T_s	E_s	350' T_s	E_s	400' T_s	E_s	500' T_s	E_s	600' T_s	E_s	
1-30																	
2-00																	
2-30																	
3-00																	
3-30	1401.09	470.2	1426.45	470.7	1451.90	471.5	1477.45	472.1	1503.09	473.4	1528.83	474.7	1580.59	477.6	1632.71	481.2	70 mph
4-00	1235.45	411.6	1260.86	412.2	1286.37	413.1	1311.99	414.1	1337.73	415.3	1363.57	416.7	1415.56	420.1	1467.96	424.2	
5	1003.60	329.7	1029.10	330.5	1054.73	331.5	1080.51	332.8	1106.41	334.3	1132.45	336.1	1184.90	340.3	1237.83	345.4	60 mph
6	849.07	275.1	874.66	276.1	900.42	277.3	926.34	278.9	952.42	280.7	978.64	282.8	1031.53	287.8	1084.98	294.0	
7	738.72	236.2	764.42	237.3	790.30	238.8	816.36	240.6	842.59	242.7	869.00	245.2	922.31	251.0	976.25	258.2	
8	656.00	207.1	681.78	208.4	707.78	210.1	733.98	212.1	760.38	214.5	786.96	217.3	840.68	224.0	895.07	232.2	50 mph
9	591.68	184.5	617.56	185.9	643.67	187.8	670.01	190.1	696.56	192.8	723.32	196.0	777.43	203.5	832.25	212.6	
10	540.26	166.4	566.22	168.0	592.45	170.1	618.92	172.7	645.62	175.7	672.55	179.2	727.01	187.5	782.24	197.7	
11	498.20	151.7	524.26	153.5	550.60	155.8	577.19	158.6	604.04	161.9	631.12	165.7	685.95	174.9	741.55	186.0	
12	463.17	139.4	489.32	141.4	515.76	143.9	542.49	147.0	569.48	150.6	596.72	154.8	651.87	164.7	707.82	176.8	
13	433.55	129.1	459.79	131.2	486.34	134.0	513.19	137.3	540.31	141.2	567.69	`145.7	623.17	156.5	679.44	169.46	
14	408.18	120.3	434.50	122.6	461.16	125.5	488.13	129.1	515.38	133.3	542.91	138.1	598.67	149.7			40 mph
15	386.20	112.7	412.61	115.1	439.37	118.3	466.46	122.1	493.84	126.6	521.50	131.8	577.54	144.1			
16	366.99	106.1	393.48	108.7	420.34	112.0	447.54	116.1	475.04	120.9	502.83	126.4					
17	350.05	100.2	376.63	103.0	403.58	106.5	430.89	110.9	458.51	115.9	486.42	121.8					
18	335.01	95.1	361.66	98.0	388.71	101.7	416.12	106.3	443.86	111.7	471.88	117.9					
19	321.55	90.5	348.29	93.6	375.43	97.5	402.95	102.3	430.79	108.0	458.92	114.5					
20	309.46	86.4	336.27	89.6	363.51	93.8	391.12	98.8	419.07	104.8							
21	298.52	82.6	325.42	86.1	352.74	90.4	380.45	95.7	408.49	102.0							
22	288.60	79.3	315.56	82.9	342.97	87.4	370.78	93.0	398.91	99.5							
23	279.54	76.3	306.58	80.0	334.07	84.8	361.96	90.6									30 mph
24	271.24	73.5	298.36	77.4	325.93	82.4	353.91	88.4									
25	263.62	71.0	290.81	75.0	318.46	80.2	346.52	86.5									

TABLE IV
T_s AND E_s

Δ = 79°

D_c	$L_s = 150'$ T_s	E_s	200' T_s	E_s	250' T_s	E_s	300' T_s	E_s	350' T_s	E_s	400' T_s	E_s	500' T_s	E_s	600' T_s	E_s
1-30																
2-00																
2-30																
3-00	1424.92	485.2	1450.28	485.8	1475.74	486.6	1501.30	487.5	1526.36	488.5	1552.71	489.8	1604.51	492.8	1656.67	496.4
3-30	1256.31	424.8	1281.72	425.5	1307.24	426.3	1332.88	427.3	1358.63	428.5	1384.48	430.0	1436.51	433.4	1488.96	437.5
4-00																
5	1020.28	340.2	1045.79	341.0	1071.44	342.1	1097.23	343.4	1123.15	344.9	1149.21	346.7	1201.71	350.9	1254.70	356.1
6	862.98	283.9	888.59	284.9	914.36	286.2	940.30	287.7	966.39	289.6	992.64	291.7	1045.58	296.7	1099.10	302.9
7	750.65	243.7	776.36	244.9	802.25	246.4	828.33	248.2	854.59	250.3	881.03	252.8	934.41	258.7	988.43	265.9
8	666.44	213.7	692.24	215.0	718.26	216.7	744.48	218.7	770.90	221.2	797.52	224.0	851.31	230.7	905.80	238.9
9	600.97	190.3	626.86	191.8	653.00	193.7	679.36	196.0	705.94	198.8	732.73	201.9	786.93	209.5	841.85	218.7
10	548.62	171.7	574.60	173.3	600.85	175.5	627.35	178.0	654.09	181.1	681.05	184.6	735.61	193.0	790.96	203.2
11	505.80	156.5	531.89	158.3	558.25	160.6	584.88	163.5	611.76	166.8	638.89	170.7	693.81	179.9	749.54	191.0
12	470.15	143.9	496.32	145.8	522.79	148.4	549.55	151.5	576.58	155.1	603.87	159.3	659.13	169.0	715.22	181.5
13	440.00	133.2	466.26	135.3	492.84	138.1	519.72	141.4	546.90	145.4	574.32	149.5	629.92	160.7	686.34	173.8
14	414.17	122.1	440.52	126.4	467.21	129.3	494.21	132.9	521.52	137.2	549.10	142.1	604.99	153.7		
15	391.80	116.2	418.23	118.7	445.03	121.9	472.16	125.7	499.59	130.2	527.31	135.5	583.49	147.9		
16	372.24	109.4	398.76	112.0	425.66	115.4	452.90	119.5	480.46	124.3	508.30	129.8				
17	355.00	103.4	381.60	106.1	408.60	109.7	435.95	114.1	463.63	119.2	491.61	125.1				
18	339.68	98.0	366.37	101.0	393.46	104.8	420.93	109.4	448.72	114.8	476.82	121.0				
19	325.99	93.3	352.76	96.4	379.95	100.4	407.51	105.2	435.42	110.9	463.63	117.5				
20	313.68	89.0	340.53	92.3	367.81	96.5	395.48	101.6	423.50	107.6						
21	302.55	85.2	329.48	88.6	356.85	93.0	384.62	98.4	412.73	104.6						
22	292.44	81.7	319.44	85.3	346.91	89.9	374.77	95.5	402.98	102.1						
23	283.22	78.6	310.30	82.4	337.85	87.2	365.80	93.0								
24	274.77	75.7	301.93	79.6	329.57	84.7	357.61	90.7								
25	267.02	73.1	294.25	77.2	321.96	82.4	350.09	88.7								

Speed annotations (right margin): 70 mph, 60 mph, 50 mph, 40 mph, 30 mph

140

TABLE IV
T_s AND E_s
$\Delta = 80°$

D_c	$L_s=150'$ T_s	E_s	$200'$ T_s	E_s	$250'$ T_s	E_s	$300'$ T_s	E_s	$350'$ T_s	E_s	$400'$ T_s	E_s	$500'$ T_s	E_s	$600'$ T_s	E_s	
1-30																	
2-00																	
2-30																	
3-00	1449.10	500.7	1474.47	501.3	1499.93	502.0	1525.51	503.0	1551.17	504.0	1576.94	505.2	1628.77	508.3	1680.97	511.9	70 mph
3-30	1277.16	438.3	1302.88	439.0	1328.41	439.8	1354.06	440.9	1379.82	442.1	1405.69	443.5	1457.76	447.0	1510.26	451.1	
4-00																	
5	1037.09	351.0	1062.73	351.9	1088.39	352.9	1114.20	354.2	1140.14	355.8	1166.21	357.6	1218.76	361.8	1271.81	367.0	60 mph
6	877.39	292.9	902.71	293.9	928.50	295.2	954.45	296.8	980.57	298.6	1006.84	300.7	1059.84	305.8	1113.43	312.1	
7	762.75	251.5	788.47	252.6	814.38	254.1	840.49	256.0	866.77	258.1	893.24	260.6	946.68	266.5	1000.78	273.8	
8	677.03	220.4	702.85	221.8	728.88	223.5	755.13	225.6	781.58	228.0	808.23	230.8	862.10	237.6	916.68	245.9	50 mph
9	610.39	196.4	636.30	197.8	662.46	199.8	688.85	202.1	715.45	204.9	742.29	208.0	796.57	215.7	851.59	224.9	
10	557.10	177.1	583.11	178.8	609.38	180.9	635.90	183.5	662.68	186.6	689.68	190.1	744.34	198.6	799.80	208.8	
11	513.52	161.4	539.62	163.3	566.01	165.6	592.67	168.5	619.59	171.8	646.77	175.7	701.80	185.0	757.65	196.2	
12	477.23	148.4	503.42	150.4	529.92	152.9	556.71	156.0	583.79	159.7	611.12	163.9	666.50	174.0	722.73	186.3	
13	446.53	137.4	472.82	139.5	499.43	142.3	526.36	145.7	553.57	149.6	581.05	154.2	636.77	165.1	693.34	178.3	
14	420.24	128.0	446.62	130.3	473.34	133.3	500.39	136.9	527.74	141.2	555.38	146.1	611.41	157.8			40 mph
15	397.47	119.9	423.94	122.3	450.77	125.5	477.94	129.4	505.42	134.0	533.20	139.2	589.52	151.7			
16	377.57	112.8	404.11	115.4	431.05	118.8	458.34	123.0	485.96	127.8	513.86	133.4	570.47	146.69			
17	360.01	106.6	386.65	109.4	413.69	113.0	441.09	117.4	468.83	122.5	496.87	128.4					
18	344.42	101.1	371.14	104.0	398.28	107.8	425.80	112.5	453.65	117.9	481.82	124.2					
19	330.49	96.1	357.29	99.3	384.53	103.3	412.15	108.2	440.12	113.9	468.40	120.5					
20	317.95	91.8	344.84	95.1	372.17	99.3	399.90	104.4	427.99	110.4	456.37	117.35					
21	306.62	87.8	333.59	91.3	361.02	95.7	388.85	101.1	417.03	107.4							
22	296.34	84.2	323.38	87.9	350.90	92.5	378.83	98.1	407.11	104.7							
23	286.95	81.0	314.08	84.8	341.68	89.6	369.70	95.5									
24	278.36	78.0	305.56	82.0	333.25	87.0	361.36	93.1									
25	270.46	75.3	297.74	79.4	325.51	84.7	353.71	91.0									

30 mph

$\Delta = 80°$

141

TABLE IV
T_s AND E_s

$\triangle = 81°$ $L_s = 150'$

D_c	150' T_s	150' E_s	200' T_s	200' E_s	250' T_s	250' E_s	300' T_s	300' E_s	350' T_s	350' E_s	400' T_s	400' E_s	500' T_s	500' E_s	600' T_s	600' F_{-s}
1-30																
2-00																
2-30																
3-00																
3-30	1473.63	516.6	1492.01	517.1	1524.48	517.9	1550.06	518.8	1575.75	513.9	1601.53	521.2	1653.39	524.2	1705.63	527.9
4-00	1298.93	452.1	1324.36	452.9	1349.90	453.7	1375.56	454.8	1401.34	456.0	1427.22	457.5	1479.33	460.9	1531.87	465.1
5	1054.39	362.1	1079.92	363.0	1105.60	364.1	1131.41	365.4	1157.37	366.9	1183.47	368.7	1236.06	373.0	1289.17	378.2
6	891.41	302.2	917.04	303.2	942.85	304.5	968.82	306.0	994.95	307.9	1021.25	310.1	1074.31	315.2	1127.97	321.5
7	775.03	259.4	800.76	260.6	826.69	262.1	852.82	263.9	879.13	266.1	905.62	268.6	959.13	274.6	1013.32	281.9
8	687.78	227.4	713.61	228.7	739.67	230.4	765.94	232.5	792.42	235.0	819.10	237.9	873.05	244.7	927.72	253.0
9	619.95	202.5	645.88	204.0	672.06	206.0	698.47	208.3	725.11	211.1	751.98	214.3	806.35	222.0	861.48	231.3
10	565.71	182.7	591.73	184.4	618.03	186.5	644.59	189.1	671.40	192.2	698.44	195.8	753.19	204.3	808.77	214.6
11	521.35	166.5	547.47	168.3	573.89	170.7	600.58	173.6	627.54	177.0	654.76	180.9	709.90	190.2	765.88	201.5
12	484.41	153.0	510.63	155.0	537.16	157.6	563.98	160.7	591.10	164.4	618.48	168.7	673.98	178.9	730.35	191.2
13	453.17	141.7	479.48	143.8	506.12	146.6	533.09	150.0	560.35	154.0	587.88	158.6	643.73	169.6	700.44	182.9
14	426.41	132.0	452.81	134.3	479.57	137.3	506.66	140.9	534.06	145.2	561.75	150.2	617.91	162.0		
15	403.23	123.6	429.72	126.1	456.59	129.3	483.81	133.2	511.34	137.8	539.18	143.1	595.65	155.7		
16	382.97	116.3	409.55	118.9	436.52	122.4	463.86	126.5	491.53	131.4	519.50	137.0	576.26	150.4		
17	365.10	109.8	391.77	112.7	418.85	116.3	446.30	120.7	474.10	125.9	502.21	131.9				
18	349.24	104.2	375.99	107.2	403.17	111.0	430.74	115.7	458.66	121.2	486.90	127.5				
19	335.05	99.1	361.89	102.3	389.17	106.3	416.85	111.1	444.89	117.0	473.25	123.6				
20	322.29	94.6	349.22	97.9	376.60	102.1	404.39	107.3	432.54	113.4	461.01	120.3				
21	310.76	90.5	337.77	94.0	365.25	98.4	393.14	103.8	421.40	110.2						
22	300.29	86.8	327.38	90.4	354.95	95.1	382.94	100.8	411.30	107.4						
23	290.74	83.4	317.91	87.2	345.57	92.1	373.66	98.0	402.12	105.0						
24	281.99	80.4	309.24	84.3	336.99	89.4	365.17	95.6								
25	273.95	77.6	301.28	81.7	329.11	87.0	357.39	93.4								

Design speed regions (stepped boundaries across table): 70 mph, 60 mph, 50 mph, 40 mph, 30 mph

$\triangle = 81°$

TABLE IV — T_s AND E_s — Δ=82°

D_c	Ls=150' T_s	E_s	200' T_s	E_s	250' T_s	E_s	300' T_s	E_s	350' T_s	E_s	400' T_s	E_s	500' T_s	E_s	600' T_s	E_s
1-30																
2-00																
2-30																
3-00																
3-30	1498.53	532.8	1523.91	533.8	1549.40	534.2	1574.99	535.1	1600.69	536.2	1626.48	537.4	1678.38	540.5	1730.67	544.2
4-00	1320.72	466.4	1346.16	467.1	1371.71	468.0	1397.38	469.0	1423.17	470.1	1449.07	471.7	1501.22	475.2	1553.81	479.4
5	1071.83	373.5	1097.37	374.4	1123.06	375.4	1148.89	376.8	1174.86	378.3	1200.98	380.1	1253.62	384.5	1306.80	389.7
6	905.95	311.7	931.59	312.5	957.41	314.0	983.40	315.6	1009.56	317.4	1035.88	319.6	1089.00	324.8	1142.73	331.1
7	787.50	267.5	813.24	268.7	839.19	270.2	865.33	272.1	891.67	274.3	918.19	276.8	971.77	282.8	1026.04	290.2
8	698.69	234.5	724.54	235.9	750.61	237.6	776.91	239.7	803.42	242.2	830.13	245.1	884.16	252.0	938.93	260.4
9	629.65	208.9	655.60	210.4	681.80	212.3	708.24	214.7	734.91	217.5	761.82	220.7	816.27	228.5	871.52	237.9
10	574.45	188.4	600.49	190.1	626.81	192.2	653.40	194.9	680.24	198.0	707.33	201.6	762.18	210.1	817.88	220.6
11	529.30	171.7	555.44	173.5	581.89	175.9	608.61	178.8	635.61	182.1	662.87	186.2	718.12	195.6	774.24	207.0
12	491.70	157.8	517.94	159.8	544.50	162.4	571.36	165.5	598.52	169.3	625.95	173.6	681.57	183.8	738.08	196.2
13	459.90	146.1	486.24	148.2	512.91	151.1	539.92	154.5	567.22	158.5	594.81	163.1	650.78	174.2	707.65	187.6
14	432.67	136.0	459.10	138.4	485.89	141.4	513.02	145.1	540.47	149.4	568.22	154.4	624.52	166.3		
15	409.08	127.4	435.60	129.9	462.50	133.1	489.76	137.0	517.35	141.7	545.25	147.0	601.86	159.7		
16	388.46	119.9	415.06	122.5	442.08	126.0	469.46	130.2	497.19	135.1	525.23	140.8	582.14	154.3		
17	370.27	113.2	396.97	116.1	424.09	119.7	451.60	124.2	479.46	129.4	507.63	135.4				
18	354.12	107.3	380.91	110.4	408.14	114.2	435.76	118.9	463.74	124.5	492.05	130.8				
19	339.68	102.1	366.56	105.3	393.89	109.4	421.62	114.3	449.73	120.2	478.16	126.8				
20	326.70	97.4	353.66	100.8	381.09	105.1	408.94	110.3	437.16	116.4	465.71	123.4				
21	314.96	93.2	342.01	96.7	369.54	101.2	397.49	106.7	425.82	113.1						
22	304.31	89.4	331.44	93.1	359.06	97.8	387.12	103.5	415.55	110.2						
23	294.59	85.9	321.80	89.8	349.51	94.7	377.67	100.7	406.21	107.6						
24	285.68	82.8	312.98	86.8	340.78	91.9	369.04	98.1								
25	277.50	79.9	304.87	84.1	332.77	89.4	361.12	95.8								

Speed designations: 70 mph, 60 mph, 50 mph, 40 mph, 30 mph

143

Δ = 83°

Table IV — T_s and E_s, Δ = 83°

D_c	$L_s=150'$ T_s	E_s	$200'$ T_s	E_s	$250'$ T_s	E_s	$300'$ T_s	E_s	$350'$ T_s	E_s	$400'$ T_s	E_s	$500'$ T_s	E_s	$600'$ T_s	E_s	
1-30																	
2-00																	
2-30																	
3-00																	
3-30	1523.81	549.5	1549.20	550.1	1574.70	550.8	1600.30	551.8	1626.01	552.9	1651.82	554.2	1703.75	557.2	1756.08	560.9	70 mph
4-00	1342.85	481.0	1368.29	481.7	1393.85	482.6	1419.54	483.6	1445.34	484.9	1471.26	486.3	1523.45	489.8	1576.09	494.1	
5	1089.53	385.1	1115.08	386.0	1140.78	387.1	1166.63	388.5	1192.62	390.0	1218.76	391.9	1271.46	396.2	1324.69	401.5	60 mph
6	920.70	321.4	946.36	322.4	972.19	323.7	998.20	325.3	1024.38	327.2	1050.73	329.4	1103.91	334.6	1157.71	341.0	
7	800.15	275.9	825.91	277.1	851.87	278.6	878.04	280.5	904.40	282.5	930.95	285.2	984.61	291.3	1038.96	298.7	
8	709.77	241.8	735.63	243.2	761.73	244.9	788.05	247.0	814.58	249.6	841.33	252.5	895.44	259.4	950.31	267.9	50 mph
9	639.50	215.4	665.47	216.9	691.69	218.8	718.16	221.2	744.87	224.1	771.81	227.3	826.35	235.1	881.71	244.6	
10	583.32	194.2	609.38	195.9	635.73	198.1	662.34	200.8	689.23	203.9	716.35	207.5	771.30	216.2	827.12	226.7	
11	537.37	177.0	563.53	178.9	590.00	181.3	616.77	184.2	643.80	187.6	671.11	191.6	726.47	201.1	782.72	212.6	
12	499.10	162.7	525.36	164.7	551.95	167.3	578.86	170.5	606.06	174.2	635.54	178.6	689.27	188.6	745.93	201.4	
13	466.74	150.6	493.10	152.8	519.81	155.6	546.85	159.0	574.21	163.1	601.85	167.8	657.95	178.9	714.97	192.4	
14	439.04	140.2	465.48	142.6	492.30	145.6	519.48	149.4	546.98	153.7	574.79	158.7	631.22	170.7			40 mph
15	415.01	131.3	441.56	133.8	468.50	137.1	495.81	141.1	523.46	145.7	551.42	151.1	608.18	163.9			
16	394.02	123.5	420.66	126.2	447.72	129.7	475.15	133.9	502.94	138.9	531.04	144.6	588.11	158.2			
17	375.52	116.7	402.25	119.6	429.41	123.2	456.97	127.7	484.89	133.0	515.14	139.0					
18	359.08	110.6	385.90	113.7	413.18	117.6	440.85	122.3	468.90	127.9	497.28	134.3					
19	344.39	105.2	371.30	108.4	398.68	112.5	426.47	117.5	454.64	123.4	483.15	130.1					
20	331.17	100.4	358.18	103.8	385.65	108.1	413.56	113.3	441.86	119.5	470.49	126.6					30 mph
21	319.23	96.0	346.32	99.6	373.90	104.1	401.92	109.6	430.32	116.1							
22	308.38	92.1	335.56	95.8	363.23	100.5	391.36	106.3	419.87	113.0							
23	298.49	88.5	325.75	92.4	353.52	97.3	381.76	103.3	410.37	110.4							
24	289.43	85.2	316.77	89.3	344.64	94.4	372.95	100.7									
25	281.10	82.3	308.52	86.5	336.48	91.8	364.91	98.3									

144

TABLE IV — T_s AND E_s

$\Delta = 84°$

Design-speed zones marked along the staircase boundary: 70 mph, 60 mph, 50 mph, 40 mph, 30 mph.

D_c	150′ T_s	150′ E_s	200′ T_s	200′ E_s	250′ T_s	250′ E_s	300′ T_s	300′ E_s	350′ T_s	350′ E_s	400′ T_s	400′ E_s	500′ T_s	500′ E_s	600′ T_s	600′ E_s
1-30																
2-00																
2-30																
3-00																
3-30	1549.49	566.6	1574.88	567.2	1600.39	567.9	1626.00	568.9	1651.72	570.0	1677.55	571.3	1729.51	574.4	1781.89	578.1
4-00	1365.31	496.0	1390.76	496.6	1416.34	497.5	1442.04	498.6	1467.85	499.9	1493.79	501.3	1546.02	504.9	1598.71	509.2
5	1107.51	397.2	1133.07	398.0	1158.78	399.1	1184.65	400.5	1210.66	402.1	1236.82	403.9	1289.56	408.3	1342.86	413.6
6	935.69	331.4	961.36	332.4	987.21	333.7	1013.23	335.3	1039.44	337.2	1065.81	339.4	1119.05	344.7	1172.93	351.1
7	813.00	284.4	838.77	285.6	864.76	287.0	890.95	289.1	917.33	291.3	943.91	293.8	997.64	300.0	1052.08	307.4
8	721.02	249.3	746.90	250.7	773.01	252.4	799.36	254.6	825.92	257.1	852.70	260.0	906.89	267.0	961.86	275.5
9	649.51	222.0	675.49	223.6	701.73	225.5	728.23	227.9	754.97	230.8	781.95	234.1	836.59	241.9	892.06	251.5
10	592.33	200.2	618.41	201.9	644.78	204.1	671.43	206.8	698.35	210.0	725.52	213.6	780.57	222.3	836.51	232.9
11	545.56	182.4	571.75	184.3	598.25	186.7	625.04	189.7	652.12	193.2	679.48	197.2	734.94	206.7	791.33	218.3
12	506.62	167.7	532.90	169.7	559.53	172.3	586.46	175.6	613.71	179.3	641.24	183.7	697.10	194.1	753.90	206.7
13	473.68	155.2	500.07	157.4	526.81	160.0	553.89	163.7	581.30	167.8	608.99	172.5	665.22	183.8	722.41	197.4
14	445.47	144.5	471.96	146.9	498.82	150.0	526.04	153.7	553.59	158.1	581.46	163.2	638.03	175.2	695.58	189.84
15	421.04	135.3	447.62	137.9	474.60	141.2	501.95	145.2	529.65	149.9	557.68	155.1	614.58	168.2		
16	399.16	127.3	426.35	130.0	453.45	133.5	480.93	137.8	508.77	142.8	536.94	148.5	594.17	162.2		
17	380.84	120.2	407.61	123.1	434.82	126.8	462.43	131.4	490.41	136.7	518.73	142.8				
18	364.12	114.0	390.98	117.0	418.30	121.0	446.03	125.7	474.14	131.4	502.60	137.8				
19	349.16	108.4	376.11	111.6	403.54	115.8	431.39	120.8	459.63	126.7	488.22	133.5				
20	335.72	103.4	362.76	106.8	390.29	111.2	418.26	116.5	446.63	122.7	475.34	129.8				
21	323.56	98.9	350.69	102.5	378.32	107.0	406.41	112.6	434.89	119.1	463.72	126.56				
22	312.52	94.8	339.74	98.6	367.47	103.4	395.67	109.2	424.26	116.0						
23	302.45	91.1	329.76	95.1	357.59	100.0	385.88	106.1	414.59	113.2						
24	293.23	87.8	320.62	91.8	348.55	97.1	376.95	103.3	405.76	110.7						
25	284.76	84.7	312.23	88.9	340.25	94.3	368.75	100.9								

TABLE IV — T_s AND E_s — Δ = 85°

D_c	$L_s=150'$ T_s	E_s	$200'$ T_s	E_s	$250'$ T_s	E_s	$300'$ T_s	E_s	$350'$ T_s	E_s	$400'$ T_s	E_s	$500'$ T_s	E_s	$600'$ T_s	E_s	mph
1-30																	
2-00																	
2-30																	
3-00																	
3-30	1575.57	584.1	1600.97	584.7	1626.49	585.5	1652.11	586.4	1677.85	587.6	1703.69	588.9	1755.69	592.0	1808.11	595.8	70 mph
4-00	1388.14	511.3	1413.60	512.0	1439.18	512.9	1464.89	514.0	1490.73	515.3	1516.68	516.7	1568.95	520.3	1621.69	524.6	
5	1125.78	409.4	1151.35	410.3	1177.07	411.4	1202.95	412.8	1228.98	414.4	1255.16	416.2	1307.96	420.6	1361.32	426.0	60 mph
6	950.92	341.6	976.59	342.6	1002.46	344.0	1028.51	345.6	1054.73	347.5	1081.13	349.7	1134.43	355.0	1188.39	361.5	
7	826.06	299.2	851.84	294.4	877.84	296.0	904.05	297.9	930.47	300.1	957.08	302.7	1010.88	308.9	1065.40	316.4	
8	732.45	257.0	758.34	258.4	784.48	260.1	810.85	262.3	837.45	264.9	864.26	267.8	918.53	274.8	973.60	283.4	50 mph
9	659.67	228.9	685.67	230.4	711.94	232.4	738.47	234.8	765.24	237.7	792.26	241.0	846.99	248.9	902.57	258.6	
10	601.48	206.4	627.58	208.1	653.98	210.3	680.66	213.0	707.61	216.2	734.83	219.9	789.98	228.7	846.05	239.3	
11	553.89	188.0	580.10	189.9	606.62	192.4	633.46	195.3	660.57	198.8	687.98	202.9	743.56	212.5	800.08	224.2	
12	514.25	172.8	540.56	174.9	567.22	177.5	594.19	180.8	621.49	184.6	649.07	189.0	705.04	199.4	762.00	212.2	
13	480.74	159.9	507.15	162.2	533.92	165.0	561.05	168.5	588.50	172.7	616.25	177.4	672.62	188.7	729.96	202.5	
14	452.03	148.9	478.54	151.3	505.44	154.4	532.70	158.2	560.31	162.6	588.23	167.7	644.95	179.9	702.67	194.6	40 mph
15	427.16	139.4	453.77	142.0	480.79	145.3	508.19	149.4	535.95	154.1	564.04	159.6	621.10	172.5			
16	405.42	131.2	432.13	133.9	459.27	137.4	486.80	141.7	514.70	146.8	542.94	152.6	600.33	166.4			
17	386.26	123.9	413.06	126.8	440.31	130.5	467.97	135.1	496.02	140.4	524.41	146.6	582.09	161.2			30 mph
18	369.23	117.4	396.13	120.5	423.50	124.5	451.28	129.3	479.46	134.9	508.00	141.4					
19	354.02	111.7	381.00	114.9	408.48	119.1	436.39	124.2	464.70	130.1	493.37	137.0					
20	340.33	106.5	367.41	109.9	394.99	114.3	423.03	119.7	451.47	125.9	480.26	133.1					
21	327.96	101.9	355.13	105.5	382.82	110.1	410.97	115.7	439.53	122.2	468.45	129.7					
22	316.73	97.7	343.99	101.4	371.78	106.3	400.04	112.1	428.71	119.0							
23	306.48	93.9	333.83	97.8	361.72	102.8	390.09	108.9	418.88	116.1							
24	297.10	90.4	324.53	94.5	352.52	99.7	381.00	106.1	409.89	113.5							
25	288.47	87.2	315.99	91.5	344.08	96.9	372.66	103.5									

Δ = 85°

146

TABLE IV — T_s AND E_s △ = 86°

D_c	$L_s=150'$ T_s	E_s	$200'$ T_s	E_s	$250'$ T_s	E_s	$300'$ T_s	E_s	$350'$ T_s	E_s	$400'$ T_s	E_s	$500'$ T_s	E_s	$600'$ T_s	E_s	mph
1-30																	
2-00																	
2-30																	
3-00																	
3-30																	
4-00	1411.33	527.1	1436.80	527.8	1462.39	528.6	1488.11	529.7	1513.97	531.0	1539.94	532.5	1592.25	536.1	1645.04	540.5	
5	1144.34	422.0	1169.91	422.9	1195.65	424.0	1221.55	425.4	1247.60	427.1	1273.80	428.9	1326.65	433.3	1380.08	438.8	70 mph
6	966.39	352.1	992.08	352.2	1017.96	354.5	1044.02	356.1	1070.27	358.1	1096.70	360.3	1150.06	365.1	1204.10	372.2	60 mph
7	839.32	302.2	865.12	303.4	891.14	305.0	917.38	306.9	943.81	309.2	970.46	311.8	1024.33	318.0	1078.95	325.6	
8	744.06	264.9	769.97	266.3	796.13	268.0	822.52	270.2	849.15	272.8	876.00	275.8	930.36	282.9	985.53	291.5	
9	670.00	235.9	696.02	237.4	722.31	239.4	748.87	241.9	775.67	244.8	802.73	248.1	857.56	256.1	913.25	265.8	50 mph
10	610.78	212.7	636.90	214.4	663.33	216.7	690.04	219.4	717.03	222.6	744.29	226.3	799.55	235.2	855.74	245.9	
11	562.35	193.8	588.58	195.7	615.13	198.2	642.00	201.1	669.16	204.7	696.61	208.7	752.31	218.5	808.97	230.2	
12	522.01	178.1	548.35	180.2	575.03	182.8	602.05	186.1	629.39	189.9	657.02	194.4	713.12	204.9	770.23	217.7	
13	487.90	164.8	514.34	167.1	541.15	170.0	568.32	173.5	595.82	177.6	623.63	182.4	680.13	193.8	737.64	207.7	
14	458.69	153.5	485.23	155.9	512.17	159.0	539.47	162.8	567.13	167.3	595.12	172.4	651.98	184.7	709.88	199.5	40 mph
15	433.39	143.7	460.03	146.5	487.08	149.6	514.53	153.7	542.34	158.4	570.50	163.9	627.71	177.0			
16	411.26	135.1	438.00	137.9	465.18	141.4	492.76	145.8	520.73	150.9	549.03	156.7	606.59	170.6			
17	391.76	127.6	418.60	130.5	445.89	134.3	473.61	138.9	501.71	144.3	530.18	150.5	588.03	165.2			
18	374.43	120.9	401.37	124.1	428.78	128.0	456.62	132.9	484.87	138.6	513.48	145.2					
19	358.95	115.0	385.97	118.3	413.50	122.5	441.47	127.6	469.85	133.6	498.61	140.5					
20	345.02	109.7	372.14	113.2	399.78	117.6	427.87	123.0	456.39	129.3	485.27	136.5					
21	332.43	104.7	359.65	108.5	387.39	113.2	415.60	118.8	444.24	125.4	473.25	133.0					
22	321.00	100.6	348.31	104.4	376.15	109.2	404.48	115.1	433.24	122.0							
23	310.57	96.6	337.97	100.6	365.92	105.7	394.36	111.8	423.23	119.0							30 mph
24	301.02	93.0	328.51	97.2	356.56	102.5	385.11	108.9	414.10	116.4							
25	292.25	89.8	319.82	94.1	347.97	99.6	376.63	106.2									

△ = 86°

147

TABLE IV

T_s AND E_s

$\Delta = 87°$

D_c	$L_s=150'$ T_s	E_s	$200'$ T_s	E_s	$250'$ T_s	E_s	$300'$ T_s	E_s	$350'$ T_s	E_s	$400'$ T_s	E_s	$500'$ T_s	E_s	$600'$ T_s	E_s
1-30																
2-00																
2-30																
3-00																
3-30																
4-00	1434.90	543.2	1460.38	543.9	1485.98	544.8	1511.72	545.9	1537.59	547.2	1563.57	548.7	1615.93	552.3	1668.78	556.7
5	1163.20	435.0	1188.79	435.8	1214.54	437.0	1240.45	438.4	1266.52	440.0	1292.75	441.9	1345.65	446.4	1399.14	451.8
6	982.11	362.9	1007.81	363.9	1033.71	365.3	1059.80	366.9	1086.07	368.9	1112.52	371.1	1165.95	376.5	1220.06	383.1
7	852.83	311.5	878.62	312.7	904.66	314.3	930.91	316.2	957.38	318.5	984.06	321.1	1038.00	327.4	1092.71	335.0
8	755.86	273.0	781.79	274.4	807.97	276.2	834.39	278.4	861.05	281.0	887.93	283.9	942.38	291.1	997.65	299.8
9	680.49	243.1	706.53	244.6	732.85	246.7	759.43	249.1	786.28	252.0	813.37	255.4	868.29	263.5	924.11	273.3
10	620.23	219.2	646.37	220.9	672.83	223.2	699.57	225.9	726.60	229.2	753.90	232.9	809.27	241.8	865.60	252.7
11	570.94	199.7	597.20	201.6	623.78	204.1	650.69	207.1	677.89	210.7	705.39	214.8	761.20	224.5	818.01	236.4
12	529.90	183.5	556.26	185.6	582.98	188.3	610.03	191.6	637.41	195.4	665.10	199.9	721.33	210.6	778.59	223.5
13	495.19	169.8	521.65	172.1	548.50	175.0	575.71	178.5	603.26	182.7	631.12	187.6	687.76	199.1	745.44	213.0
14	465.46	158.1	492.03	160.5	519.00	162.7	546.36	167.7	574.07	172.0	602.11	177.2	659.13	189.6	717.20	204.5
15	439.71	148.0	466.38	150.6	493.48	154.0	520.98	158.1	548.85	162.9	577.06	168.4	634.64	181.6		
16	417.20	139.2	443.97	142.0	471.19	145.6	498.83	149.9	526.85	155.1	555.23	161.0	612.95	175.0		
17	397.35	131.4	424.22	134.4	451.56	138.2	479.33	142.8	507.50	148.3	536.05	154.5	594.08	169.4		
18	379.72	124.6	406.69	127.7	434.15	131.7	462.05	136.6	490.37	142.4	519.06	149.0				
19	363.96	118.4	391.02	121.8	418.60	126.0	446.63	131.2	475.09	137.2	503.92	144.2				
20	349.79	113.0	376.95	116.4	404.64	120.9	432.80	126.3	461.39	132.7	490.36	140.0				
21	336.98	108.0	364.24	111.7	392.03	116.4	420.32	122.0	449.03	128.7	478.13	136.3				
22	325.34	103.6	352.70	107.4	380.60	112.3	409.00	118.2	437.84	125.2						
23	314.73	99.5	342.18	103.5	370.19	108.6	398.70	114.8	427.66	122.1						
24	305.02	95.8	332.55	99.9	360.67	105.3	389.29	111.7	418.37	119.3						
25	296.09	92.4	323.71	96.7	351.93	102.3	380.66	109.0								

Speed designations: 70 mph, 60 mph, 50 mph, 40 mph, 30 mph.

148

TABLE IV — T_s AND E_s, $\Delta = 88°$

D_c	$L_s=150'$ T_s	E_s	$200'$ T_s	E_s	$250'$ T_s	E_s	$300'$ T_s	E_s	$350'$ T_s	E_s	$400'$ T_s	E_s	$500'$ T_s	E_s	$600'$ T_s	E_s	
1-30																	
2-00																	
2-30																	
3-00																	
3-30																	
4-00	1458.87	559.8	1484.35	560.5	1509.97	561.4	1535.72	562.5	1561.60	563.8	1587.61	565.2	1640.01	569.0	1692.91	573.4	70 mph
5	1182.38	448.2	1207.98	449.1	1233.74	450.2	1259.67	451.6	1285.76	453.3	1312.01	455.2	1364.97	459.7	1418.52	465.2	
6	998.10	373.9	1023.81	375.0	1049.73	376.4	1075.83	378.0	1102.13	380.0	1128.61	382.3	1182.10	387.7	1236.29	394.3	60 mph
7	866.51	320.9	892.34	322.2	918.40	323.8	944.68	325.7	971.17	328.0	997.88	330.6	1051.99	337.0	1106.79	344.7	
8	767.86	281.3	793.80	282.7	820.01	284.5	846.45	286.7	873.15	289.3	900.07	292.3	954.60	299.6	1009.98	308.4	
9	691.16	250.4	717.22	252.0	743.56	254.1	770.18	256.6	797.06	259.5	824.20	262.9	879.21	271.0	935.14	280.9	50 mph
10	629.84	225.8	656.00	227.6	682.48	229.9	709.26	232.6	736.33	235.9	763.68	239.6	819.16	248.6	875.61	259.6	
11	579.69	205.7	605.96	207.7	632.58	210.2	659.52	213.2	686.76	216.8	714.31	220.9	770.24	230.8	827.19	242.8	
12	537.92	189.0	564.30	191.1	591.05	193.9	618.15	197.2	645.58	201.1	673.32	205.6	729.68	216.3	787.09	229.4	
13	502.60	174.9	529.09	177.2	555.97	180.1	583.22	183.7	610.82	188.0	638.74	192.8	695.52	204.4	753.37	218.5	
14	472.34	162.9	498.94	165.3	525.95	168.5	553.35	172.4	581.12	176.9	609.23	182.1	666.39	194.6	724.65	209.7	40 mph
15	446.14	152.4	472.84	155.1	499.98	158.5	527.53	162.6	555.46	167.5	583.74	173.1	641.28	186.4			
16	423.23	143.4	450.03	146.2	477.30	149.8	504.99	154.2	533.08	159.4	561.53	165.3	619.42	179.5			
17	403.03	135.4	429.94	138.4	457.32	142.2	485.15	146.9	513.39	152.3	542.01	158.7	600.22	173.6			
18	385.09	128.3	412.10	131.4	439.61	135.5	467.57	140.4	495.96	146.2	524.73	152.9					
19	369.05	122.0	396.16	125.3	423.79	129.6	451.88	134.8	480.41	140.9	509.33	147.9					30 mph
20	354.63	116.3	381.84	119.8	409.58	124.3	437.81	129.8	466.48	136.2	495.53	143.6					
21	341.60	111.2	368.90	114.9	396.75	119.6	425.11	125.4	453.90	132.1	483.10	139.8					
22	329.76	106.6	357.16	110.5	385.12	115.4	413.60	121.4	442.52	128.4	471.84	136.46					
23	318.96	102.4	346.45	106.4	374.53	111.6	403.12	117.9	432.17	125.2							
24	309.07	98.6	336.66	102.8	364.84	108.2	393.55	114.7	422.71	122.3							
25	299.99	95.1	327.66	99.5	355.95	105.0	384.77	111.8	414.04	119.7							

Δ = 89°

TABLE IV — T_s AND E_s — Δ = 89°

Speed designations: 70 mph, 60 mph, 50 mph, 40 mph, 30 mph

D_c	150' T_s	150' E_s	200' T_s	200' E_s	250' T_s	250' E_s	300' T_s	300' E_s	350' T_s	350' E_s	400' T_s	400' E_s	500' T_s	500' E_s	600' T_s	600' E_s
1-30																
2-00																
2-30																
3-00																
3-30																
4-00	1483.24	576.8	1508.74	577.5	1534.36	578.4	1560.13	579.5	1586.02	580.9	1612.05	582.4	1664.49	586.1	1717.45	590.5
5	1201.88	461.8	1227.49	462.7	1253.27	463.9	1279.22	465.3	1305.33	466.9	1331.60	468.8	1384.61	473.4	1438.24	479.0
6	1014.36	385.3	1040.02	386.4	1066.02	387.7	1092.14	389.4	1118.46	391.4	1144.97	393.7	1198.53	399.2	1252.80	405.8
7	880.45	330.7	906.30	331.9	932.38	333.5	958.68	335.5	985.20	337.8	1011.94	340.5	1066.04	346.9	1123.94	354.6
8	780.06	289.8	806.03	291.2	832.25	293.0	858.72	295.3	885.45	297.9	912.40	300.9	967.02	308.2	1022.51	317.1
9	702.02	258.0	728.09	259.6	754.46	261.7	781.11	264.2	808.02	267.1	835.20	270.6	890.32	278.8	946.37	288.7
10	639.61	232.6	665.80	234.4	692.31	236.7	719.12	239.5	746.23	242.8	773.62	246.6	829.21	255.7	885.80	266.7
11	588.57	211.9	614.88	213.9	641.52	216.4	668.50	219.5	695.79	223.1	723.39	227.3	779.44	237.2	836.54	249.3
12	546.07	194.7	572.48	196.8	599.26	199.6	626.40	202.9	653.88	206.9	681.68	211.4	738.17	222.2	795.74	235.4
13	510.13	180.2	536.65	182.5	563.57	185.4	590.86	189.1	618.51	193.3	646.50	198.2	703.42	209.9	761.43	224.1
14	479.34	167.7	505.97	170.2	533.02	173.4	560.47	177.3	588.29	181.9	616.46	187.2	673.78	199.7	732.22	214.9
15	452.68	157.0	479.41	159.7	506.59	163.1	534.19	167.3	562.18	172.2	590.53	177.8	648.23	191.2		
16	429.30	147.6	456.20	150.5	483.51	154.1	511.26	158.6	539.41	163.8	567.93	169.8	625.99	184.1		
17	408.81	139.4	435.76	142.4	463.19	146.3	491.07	151.0	519.38	156.5	548.07	162.9	606.47	178.0		
18	390.55	132.1	417.60	135.3	445.16	139.4	473.18	144.4	501.64	150.2	530.49	156.9				
19	374.23	125.6	401.38	129.0	429.06	133.3	457.22	138.5	485.83	144.7	514.83	151.7				
20	359.56	119.7	386.81	123.3	414.60	127.8	442.90	133.3	471.65	139.8	500.79	147.2				
21	346.29	114.5	373.65	118.2	401.56	123.0	429.98	128.8	458.86	135.5	488.15	143.3				
22	334.25	109.7	361.70	113.6	389.72	118.6	418.27	124.7	447.28	131.7	476.69	139.8				
23	323.26	105.4	350.81	109.5	378.94	114.7	407.61	121.0	436.75	128.4						
24	313.20	101.5	340.84	105.7	369.08	111.1	397.87	117.7	427.13	125.4						
25	303.95	97.9	331.68	102.3	360.04	107.9	388.94	114.7	418.31	122.7						

$L_s = 150'$

30 mph

TABLE IV
Ts AND Es   Δ = 90°

D_c	L_s=150′ Ts	Es	200′ Ts	Es	250′ Ts	Es	300′ Ts	Es	350′ Ts	Es	400′ Ts	Es	500′ Ts	Es	600′ Ts	Es	mph
1-30																	
2-00																	
2-30																	
3-00																	
3-30																	
4-00	1508.04	594.2	1533.54	595.0	1559.18	595.9	1584.96	597.0	1610.87	598.4	1636.91	599.9	1689.40	603.6	1742.41	608.1	
5	1221.72	475.8	1247.34	476.7	1273.14	477.9	1299.10	479.3	1325.23	480.9	1351.52	482.9	1404.60	487.5	1458.29	493.1	70 mph
6	1030.90	396.9	1056.64	398.0	1082.59	399.4	1108.73	401.1	1135.08	403.1	1161.61	405.4	1215.24	410.9	1269.59	417.7	60 mph
7	894.64	340.7	920.50	341.9	946.59	343.5	972.92	345.5	999.47	347.5	1026.24	350.5	1080.42	357.0	1135.41	364.8	
8	792.48	298.5	818.46	299.9	844.70	301.8	871.21	304.1	897.96	306.7	924.96	309.8	979.67	317.1	1035.27	326.1	50 mph
9	713.06	265.8	739.15	267.4	765.55	269.5	792.22	272.0	819.17	275.0	846.40	278.4	901.62	286.7	957.79	296.8	
10	649.55	239.6	675.76	241.4	702.30	243.7	729.14	246.6	756.30	249.9	783.73	253.7	839.43	262.9	896.16	274.0	
11	597.62	218.3	623.95	220.3	650.62	222.8	677.64	225.9	704.97	229.6	732.62	233.8	788.80	243.8	846.04	256.0	
12	554.37	200.5	580.81	202.7	607.62	205.5	634.80	208.8	662.33	212.8	690.18	217.4	746.80	228.3	804.54	241.6	
13	517.79	185.6	544.34	187.9	571.29	190.9	598.63	194.5	626.34	198.8	654.38	203.8	711.45	215.6	769.64	229.9	
14	486.46	172.8	513.12	175.3	540.21	178.5	567.71	182.4	595.59	187.0	623.82	192.4	681.30	205.0	739.92	220.4	40 mph
15	459.33	161.7	486.10	164.4	513.32	167.8	540.97	172.0	569.02	177.0	597.44	182.7	655.30	196.2	714.33	212.55	
16	435.61	152.0	462.48	154.9	489.83	158.6	517.53	163.0	545.85	168.3	574.44	174.4	632.68	188.8			
17	414.69	143.5	441.67	146.6	469.15	150.5	497.10	155.2	525.47	160.8	554.24	167.2	612.82	182.5			30 mph
18	396.11	136.0	423.20	139.2	450.81	143.3	478.89	148.4	507.42	154.3	536.36	161.1	595.28	177.12			
19	379.51	129.3	406.70	132.7	434.43	137.0	462.65	142.3	491.33	148.6	520.43	155.7					
20	364.57	123.3	391.87	126.9	419.72	131.4	448.08	137.0	476.91	143.5	506.15	151.0					
21	351.07	117.9	378.47	121.6	406.44	126.4	434.93	132.2	463.90	139.1	493.28	146.9					
22	338.82	113.0	366.31	116.9	394.40	121.9	423.02	128.0	452.12	135.1	481.63	143.3					
23	327.64	108.5	355.23	112.6	383.43	117.8	412.17	124.2	441.40	131.7							
24	317.40	104.4	345.09	108.7	373.40	114.2	402.27	120.8	431.62	128.6							
25	307.99	100.7	335.77	105.1	364.20	110.8	393.18	117.7	422.65	125.8							

151

Δ = 91°

TABLE IV
T_s AND E_s

D_c	$L_s=150'$ T_s	E_s	$200'$ T_s	E_s	$250'$ T_s	E_s	$300'$ T_s	E_s	$350'$ T_s	E_s	$400'$ T_s	E_s	$500'$ T_s	E_s	$600'$ T_s	E_s
1-30																
2-00																
2-50																
3-00																
3-30																
4-00																
5	1241.91	490.2	1267.55	491.1	1293.36	492.2	1319.34	493.7	1345.49	495.3	1371.80	497.3	1424.93	501.9	1478.69	507.6
6	1047.73	408.9	1073.48	410.0	1099.45	411.4	1125.61	413.1	1151.98	415.1	1178.55	417.4	1232.25	423.0	1286.68	429.8
7	909.07	350.9	934.95	352.2	961.06	353.8	987.41	355.8	1013.99	358.1	1040.80	360.9	1095.06	367.4	1150.15	375.3
8	805.11	307.5	831.11	308.9	857.38	310.8	883.91	313.1	910.70	315.8	937.73	318.9	992.53	326.3	1048.24	335.3
9	724.29	273.8	750.41	275.4	776.83	277.5	803.54	280.0	830.52	283.1	857.79	286.5	913.11	294.9	969.41	305.0
10	659.67	246.8	685.90	248.8	712.47	251.0	739.35	253.8	766.54	257.2	794.03	261.0	849.84	270.3	906.71	281.5
11	606.82	224.8	633.17	226.8	659.88	229.4	686.93	232.5	714.31	236.2	742.02	240.4	798.32	250.6	855.71	262.9
12	562.81	206.5	589.27	208.7	616.12	211.5	643.34	214.9	670.92	218.9	698.83	223.5	755.59	234.6	813.49	247.9
13	525.59	191.1	552.17	193.5	579.16	196.5	606.54	200.2	634.30	204.5	662.41	209.5	719.62	221.4	777.99	235.8
14	493.71	177.9	520.40	180.4	547.53	183.7	575.07	187.6	603.01	192.3	631.31	197.7	688.94	210.5	747.76	225.9
15	466.10	166.5	492.90	169.2	520.16	172.7	547.87	176.9	575.98	181.9	604.47	187.7	662.50	201.3	721.73	217.8
16	441.96	156.5	468.87	159.4	496.27	163.1	524.12	167.7	552.40	173.0	581.07	179.1	639.49	193.6		
17	420.67	147.8	447.69	150.9	475.22	154.8	503.23	159.6	531.67	165.2	560.52	171.7	619.29	187.1		
18	401.77	140.0	428.89	143.3	456.56	147.4	484.70	152.5	513.31	158.5	542.33	165.3	601.44	181.5		
19	384.87	133.1	412.10	136.5	439.89	140.9	468.18	146.3	496.94	152.5	526.12	159.7				
20	369.67	126.9	397.01	130.5	424.92	135.1	453.35	140.7	482.26	147.3	511.59	154.9				
21	355.94	121.3	383.38	125.1	411.41	129.9	439.98	135.8	469.03	142.7	498.51	150.6				
22	343.47	116.3	371.01	120.2	399.16	125.3	427.86	131.4	457.04	138.6	486.66	146.9				
23	332.09	111.7	359.73	115.8	388.00	121.1	416.82	127.5	446.15	135.0						
24	321.67	107.5	349.41	111.8	377.79	117.3	406.74	124.0	436.19	131.8						
25	312.10	103.6	339.94	108.1	368.43	113.8	397.50	120.8	427.07	128.9						

70 mph · 60 mph · 50 mph · 40 mph · 30 mph

Δ = 91°

Table IV — T_s and E_s — $\Delta = 92°$

Design-speed annotations along the stepped minimum-length line (right side of table): 70 mph, 60 mph, 50 mph, 40 mph, 30 mph.

D_c	$L_s=150'$ T_s	E_s	$200'$ T_s	E_s	$250'$ T_s	E_s	$300'$ T_s	E_s	$350'$ T_s	E_s	$400'$ T_s	E_s	$500'$ T_s	E_s	$600'$ T_s	E_s
1-30																
2-00																
2-30																
3-00																
3-30																
4-00																
5	1262.47	504.9	1288.11	505.8	1313.93	507.0	1339.93	508.4	1366.11	510.1	1392.45	512.1	1445.63	516.8	1499.47	522.5
6	1064.86	421.2	1090.63	422.3	1116.61	423.7	1142.80	425.4	1169.19	427.4	1195.79	429.8	1249.56	435.4	1304.08	442.3
7	923.76	361.4	949.65	362.7	975.79	364.4	1002.17	366.4	1028.77	368.7	1055.61	371.5	1109.95	378.0	1165.14	386.0
8	817.97	316.7	843.99	318.2	870.28	320.0	896.84	322.3	923.66	325.1	950.73	328.2	1005.63	335.7	1061.45	344.8
9	735.73	282.0	761.87	283.6	788.31	285.8	815.05	288.3	842.08	291.3	869.39	294.9	924.81	303.3	981.24	313.5
10	669.97	254.2	696.22	256.0	722.82	258.4	749.73	261.2	776.97	264.6	804.50	268.5	860.43	277.8	917.44	289.2
11	616.19	231.5	642.57	233.6	669.31	236.1	696.40	239.3	723.82	243.0	751.58	247.3	808.01	257.5	865.56	269.9
12	571.40	212.7	597.89	214.9	624.78	217.7	652.04	221.7	679.67	225.2	707.63	229.9	764.53	241.0	822.60	254.5
13	533.53	196.8	560.13	199.2	587.16	202.2	614.59	205.9	642.41	210.3	670.57	215.3	727.94	227.4	786.49	241.9
14	501.08	183.2	527.81	185.7	554.98	189.0	582.57	193.0	610.57	197.7	638.94	203.1	696.73	216.0	755.74	231.7
15	472.99	171.4	499.82	174.2	527.13	177.7	554.83	182.0	583.06	187.7	611.63	192.8	669.83	206.6	729.27	223.2
16	448.42	161.2	475.37	164.1	502.82	167.8	530.73	172.4	559.07	177.7	587.82	183.0	646.42	198.6		
17	426.76	152.1	453.82	155.2	481.40	159.2	509.46	164.1	537.98	169.7	566.91	176.3	625.88	191.8		
18	407.53	144.1	434.69	147.4	462.41	151.6	490.62	156.7	519.30	162.8	548.40	169.6	607.72	186.0		
19	390.33	137.0	417.61	140.5	445.45	144.9	473.80	150.3	502.64	156.6	531.91	163.9				
20	374.87	130.6	402.25	134.3	430.22	138.9	458.72	144.6	487.71	151.2	517.14	158.9				
21	360.89	124.9	388.38	128.7	416.47	133.6	445.11	139.5	474.25	146.5	503.83	154.4				
22	348.20	119.6	375.79	123.6	404.00	128.8	432.78	135.0	462.06	142.2	491.78	150.6				
23	336.62	114.9	364.32	119.1	392.65	124.4	421.55	130.9	450.97	138.5	480.82	147.15				
24	326.02	110.6	353.82	114.9	382.27	120.5	411.30	127.2	440.85	135.1						
25	316.28	106.6	344.17	111.1	372.74	116.9	401.90	123.9	431.57	132.1						

Δ = 93°

TABLE IV
T_s AND E_s

Speed annotations (right margin, top to bottom): 70 mph, 60 mph, 50 mph, 40 mph, 30 mph (30 mph also at lower right).

D_c	$L_s = 150'$		$200'$		$250'$		$300'$		$350'$		$400'$		$500'$		$600'$	
	T_s	E_s	T_s	E_s	T_s	E_s	T_s	E_s	T_s	E_s	T_s	E_s	T_s	E_s	T_s	E_s
1–30																
2–00																
2–30																
3–00																
3–30																
4–00																
5	1283.39	520.0	1309.05	520.9	1334.89	522.1	1360.91	523.6	1387.10	525.3	1413.46	527.2	1466.71	532.0	1520.62	537.8
6	1092.31	433.8	1108.09	434.9	1134.09	436.3	1160.30	438.0	1186.72	440.1	1213.34	442.5	1267.18	448.1	1321.79	455.1
7	938.72	372.2	964.53	373.5	990.79	375.2	1017.19	377.2	1043.82	379.6	1070.70	382.4	1125.12	389.0	1180.41	397.1
8	831.07	326.2	857.10	327.6	883.42	329.5	910.01	331.8	936.86	334.6	963.97	337.7	1018.96	345.3	1074.90	354.5
9	747.37	290.4	773.53	292.0	800.00	294.2	826.78	296.8	853.84	299.8	881.20	303.2	936.73	311.9	993.28	322.2
10	680.45	261.8	706.73	263.6	733.36	266.0	760.31	268.9	787.59	272.3	815.17	276.2	871.22	285.6	928.37	297.1
11	625.73	238.4	652.13	240.5	678.90	243.1	706.04	246.2	733.51	250.0	761.32	254.3	817.88	264.6	875.58	277.2
12	580.15	219.0	606.67	221.2	633.59	224.1	660.90	227.5	688.58	231.6	716.60	236.3	773.64	247.6	831.88	261.2
13	541.61	202.6	568.25	205.0	595.31	208.1	622.79	211.8	650.66	216.3	678.89	221.3	736.41	233.5	795.14	248.2
14	508.59	188.6	535.35	191.2	562.56	194.5	590.21	198.5	618.26	203.2	646.70	208.7	704.66	221.8	763.87	237.5
15	480.00	176.5	506.87	179.3	534.23	182.8	562.04	187.1	590.27	192.2	618.91	198.0	677.29	211.9	736.94	228.7
16	455.00	165.9	481.99	168.9	509.48	172.6	537.45	177.2	565.87	182.7	594.69	188.9	653.48	203.7		
17	432.96	156.5	460.06	159.8	487.69	163.8	515.82	168.6	544.40	174.4	573.42	181.0	632.58	196.6		
18	413.39	148.4	440.50	151.7	468.36	155.9	496.64	161.1	525.39	167.2	554.59	174.1	614.12	190.6		
19	395.89	141.0	423.21	144.5	451.11	149.0	479.53	154.4	508.45	160.8	537.81	168.1				
20	380.15	134.4	407.59	138.1	435.61	142.8	464.18	148.5	493.26	155.2	522.78	162.9				
21	365.93	128.5	393.47	132.4	421.62	137.3	450.34	143.3	479.56	150.3	509.24	158.3				
22	353.02	123.1	380.66	127.2	408.94	132.3	437.79	138.6	467.16	145.9	496.99	154.3				
23	341.24	118.2	368.99	122.4	397.38	127.8	426.37	134.4	455.88	142.0	485.85	150.8				
24	330.45	113.8	358.30	118.2	386.82	123.8	415.94	130.6	445.59	138.6						
25	320.54	109.7	348.49	114.3	377.13	120.1	406.37	127.2	436.15	135.5						

Δ = 93°

TABLE IV — T_s AND E_s △ = 94°

Speed labels (right side): 70 mph, 60 mph, 50 mph, 40 mph, 30 mph

D_c	150' T_s	150' E_s	200' T_s	200' E_s	250' T_s	250' E_s	300' T_s	300' E_s	350' T_s	350' E_s	400' T_s	400' E_s	500' T_s	500' E_s	600' T_s	600' E_s
1-30																
2-00																
2-30																
3-00																
3-30																
4-00																
5	1304.71	535.5	1330.38	536.5	1356.23	537.6	1382.27	539.1	1408.48	540.8	1434.87	542.8	1488.18	547.6	1542.16	553.5
6	1100.07	446.7	1125.87	447.8	1151.89	449.3	1178.12	451.0	1204.57	453.1	1231.22	455.5	1285.13	461.2	1339.83	468.2
7	953.95	383.3	979.88	384.6	1006.06	386.3	1032.49	388.4	1059.16	390.8	1086.07	393.6	1140.57	400.3	1195.97	408.4
8	844.40	335.9	870.46	337.4	896.80	339.3	923.42	341.6	950.31	344.4	977.46	347.6	1032.55	355.2	1088.60	364.5
9	759.24	299.0	785.42	300.7	811.91	302.8	838.72	305.5	865.82	308.6	893.22	312.1	948.86	320.7	1005.55	331.1
10	691.14	269.6	717.44	271.4	744.09	273.8	771.08	276.7	798.40	280.2	826.04	284.1	882.20	293.6	939.50	305.2
11	635.44	245.5	661.87	247.6	688.68	250.2	715.85	253.4	743.37	257.2	771.24	261.5	827.93	272.0	885.80	284.6
12	589.06	225.5	615.61	227.7	642.57	230.6	669.92	234.1	697.65	238.2	725.74	243.0	782.92	254.3	841.33	268.1
13	549.84	208.5	576.51	211.0	603.62	214.1	631.14	217.9	659.07	222.4	687.36	227.5	745.03	239.8	803.96	254.6
14	516.24	194.2	543.03	196.8	570.29	200.1	597.98	204.2	626.10	209.0	654.61	214.2	712.73	227.7	772.14	243.6
15	487.15	181.7	514.05	184.5	541.45	188.1	569.32	192.4	597.62	197.6	626.33	203.4	684.89	217.5	744.75	234.4
16	461.71	170.8	488.73	173.8	516.27	177.6	544.30	182.2	572.79	187.7	601.69	194.0	660.67	208.9		
17	439.28	161.2	466.42	164.4	494.10	168.4	522.29	173.4	550.95	179.1	580.05	185.8	639.41	201.6		
18	419.36	152.7	446.61	156.1	474.43	160.4	502.78	165.6	531.61	171.7	560.89	178.7	620.63	195.4		
19	401.55	145.2	428.92	148.7	456.87	153.2	485.37	158.7	514.37	165.1	543.82	172.5				
20	385.54	138.4	413.02	142.1	441.10	146.8	469.75	152.6	498.91	159.4	528.53	167.1				
21	371.07	132.2	398.66	136.1	426.87	141.1	455.66	147.2	484.98	154.2	514.76	162.4				
22	357.93	126.7	385.62	130.8	413.96	136.0	442.90	142.3	472.36	149.7	502.29	158.2				
23	345.94	121.7	373.74	125.9	402.21	131.3	431.28	137.9	460.89	145.7	490.96	154.7				
24	334.96	117.1	362.87	121.5	391.46	127.2	420.67	134.0	450.42	142.1						
25	324.87	112.8	352.88	117.5	381.60	123.3	410.93	130.5	440.81	138.8						

30 mph

Δ = 95°   **TABLE IV — T_s AND E_s**   **Δ = 95°**

Speed bands (right margin): 70 mph, 60 mph, 50 mph, 40 mph, 30 mph

D_c	$L_s=150'$ T_s	E_s	$200'$ T_s	E_s	$250'$ T_s	E_s	$300'$ T_s	E_s	$350'$ T_s	E_s	$400'$ T_s	E_s	$500'$ T_s	E_s	$600'$ T_s	E_s
1-30																
2-00																
2-30																
3-00																
3-30																
4-00																
5	1326.43	551.5	1352.11	552.4	1377.98	553.6	1404.03	555.1	1430.27	556.8	1456.69	558.9	1510.06	563.7	1564.11	569.6
6	1118.18	460.0	1143.99	461.1	1170.03	462.6	1196.28	464.4	1222.76	466.5	1249.44	468.9	1303.43	474.7	1358.22	481.7
7	969.48	394.7	995.42	396.1	1021.62	397.7	1048.08	399.8	1074.78	402.3	1101.72	405.1	1156.32	411.8	1211.82	420.0
8	857.99	345.8	884.06	347.4	910.43	349.3	937.08	351.7	964.01	354.4	991.20	357.6	1046.38	365.3	1102.56	374.7
9	771.32	307.9	797.52	309.6	824.05	311.7	850.89	314.4	878.03	317.5	905.48	321.1	961.23	329.8	1018.05	340.3
10	702.02	277.6	728.34	279.4	755.03	281.8	782.06	284.8	809.42	288.3	837.11	292.3	893.40	301.9	950.84	313.5
11	645.34	252.8	671.80	254.8	698.64	257.5	725.85	260.7	753.42	264.6	781.35	269.0	838.17	279.5	896.20	292.2
12	598.14	232.2	624.72	234.4	651.71	237.3	679.11	240.9	706.89	245.0	735.04	249.8	792.37	261.3	850.96	275.1
13	558.23	214.8	584.93	217.2	612.07	220.4	639.65	224.2	667.63	228.7	696.00	233.9	753.82	246.2	812.94	261.2
14	524.04	199.9	550.86	202.5	578.16	205.9	605.91	210.0	634.09	214.9	662.67	220.4	720.96	233.7	780.57	249.7
15	494.43	187.0	521.37	189.9	548.81	193.5	576.74	197.9	605.10	203.0	633.90	209.0	692.63	223.2	752.72	240.3
16	468.54	175.8	495.60	178.8	523.19	182.7	551.28	187.4	579.84	192.9	608.82	199.2	667.99	214.3		
17	445.72	166.0	472.90	169.1	500.63	173.2	528.88	178.2	557.61	184.0	586.80	190.8	646.37	206.7		
18	425.45	157.2	452.74	160.6	480.62	164.9	509.03	170.2	537.94	176.3	567.31	183.4	627.26	200.2		
19	407.32	149.4	434.73	153.0	462.75	157.5	491.31	163.0	520.39	169.6	549.95	177.0	610.25	194.69		
20	391.03	142.4	418.55	146.1	446.70	150.0	475.42	156.8	504.67	163.6	534.39	171.4				
21	376.30	136.1	403.94	140.0	432.22	145.0	461.09	151.1	490.49	158.3	520.38	166.5				
22	362.93	130.4	390.67	134.5	419.08	139.7	448.10	146.1	477.66	153.6	507.70	162.2				
23	350.73	125.2	378.58	129.5	407.12	135.0	436.28	141.6	465.99	149.4	496.18	158.3				
24	339.55	120.4	367.52	124.9	396.19	130.6	425.48	137.6	455.34	145.7						
25	329.29	116.1	357.36	120.7	386.15	126.7	415.58	133.9	445.57	142.3						

30 mph

156

Δ = 96°

TABLE IV — T_s AND E_s — Δ = 96°

D_c	L_s=150' T_s	E_s	200' T_s	E_s	250' T_s	E_s	300' T_s	E_s	350' T_s	E_s	400' T_s	E_s	500' T_s	E_s	600' T_s	E_s
1-30																
2-00																
2-30																
3-00																
3-30																
4-00																
5	1348.57	567.9	1374.26	568.8	1400.14	570.0	1426.22	571.5	1452.48	573.3	1478.92	575.3	1532.35	580.2	1586.49	586.1
6	1136.63	473.7	1162.46	474.8	1188.52	476.3	1214.79	478.1	1224.29	480.2	1268.01	482.5	1322.07	488.5	1376.95	495.6
7	985.30	406.4	1011.26	407.8	1037.48	409.5	1063.97	411.6	1090.70	414.0	1117.68	416.9	1172.36	423.7	1227.97	432.0
8	871.84	356.1	897.94	357.6	924.33	359.6	951.01	362.0	977.97	364.8	1005.20	368.0	1060.49	375.8	1116.79	385.3
9	783.64	317.0	809.86	318.7	836.42	320.9	863.29	323.6	890.48	326.7	917.97	330.4	973.83	339.1	1030.79	349.7
10	713.11	285.8	739.46	287.7	766.18	290.1	793.24	293.1	820.66	296.6	848.39	300.6	904.81	310.3	962.40	322.1
11	655.43	260.1	681.91	262.3	708.79	265.0	736.05	268.3	763.67	272.1	791.65	276.6	848.61	287.2	906.80	300.1
12	607.40	239.1	634.00	241.3	661.04	244.2	688.48	247.8	716.32	252.0	744.53	256.8	802.00	268.4	860.78	282.4
13	566.78	221.1	593.51	223.6	620.70	226.7	648.32	230.6	676.36	235.1	704.79	240.4	762.78	252.9	822.09	268.0
14	531.98	205.8	558.84	208.4	586.18	211.8	613.99	216.0	642.23	220.9	670.88	226.5	729.34	239.9	789.17	256.1
15	501.85	192.5	528.83	195.4	556.32	199.1	584.30	203.5	612.73	208.7	641.60	214.7	700.52	229.0	760.83	246.3
16	475.50	181.0	502.60	184.0	530.25	187.9	558.39	192.6	587.02	198.2	616.09	204.6	675.46	219.8	736.19	238.12
17	452.27	170.8	479.50	174.0	507.28	178.1	535.60	183.2	564.41	189.1	593.68	195.8	653.46	211.9		
18	431.65	161.8	458.98	165.2	486.92	169.6	515.40	174.9	544.39	181.1	573.85	188.3	634.03	205.2		
19	413.20	153.8	440.66	157.2	468.73	161.9	497.37	167.5	526.54	174.1	556.19	181.6	616.73	199.5		
20	396.62	146.5	424.20	150.0	452.40	155.2	481.20	161.0	510.54	167.9	540.37	175.8				
21	381.63	140.0	409.32	144.0	437.67	149.1	466.62	155.2	496.12	162.5	526.11	170.7				
22	368.02	134.1	395.82	138.1	424.30	143.6	453.40	150.0	483.06	157.6	513.21	166.2				
23	355.61	128.8	383.52	133.1	412.13	138.7	441.37	145.4	471.19	153.3	501.49	162.3				
24	344.24	123.9	372.26	128.4	401.00	134.2	430.39	141.2	460.35	149.4	490.79	158.75				
25	333.79	119.4	361.92	124.1	390.79	130.1	420.31	137.4	450.41	145.9						

Speed annotations: 70 mph (≈rows 5), 60 mph (≈rows 6–7), 50 mph (≈rows 8–10), 40 mph (≈rows 14–16), 30 mph (≈rows 23–25).

TABLE IV
T_s AND E_s

Δ = 97°

Speed annotations: 70 mph, 60 mph, 50 mph, 40 mph, 30 mph

D_c	$L_s=150'$ T_s	E_s	$200'$ T_s	E_s	$250'$ T_s	E_s	$300'$ T_s	E_s	$350'$ T_s	E_s	$400'$ T_s	E_s	$500'$ T_s	E_s	$600'$ T_s	E_s
1-30																
2-00																
2-30																
3-00																
3-30																
4-00																
5	1371.14	584.7	1396.84	585.6	1422.74	586.6	1448.84	588.4	1475.12	590.1	1501.59	592.2	1555.09	597.2	1609.30	603.2
6	1155.45	487.7	1181.29	488.8	1207.36	490.1	1233.66	492.1	1260.19	494.3	1286.94	496.7	1341.08	502.6	1396.06	509.8
7	1001.43	418.5	1027.41	419.8	1053.66	421.6	1080.17	423.7	1106.93	426.2	1133.95	429.0	1188.72	435.9	1244.44	444.3
8	885.97	366.6	912.08	368.2	938.49	370.1	965.21	372.6	992.21	375.4	1019.48	378.7	1074.87	386.5	1131.29	396.1
9	796.20	326.4	822.44	328.1	849.03	330.3	875.94	333.0	903.16	336.2	930.70	339.9	986.68	348.7	1043.78	359.4
10	724.42	294.2	750.79	296.1	777.54	298.6	804.65	301.6	832.11	305.1	859.90	309.2	916.44	319.0	974.19	330.9
11	665.72	267.9	692.23	270.0	719.14	272.7	746.44	276.0	774.11	279.9	802.15	284.4	859.25	295.2	917.62	308.2
12	616.83	246.1	643.47	248.4	670.54	251.3	698.03	254.9	725.92	259.2	754.20	264.0	811.83	275.7	870.78	289.9
13	575.49	227.6	602.26	230.1	629.49	233.3	657.16	237.2	685.27	241.8	713.76	247.1	771.92	259.7	831.43	274.9
14	540.08	211.8	566.98	214.5	594.36	217.9	622.01	222.1	650.52	227.1	679.25	232.7	737.89	246.3	797.93	262.6
15	509.42	198.2	536.43	201.1	563.97	204.7	592.01	209.2	620.51	214.5	649.46	220.6	708.57	235.0	769.10	252.5
16	482.60	186.3	509.74	189.3	537.44	193.1	565.65	198.0	594.35	203.7	623.50	210.1	683.07	225.5	744.04	244.0
17	458.96	175.8	486.23	179.0	514.07	183.2	542.45	188.3	571.34	194.2	600.70	201.1	660.69	217.3		
18	437.97	166.5	465.35	169.9	493.34	174.1	521.89	179.7	550.96	186.0	580.52	193.2	640.92	210.4		
19	419.20	158.2	446.70	161.8	474.84	166.5	503.55	172.1	532.80	178.8	562.55	186.4	623.33	204.4		
20	402.32	150.8	429.95	154.6	458.22	159.5	487.10	165.4	516.53	172.4	546.45	180.4				
21	387.07	144.1	414.81	148.1	443.22	153.2	472.25	159.4	501.85	166.7	531.95	175.1				
22	373.22	138.0	401.07	142.2	429.62	147.6	458.81	154.1	488.56	161.7	518.83	170.4				
23	360.59	132.5	388.56	136.9	417.24	142.5	446.57	149.3	476.49	157.2	506.91	166.2				
24	349.01	127.5	377.10	132.0	405.49	137.9	435.49	144.9	465.46	153.2	496.03	162.7				
25	338.38	122.8	366.58	127.6	395.52	133.7	425.14	141.0	455.35	149.6						

Δ = 98°

TABLE IV
T_s AND E_s
Δ = 98°

Speed region labels (right side, by diagonal): 70 mph, 60 mph, 50 mph, 40 mph, 30 mph

D_c	$L_s=150'$ T_s	E_s	$200'$ T_s	E_s	$250'$ T_s	E_s	$300'$ T_s	E_s	$350'$ T_s	E_s	$400'$ T_s	E_s	$500'$ T_s	E_s	$600'$ T_s	E_s
1-30																
2-00																
2-30																
3-00																
3-30																
4-00																
5	1394.16	602.0	1419.87	603.0	1445.79	604.2	1471.90	605.7	1498.21	607.5	1524.71	609.6	1578.27	611.6	1632.56	620.6
6	1174.64	502.1	1200.49	503.3	1226.59	504.8	1252.91	506.6	1279.47	508.8	1306.25	511.2	1360.47	517.2	1415.54	524.5
7	1017.89	430.9	1043.88	432.2	1070.15	434.0	1096.69	436.1	1123.49	438.6	1150.54	441.5	1205.41	448.4	1261.23	456.9
8	900.37	377.5	926.50	379.0	952.94	381.0	979.69	383.4	1006.73	386.3	1034.05	389.6	1089.54	397.5	1146.09	407.2
9	809.01	336.0	835.28	337.7	861.89	340.0	888.84	342.7	916.10	345.9	943.69	349.6	999.79	358.5	1057.03	369.4
10	735.95	302.9	762.35	304.8	789.14	307.3	816.28	310.3	843.79	313.9	871.63	318.0	928.30	327.9	986.21	339.9
11	676.21	275.8	702.75	277.9	729.70	280.7	757.04	284.0	784.76	287.7	812.86	292.5	870.10	303.3	928.64	316.4
12	626.46	253.3	653.13	255.6	680.23	258.6	707.77	262.2	735.72	266.5	764.06	271.5	821.84	283.2	880.99	297.5
13	584.38	234.3	611.18	236.8	638.45	240.0	666.18	244.0	694.34	248.6	722.91	253.9	781.23	266.7	840.95	282.1
14	548.34	218.0	575.27	220.7	602.71	224.2	630.62	228.5	658.99	233.2	687.79	239.2	746.61	252.8	806.87	269.4
15	517.13	204.0	544.19	206.9	571.78	210.6	599.87	215.1	628.45	220.5	657.48	226.6	716.78	241.2	777.54	258.8
16	489.85	191.7	517.02	194.8	544.77	198.8	573.05	203.6	601.82	209.3	631.06	215.8	690.83	231.3	752.05	250.0
17	465.78	180.9	493.09	184.2	520.99	188.4	549.44	193.5	578.41	199.6	607.86	206.5	668.06	222.9		
18	444.42	171.4	471.85	174.8	499.90	179.3	528.52	184.7	557.67	191.1	587.33	198.4	647.95	215.7		
19	425.32	162.8	452.87	166.5	481.06	171.2	509.85	176.9	539.19	183.6	569.04	191.3	630.06	209.5		
20	420.14	155.2	435.82	159.0	464.15	163.9	493.11	169.9	522.63	177.0	552.66	185.0				
21	392.62	148.3	420.41	152.3	448.89	157.5	478.00	163.8	507.70	171.1	537.91	179.6				
22	378.52	142.0	406.43	146.2	435.05	151.7	464.32	158.2	494.18	165.9	524.56	174.7				
23	365.66	136.3	393.69	140.7	422.45	146.4	451.87	153.2	481.89	161.3	512.44	170.5				
24	353.88	131.1	382.03	135.7	410.92	141.6	440.50	148.8	470.67	157.1	501.37	166.7				
25	343.06	126.4	371.32	131.2	400.35	137.3	430.07	144.7	460.39	153.4						

159

TABLE IV — T_s AND E_s Δ = 99°

D_c	$L_s=150'$ T_s	E_s	$200'$ T_s	E_s	$250'$ T_s	E_s	$300'$ T_s	E_s	$350'$ T_s	E_s	$400'$ T_s	E_s	$500'$ T_s	E_s	$600'$ T_s	E_s
1-30																
2-00																
2-30																
3-00																
3-30																
4-00																
5	1417.64	619.8	1443.37	620.8	1469.31	622.0	1495.44	623.6	1521.77	625.4	1548.30	627.5	1601.93	632.5	1656.30	638.6
6	1194.21	517.0	1220.09	518.1	1246.20	519.6	1272.55	521.5	1299.14	523.5	1325.95	526.2	1380.25	532.2	1435.42	539.5
7	1034.60	443.6	1060.69	444.9	1086.98	446.7	1113.55	448.6	1140.38	451.7	1167.47	454.3	1222.43	461.3	1278.37	469.9
8	915.06	388.6	941.22	390.2	967.69	392.2	994.46	394.6	1021.54	397.5	1048.95	400.9	1104.50	408.9	1161.18	418.6
9	822.08	345.9	848.37	347.7	875.01	349.9	902.00	352.7	929.31	355.9	956.95	359.3	1013.16	368.7	1070.55	379.6
10	747.72	311.8	774.15	313.7	800.96	316.3	828.15	319.3	855.70	322.9	883.60	327.1	940.41	337.1	998.48	349.2
11	686.92	283.9	713.48	286.1	740.47	288.8	767.85	292.2	795.63	296.2	823.79	300.8	881.18	311.7	939.89	325.0
12	636.28	260.7	662.98	263.1	690.12	266.1	717.71	269.8	745.72	274.1	774.12	279.1	832.07	291.0	891.40	305.4
13	593.45	241.2	620.28	243.7	647.60	247.0	675.38	250.9	703.61	255.6	732.25	261.0	790.74	273.9	850.66	289.4
14	556.77	224.4	583.74	227.2	611.22	230.7	639.19	234.9	667.62	240.0	696.50	245.8	755.51	259.6	815.99	276.3
15	525.01	210.0	552.10	213.0	579.74	216.6	607.90	221.2	636.54	226.6	665.65	232.8	725.15	247.5	786.15	265.3
16	497.23	197.3	524.45	200.4	552.25	204.4	580.59	209.3	609.44	215.0	638.77	221.6	698.75	237.1	760.22	256.2
17	472.74	186.2	500.10	189.5	528.05	193.8	556.57	198.9	585.62	205.0	615.16	212.0	675.58	228.6		
18	451.00	176.3	478.47	179.8	506.58	184.3	535.27	189.8	564.52	196.2	594.27	203.6	655.13	221.1		
19	431.56	167.5	459.16	171.2	487.42	176.0	516.28	181.7	545.71	188.5	575.66	196.3	636.92	214.7		
20	414.07	159.7	441.80	163.6	470.20	168.5	499.24	174.6	528.86	181.7	559.00	189.9				
21	398.27	152.5	426.12	156.6	454.67	161.9	483.87	168.2	513.66	175.7	543.99	184.2				
22	383.93	146.1	411.89	150.4	440.59	155.8	469.95	162.5	499.91	170.3	530.41	179.2				
23	370.84	140.2	398.93	144.7	427.76	150.4	457.27	157.3	487.40	165.5	518.07	174.7				
24	358.85	134.9	387.06	139.5	416.03	145.5	445.70	152.7	475.99	161.2	506.81	170.8				
25	347.84	130.0	376.16	134.8	405.27	141.0	435.09	148.5	465.53	157.3						

Speed markers: 70 mph, 60 mph, 50 mph, 40 mph, 30 mph

TABLE IV — T_s AND E_s Δ=100°

D_c	150' T_s	150' E_s	200' T_s	200' E_s	250' T_s	250' E_s	300' T_s	300' E_s	350' T_s	350' E_s	400' T_s	400' E_s	500' T_s	500' E_s	600' T_s	600' E_s	mph
1-30																	
2-00																	
2-30																	
3-00																	
3-30																	
4-00																	
5	1441.61	638.1	1467.36	639.1	1493.31	640.3	1519.46	641.2	1545.82	643.7	1572.37	645.9	1626.07	650.9	1680.53	657.1	70 mph
6	1214.20	532.2	1240.08	533.4	1266.22	534.9	1292.60	536.8	1319.21	539.0	1346.06	541.5	1400.44	547.6	1455.71	555.0	60 mph
7	1051.81	456.6	1077.84	458.0	1104.16	457.8	1130.75	462.0	1157.62	464.6	1184.75	467.5	1239.81	474.6	1295.86	483.2	
8	930.06	400.0	956.24	401.6	982.73	403.7	1009.54	406.1	1036.66	409.1	1064.07	412.4	1119.78	420.5	1176.59	430.4	
9	835.41	356.1	861.73	357.9	888.40	360.1	915.43	362.6	942.78	366.2	970.47	370.0	1026.81	379.1	1084.35	390.1	50 mph
10	759.73	321.0	786.19	322.9	813.04	325.5	840.26	328.2	867.87	332.2	895.82	336.4	952.76	346.5	1011.00	358.7	
11	697.84	292.3	724.44	294.4	751.46	297.2	778.89	300.6	806.72	304.6	834.94	309.3	892.48	320.3	951.38	333.7	
12	646.30	268.4	673.03	270.8	700.22	273.8	727.85	277.5	755.92	281.9	784.39	286.9	842.50	298.9	902.03	313.5	
13	602.71	248.2	629.58	250.8	656.94	254.1	684.77	258.1	713.06	262.8	741.77	268.3	800.44	281.3	860.57	297.0	
14	565.38	231.0	592.38	233.8	619.91	237.3	647.93	241.6	676.44	246.7	705.40	252.6	764.59	266.5	825.29	283.4	40 mph
15	533.04	216.1	560.18	219.0	587.86	222.8	616.09	227.5	644.80	232.9	674.00	239.2	733.70	254.0	794.94	272.0	
16	504.77	203.1	532.04	206.2	559.89	210.3	588.30	215.2	617.22	221.0	646.64	227.6	706.83	243.5	768.56	262.6	
17	479.85	191.6	507.25	195.0	535.25	199.3	563.84	204.5	592.97	210.6	622.62	217.7	683.26	234.4			
18	457.71	181.5	485.24	185.0	513.41	189.5	542.17	195.1	571.50	201.6	601.36	209.4	662.45	226.7			
19	437.92	172.4	465.58	176.1	493.90	180.9	522.84	186.8	552.36	193.6	582.42	201.4	643.93	220.0			
20	420.13	164.3	447.91	168.2	476.38	173.2	505.50	179.4	535.21	186.6	565.47	194.8	627.37	214.26			30 mph
21	404.05	157.0	431.95	161.1	460.57	166.4	489.86	172.8	519.75	180.3	550.20	188.9					
22	389.45	150.3	417.47	154.6	446.24	160.2	475.69	166.9	505.75	174.7	536.38	183.7					
23	376.13	144.3	404.27	148.8	433.18	154.6	462.79	161.6	493.03	169.8	523.83	179.1					
24	363.93	138.8	392.20	143.5	421.25	149.5	451.02	156.8	481.42	165.5	512.37	175.0					
25	352.72	133.7	381.10	138.6	410.30	144.9	440.22	152.4	470.78	161.3	501.90	171.4					

Δ = 101°

TABLE IV — T_s AND E_s

Speed annotations (right margin, top to bottom): 70 mph, 60 mph, 50 mph, 40 mph, 30 mph

D_c	L_s=150' T_s	E_s	200' T_s	E_s	250' T_s	E_s	300' T_s	E_s	350' T_s	E_s	400' T_s	E_s	500' T_s	E_s	600' T_s	E_s
1-30																
2-00																
2-30																
3-00																
3-30																
4-00																
5	1466.09	656.9	1491.85	657.9	1517.81	659.2	1543.99	660.8	1570.37	662.6	1596.95	664.8	1650.72	669.9	1705.26	676.1
6	1234.60	547.9	1260.50	549.1	1286.66	550.6	1313.06	552.5	1339.71	554.7	1366.59	557.3	1421.05	563.4	1476.42	570.9
7	1069.30	470.1	1095.35	471.5	1121.69	473.3	1148.32	475.5	1175.22	478.1	1202.40	481.1	1257.55	488.2	1313.72	497.0
8	945.38	411.8	971.57	413.4	998.10	415.5	1024.94	418.0	1052.10	420.9	1079.55	424.3	1135.37	432.5	1192.32	442.5
9	849.03	366.5	875.37	368.3	902.08	370.7	929.14	373.5	956.54	376.8	984.28	380.6	1040.74	389.8	1098.43	401.0
10	772.00	330.4	798.48	332.4	825.36	334.9	852.63	338.1	880.28	341.8	908.30	346.0	965.38	356.2	1023.78	368.6
11	709.00	300.8	735.62	303.0	762.68	305.9	790.16	309.3	818.05	313.3	846.33	318.0	904.02	329.2	963.10	342.7
12	656.53	276.3	683.29	278.7	710.53	281.7	738.21	285.5	766.34	289.9	794.88	295.5	853.15	307.1	912.89	321.9
13	612.16	255.5	639.06	258.1	666.47	261.4	694.36	265.5	722.71	270.3	751.50	275.8	810.35	288.9	870.69	304.8
14	574.16	237.7	601.20	240.5	628.78	244.1	656.86	248.3	685.44	253.6	714.48	259.7	773.86	272.6	834.80	290.7
15	541.25	222.4	568.42	225.4	596.16	229.2	624.45	233.9	653.24	239.4	682.52	245.7	742.42	260.8	803.91	278.9
16	512.47	209.0	539.78	212.2	567.69	216.3	596.16	221.2	625.17	227.1	654.68	233.8	715.09	249.8	777.07	269.1
17	487.10	197.2	514.54	200.6	542.61	204.9	571.27	210.2	600.49	216.4	630.23	223.5	691.10	240.5		
18	464.57	186.7	492.14	190.3	520.37	194.9	549.22	200.5	578.63	207.1	608.59	214.6	669.93	232.4		
19	444.43	177.4	472.13	181.2	500.52	186.0	529.54	191.9	559.16	198.8	589.32	206.7	651.09	225.5		
20	426.32	169.0	454.15	173.0	482.69	178.1	511.89	184.3	541.70	191.5	572.07	199.9	634.24	219.5		
21	409.95	161.5	437.91	165.7	466.60	171.0	495.97	177.0	525.97	185.1	556.53	193.8				
22	395.08	154.6	423.17	159.0	452.01	164.6	481.55	171.4	511.72	179.3	542.47	188.4				
23	381.52	148.4	409.73	153.0	438.72	158.8	468.43	165.9	498.78	174.2	529.70	183.6				
24	369.11	142.7	397.44	147.5	426.58	153.8	456.44	160.9	486.96	169.6	518.05	179.4				
25	357.70	137.5	386.15	142.5	415.43	148.8	445.45	156.5	476.14	165.4	507.39	175.6				

30 mph

Δ = 101°

162

D_c	$L_s=150'$		$200'$		$250'$		$300'$		$350'$		$400'$		$500'$		$600'$	
	T_s	E_s	T_s	E_s	T_s	E_s	T_s	E_s	T_s	E_s	T_s	E_s	T_s	E_s	T_s	E_s
1-30																
2-00																
3-00																
3-30																
4-00																
4-30																
5	1491.09	676.3	1516.86	677.3	1542.84	678.6	1569.04	680.2	1595.45	682.0	1622.06	684.2	1675.90	689.4	1730.53	695.7
6	1255.44	564.0	1281.36	565.2	1307.54	566.8	1333.96	568.7	1360.64	571.0	1387.56	573.6	1442.11	579.8	1497.58	587.3
7	1087.17	483.9	1113.24	485.4	1139.61	487.1	1166.26	489.4	1193.20	492.0	1220.42	495.0	1275.67	502.3	1331.96	511.1
8	961.02	423.9	987.24	425.6	1013.79	427.6	1040.67	430.2	1067.87	433.2	1095.37	436.6	1151.30	444.9	1208.39	454.9
9	862.94	377.3	889.31	379.1	916.05	381.5	943.15	384.3	970.59	387.7	998.39	391.6	1054.98	400.8	1112.82	412.1
10	784.52	340.1	811.03	342.1	837.95	344.7	865.26	347.9	892.97	351.6	921.04	355.9	978.26	366.2	1036.84	378.7
11	720.39	309.7	747.05	311.9	774.15	314.7	801.67	318.2	829.61	322.3	857.97	327.0	915.81	338.3	975.08	352.0
12	666.98	284.4	693.78	286.8	721.05	289.9	748.79	293.7	776.98	298.1	805.59	303.3	864.03	315.6	923.97	330.5
13	621.82	263.0	648.75	265.6	676.21	268.8	704.15	273.1	732.57	277.9	761.44	283.5	820.46	296.7	881.03	312.8
14	583.13	244.7	610.21	247.5	637.84	251.1	665.98	255.6	694.63	260.7	723.75	266.7	783.33	281.0	844.50	298.2
15	549.63	228.9	576.84	231.9	604.64	235.8	632.99	240.5	661.86	246.1	691.22	252.5	751.33	267.7	813.08	286.0
16	520.34	215.1	547.69	218.3	575.65	222.4	604.19	227.5	633.28	233.4	662.88	240.2	723.52	256.4	785.77	275.8
17	494.51	202.9	522.00	206.4	550.13	210.7	578.86	216.1	608.16	222.4	638.00	229.6	699.11	246.7		
18	471.57	192.2	499.19	195.8	527.49	200.4	556.41	206.1	585.92	212.7	615.98	220.3	677.57	238.4		
19	451.07	182.6	478.82	186.4	507.28	191.3	536.38	197.2	566.10	204.2	596.37	212.2	658.39	231.2		
20	432.63	173.9	460.52	177.9	489.13	183.1	518.42	189.3	548.33	196.7	578.81	205.1	641.26	225.0		
21	415.97	166.2	443.99	170.4	472.75	175.8	502.22	182.3	533.32	190.0	563.00	198.8				
22	400.84	159.1	428.98	163.5	457.90	169.2	487.54	176.0	517.82	184.0	548.70	192.9				
23	387.04	152.7	415.31	157.3	444.38	163.2	474.18	170.3	504.65	178.7	535.70	188.7				
24	374.39	146.8	402.80	151.6	432.02	157.8	461.98	165.2	492.63	173.9	523.85	183.9				
25	362.78	141.5	391.30	146.5	420.67	152.9	450.80	160.6	481.61	169.7	513.01	180.0				

Δ = 102°

70 mph · 60 mph · 50 mph · 40 mph · 30 mph

TABLE IV
T_s AND E_s

Δ = 102°

163

Δ=103°

TABLE IV — T_s AND E_s Δ = 103°

D_c	$L_s=150'$ T_s	E_s	$200'$ T_s	E_s	$250'$ T_s	E_s	$300'$ T_s	E_s	$350'$ T_s	E_s	$400'$ T_s	E_s	$500'$ T_s	E_s	$600'$ T_s	E_s
1-30																
2-00																
2-30																
3-00																
3-30																
4-00																
5	1516.63	696.2	1542.42	697.2	1568.42	698.5	1594.64	700.1	1621.08	702.0	1647.72	704.2	1701.63	709.5	1756.34	715.8
6	1276.73	580.6	1302.67	581.9	1328.87	583.4	1355.32	585.4	1382.03	587.6	1408.99	590.2	1463.62	596.5	1519.20	604.2
7	1105.43	498.2	1131.52	499.6	1157.91	501.4	1184.60	503.4	1211.57	506.3	1238.83	509.4	1294.18	516.7	1350.60	525.6
8	977.00	436.4	1003.24	438.0	1029.82	440.1	1056.74	442.7	1083.98	445.7	1111.53	449.2	1167.58	457.6	1224.80	467.7
9	877.16	388.4	903.55	390.2	930.32	392.6	957.46	395.5	984.95	398.9	1012.80	402.8	1069.52	412.2	1127.52	423.6
10	797.32	350.1	823.86	352.1	850.82	354.7	878.17	357.9	905.93	361.7	934.06	366.0	991.43	376.4	1050.18	389.1
11	732.03	318.7	758.72	321.0	785.86	323.9	813.44	327.4	841.43	331.5	869.85	336.3	927.85	347.7	987.31	361.6
12	677.66	292.7	704.49	295.1	731.81	298.3	759.60	302.1	787.85	306.6	816.54	311.8	875.15	324.2	935.29	339.3
13	631.68	270.7	658.66	273.3	686.15	276.7	714.16	280.9	742.65	285.8	771.59	291.4	830.80	304.8	891.59	321.0
14	592.30	251.8	619.42	254.7	647.09	258.4	675.30	262.8	704.02	268.1	733.23	274.1	793.00	288.5	854.42	305.9
15	558.19	235.6	585.45	238.6	613.30	242.5	641.71	247.3	670.66	252.8	700.12	259.4	762.44	274.8	822.44	293.3
16	528.37	221.3	555.77	224.6	583.79	228.8	612.40	233.9	641.57	239.8	671.27	246.7	732.13	263.1	794.66	282.8
17	502.08	208.8	529.62	212.3	557.81	216.7	586.61	222.1	616.00	228.5	645.94	235.8	707.29	253.1		
18	478.73	197.7	506.40	201.4	534.76	206.1	563.76	211.8	593.36	218.5	623.53	226.2	685.37	244.4		
19	457.86	187.8	485.66	191.7	514.19	196.6	543.37	202.7	573.19	209.7	603.57	217.8	665.86	237.0		
20	439.09	179.0	467.03	183.0	495.71	188.2	525.09	194.5	555.10	202.0	585.70	210.5	648.43	230.6		
21	422.12	170.9	450.20	175.2	479.04	180.7	508.60	187.3	538.80	195.1	569.61	204.0				
22	406.72	163.7	434.93	168.2	463.93	173.9	493.66	180.8	524.05	188.9	555.05	198.2				
23	392.67	157.1	421.01	161.7	450.16	167.7	480.06	174.9	510.65	183.4	541.83	193.1				
24	379.80	151.0	408.27	155.9	437.57	162.0	467.45	169.6	498.41	178.5	529.77	188.5				
25	367.98	145.5	396.57	150.6	426.03	157.0	456.26	164.9	487.20	174.0	518.74	184.5				

Speed markers (at stepped boundaries along the right): 70 mph, 60 mph, 50 mph, 40 mph, 30 mph.

164

TABLE IV — T_s AND E_s — $\triangle = 104°$

D_c	$L_s=150'$ T_s	E_s	$200'$ T_s	E_s	$250'$ T_s	E_s	$300'$ T_s	E_s	$350'$ T_s	E_s	$400'$ T_s	E_s	$500'$ T_s	E_s	$600'$ T_s	E_s
1-30																
2-00																
2-30																
3-00																
3-30																
4-00																
5	1542.74	716.7	1568.54	717.7	1594.56	719.1	1620.81	720.7	1647.27	722.6	1673.94	724.8	1727.93	730.1	1782.73	736.6
6	1298.50	597.7	1324.45	599.0	1350.67	600.6	1377.15	602.5	1403.90	604.8	1430.89	607.5	1485.61	613.8	1541.30	621.6
7	1124.09	512.8	1150.20	514.3	1176.62	516.1	1203.34	518.4	1230.35	521.1	1257.65	524.2	1313.11	531.6	1369.65	540.6
8	993.34	449.2	1019.60	450.9	1046.21	453.0	1073.16	455.6	1100.45	458.7	1128.05	462.2	1184.21	470.6	1241.59	480.9
9	891.69	399.8	918.10	401.7	944.91	404.1	972.09	407.0	999.63	410.4	1027.53	414.4	1084.39	423.9	1142.55	435.4
10	810.41	360.3	836.97	362.4	863.96	365.1	891.37	368.3	919.18	372.1	947.37	376.5	1004.88	387.0	1063.81	399.8
11	743.94	328.1	770.65	330.4	797.83	333.3	825.46	336.8	853.51	341.0	882.00	345.8	940.16	357.4	999.82	371.4
12	688.58	301.3	715.44	303.7	742.81	306.9	770.65	310.8	798.97	315.3	827.72	320.6	886.51	333.2	946.87	348.4
13	641.77	278.6	668.78	281.3	696.32	284.7	724.39	288.9	752.94	293.8	781.96	299.5	841.37	313.1	902.39	329.5
14	601.67	259.2	628.83	262.1	656.56	265.8	684.83	270.3	713.62	275.6	742.91	281.7	802.90	296.3	864.56	313.9
15	566.94	242.4	594.24	245.5	622.15	249.5	650.63	254.3	679.66	260.0	709.21	266.5	769.75	282.1	832.02	300.9
16	536.58	227.8	564.03	231.1	592.11	235.3	620.79	240.5	650.05	246.5	679.84	253.5	740.93	270.0	803.74	289.9
17	509.81	214.9	537.40	218.4	565.65	222.9	594.54	227.3	624.02	234.8	654.06	242.1	715.66	259.6		
18	486.04	203.5	513.77	207.2	542.19	211.9	571.27	217.9	600.97	224.5	631.25	232.3	693.35	250.7		
19	464.79	193.3	492.65	197.2	521.25	202.2	550.52	208.3	580.43	215.4	610.94	223.6	673.50	243.0		
20	445.68	184.1	473.69	188.2	502.44	193.5	531.91	199.9	562.03	207.4	592.75	216.0	655.76	236.3		
21	428.41	175.9	456.55	180.2	485.47	185.7	515.12	192.4	545.44	200.3	576.37	209.3				
22	412.73	168.4	441.00	172.9	470.08	178.7	499.91	185.7	530.42	193.9	561.56	203.3				
23	398.43	161.6	426.83	166.3	456.07	172.3	486.07	179.6	516.78	188.2	548.10	198.0				
24	385.32	155.4	413.86	160.3	443.26	166.6	473.44	174.0	504.32	183.1	535.83	193.3				
25	373.29	149.7	401.95	154.8	431.50	161.3	461.85	169.2	492.91	178.5	524.61	189.1				

Speed annotations (right margin): 70 mph, 60 mph, 50 mph, 40 mph, 30 mph.

165

TABLE IV
Ts AND Es

Δ = 105°

Dc	Ls = 150' Ts	Es	200' Ts	Es	250' Ts	Es	300' Ts	Es	350' Ts	Es	400' Ts	Es	500' Ts	Es	600' Ts	Es
1-30																
2-00																
2-30																
3-00																
3-30																
4-00																
5	1569.44	737.8	1595.26	738.8	1621.30	740.0	1647.57	741.8	1674.05	743.8	1700.76	746.0	1754.82	751.4	1809.72	757.9
6	1320.75	615.3	1346.73	616.6	1372.97	618.2	1399.48	620.2	1426.25	622.5	1453.28	625.2	1508.10	631.6	1563.90	639.4
7	1143.18	527.9	1169.31	529.4	1195.75	531.3	1222.50	533.6	1249.55	536.5	1276.90	539.4	1332.46	546.9	1389.14	556.0
8	1010.04	462.4	1036.33	464.1	1062.97	466.1	1089.96	468.9	1117.29	472.0	1144.94	475.5	1201.23	484.1	1258.75	494.5
9	906.54	411.6	932.99	413.4	959.82	415.9	987.05	418.8	1014.64	422.3	1042.60	426.3	1099.59	435.9	1157.92	447.5
10	823.78	370.9	850.38	373.0	877.41	375.7	904.86	379.0	932.72	382.8	960.98	387.3	1018.64	397.7	1077.76	410.8
11	756.11	337.7	782.86	340.0	810.08	343.0	837.75	346.5	865.87	350.8	894.43	355.7	952.75	367.3	1012.61	381.5
12	699.74	310.1	726.64	312.6	754.05	315.8	781.95	319.7	810.33	324.3	839.16	329.7	898.13	342.3	958.71	357.7
13	652.08	286.7	679.13	288.5	706.72	292.9	734.85	297.2	763.47	302.2	792.58	307.9	852.18	321.6	913.43	338.2
14	611.25	266.8	638.45	269.7	666.23	273.4	694.75	278.0	723.44	283.4	752.82	289.5	813.01	304.2	874.92	322.1
15	575.90	249.5	603.24	252.6	631.28	256.6	659.75	261.5	688.86	267.3	718.51	273.9	779.27	289.6	841.80	308.6
16	544.98	234.4	572.47	237.8	600.61	242.0	629.37	247.2	658.72	253.4	688.61	260.4	749.94	277.1	813.03	297.2
17	517.73	221.2	545.36	224.7	573.68	229.2	602.64	234.8	632.22	241.2	662.36	248.7	724.21	266.4		
18	493.52	209.4	521.30	213.1	549.79	217.9	578.96	223.8	608.75	230.6	639.14	238.5	701.50	257.2		
19	471.89	198.9	499.80	202.8	528.47	207.9	557.83	214.0	587.84	221.3	618.46	229.6	681.30	249.2		
20	452.43	189.5	480.49	193.6	509.32	198.9	538.88	205.4	569.11	213.0	599.95	221.7				
21	434.84	181.0	463.05	185.3	492.04	190.9	521.79	197.7	552.22	205.6	583.28	214.7				
22	418.88	173.3	447.21	177.8	476.38	183.7	506.31	190.8	536.93	199.1	568.20	208.6				
23	404.31	166.3	432.78	171.0	462.11	177.1	492.22	184.5	523.05	193.2	554.51	203.1	663.25	242.2		
24	390.97	159.9	419.58	164.8	449.07	171.2	479.35	178.9	510.37	187.9	542.02	198.2				
25	378.72	154.0	407.46	159.2	437.10	165.8	467.56	173.8	498.76	183.1	530.60	193.8				

Speed boundaries: 70 mph · 60 mph · 50 mph · 40 mph · 30 mph

TABLE IV

T_s AND E_s — Δ=106°

Speed annotations: 70 mph, 60 mph, 50 mph, 40 mph, 30 mph

D_c	$L_s=150'$ T_s	E_s	$200'$ T_s	E_s	$250'$ T_s	E_s	$300'$ T_s	E_s	$350'$ T_s	E_s	$400'$ T_s	E_s	$500'$ T_s	E_s	$600'$ T_s	E_s
1-30																
2-00																
2-30																
3-00																
3-30																
4-00																
5	1596.76	759.5	1622.59	760.6	1648.65	762.0	1674.94	763.6	1701.45	765.6	1728.19	767.8	1782.33	773.3	1837.32	779.9
6	1343.52	633.5	1369.51	634.7	1395.78	636.4	1422.32	638.3	1449.13	640.7	1476.20	643.4	1531.10	649.9	1587.02	657.8
7	1162.70	543.5	1188.85	544.9	1215.32	546.8	1242.11	549.0	1269.20	551.9	1296.59	555.1	1352.26	562.6	1409.07	571.9
8	1027.13	476.0	1053.45	477.7	1080.12	479.9	1107.15	482.6	1134.52	485.7	1162.22	489.3	1218.63	497.9	1276.30	508.5
9	921.74	423.7	948.21	425.8	975.09	428.0	1002.35	431.0	1029.99	434.5	1058.01	438.5	1115.14	448.2	1173.64	460.1
10	837.47	381.8	864.10	383.9	891.17	386.6	918.66	389.9	946.58	393.8	974.91	398.3	1032.72	409.1	1092.02	422.2
11	768.56	347.6	795.34	349.9	822.60	352.9	850.33	356.6	878.51	360.8	907.14	365.8	965.63	377.6	1025.70	391.9
12	711.16	319.2	738.10	321.7	765.55	324.9	793.51	328.9	821.96	333.6	850.87	339.0	910.02	351.8	970.82	367.4
13	662.63	295.1	689.71	297.9	717.36	301.4	745.54	305.7	774.25	310.7	803.43	316.6	863.23	330.4	924.73	347.2
14	621.06	274.6	648.30	277.5	676.13	281.3	704.54	285.9	733.48	291.4	762.95	297.6	823.36	312.5	885.53	330.5
15	585.05	256.8	612.44	260.0	640.46	264.0	669.08	268.9	698.28	274.8	728.02	281.4	789.01	297.4	851.82	316.6
16	553.58	241.3	581.11	244.6	609.32	249.0	638.15	254.2	667.58	260.4	697.58	267.5	759.15	284.4	822.53	304.8
17	525.82	227.6	553.51	231.2	581.89	235.8	610.94	241.4	640.60	247.9	670.86	255.5	732.96	273.4		
18	501.18	215.5	529.01	219.3	557.57	224.1	586.82	230.0	616.71	237.0	647.21	244.9	709.85	263.8		
19	479.14	204.7	507.12	208.7	535.86	213.8	565.30	220.0	595.42	227.3	626.17	235.7	689.29	255.5		
20	459.33	195.0	487.45	199.2	516.36	204.5	546.01	211.1	576.35	218.8	607.32	227.6	670.92	248.4		
21	441.42	186.2	469.69	190.6	498.77	196.3	528.61	203.1	559.16	211.1	590.35	220.4				
22	425.17	178.3	453.57	182.9	482.82	188.8	512.85	196.0	543.60	204.4	575.00	214.0				
23	410.34	171.1	438.88	175.9	468.29	182.0	498.50	189.5	529.46	198.5	561.07	208.3				
24	396.75	164.5	425.43	169.5	455.01	175.9	485.41	183.7	516.56	192.8	548.35	203.2				
25	384.28	158.4	413.09	163.6	442.83	170.3	473.40	178.4	504.74	187.9	536.74	198.7				

30 mph

TABLE IV — T_s AND E_s $\Delta = 107°$

D_c	$L_s=150'$ T_s	E_s	$200'$ T_s	E_s	$250'$ T_s	E_s	$300'$ T_s	E_s	$350'$ T_s	E_s	$400'$ T_s	E_s	$500'$ T_s	E_s	$600'$ T_s	E_s
1-30																
2-00																
2-30																
3-00																
3-30																
4-00																
5	1624.71	781.9	1650.56	783.0	1676.64	784.4	1702.95	786.1	1729.50	788.0	1756.27	790.3	1810.49	795.8	1865.58	802.5
6	1366.83	652.1	1392.84	653.4	1419.13	655.1	1445.69	657.1	1472.54	659.4	1499.64	662.2	1554.65	668.4	1610.68	676.8
7	1182.68	559.5	1208.86	561.0	1235.36	562.5	1262.17	565.2	1289.30	568.0	1316.74	571.2	1372.52	578.9	1429.47	588.2
8	1044.63	490.1	1070.96	491.8	1097.67	494.0	1124.73	496.6	1152.15	499.8	1179.91	503.5	1236.44	512.1	1294.27	522.8
9	937.30	436.1	963.80	438.0	990.70	440.5	1018.01	443.5	1045.71	447.1	1073.79	451.2	1131.06	461.0	1189.73	472.9
10	851.48	393.0	878.13	395.2	905.24	397.9	932.79	401.3	960.77	405.2	989.16	409.8	1047.13	420.6	1106.62	433.9
11	781.30	357.8	808.11	360.2	835.42	363.0	863.21	366.9	891.45	371.0	920.14	376.2	978.81	388.1	1039.09	402.6
12	722.85	328.5	749.82	331.1	777.32	334.4	805.34	338.4	833.86	343.1	862.85	348.6	922.18	361.6	983.22	377.3
13	673.42	303.5	700.55	306.6	728.25	310.1	756.50	314.5	785.27	319.6	814.54	325.5	874.54	339.5	936.29	356.5
14	631.09	282.6	658.37	285.6	686.26	289.4	714.73	294.1	743.76	299.6	773.32	305.9	833.94	321.0	896.38	339.2
15	594.42	264.3	621.86	267.5	649.94	271.6	678.63	276.6	707.91	282.5	737.75	289.2	798.97	305.3	862.06	322.8
16	562.37	248.3	589.95	251.7	618.22	256.1	647.13	261.4	676.66	267.7	706.76	274.9	768.58	292.0	832.26	312.6
17	534.10	234.2	561.85	237.9	590.30	242.5	619.42	248.2	649.18	254.8	679.55	262.4	741.92	280.6		
18	509.01	221.8	536.89	225.6	565.53	230.5	594.86	236.5	624.86	243.5	655.48	251.5	718.39	270.6		
19	486.57	210.6	514.60	214.7	543.42	219.8	572.96	226.1	603.18	233.5	634.05	242.0	697.46	262.1		
20	466.39	200.6	494.58	204.9	523.57	210.3	553.31	216.9	583.76	224.7	614.86	233.6	678.77	254.6		
21	448.16	191.6	476.49	196.1	505.65	201.8	535.59	208.7	566.26	216.8	597.59	226.1				
22	431.60	183.4	460.07	188.1	489.41	194.1	519.54	201.3	550.42	209.8	581.96	219.5				
23	416.50	176.0	445.11	180.9	474.61	187.1	504.94	194.7	536.02	203.5	567.78	213.7				
24	402.67	169.2	431.42	174.3	461.09	180.8	491.61	188.7	522.89	197.7	554.84	208.4				
25	389.96	163.0	418.85	168.3	448.69	175.0	479.38	183.2	510.85	192.8	543.01	203.7				

Speed annotations (right margin): 70 mph, 60 mph, 50 mph, 40 mph, 30 mph

$\Delta = 107°$

168

Δ = 108°

TABLE IV — T_s AND E_s ($\triangle = 108°$, $L_s = 150'$)

D_c	150' T_s	150' E_s	200' T_s	200' E_s	250' T_s	250' E_s	300' T_s	300' E_s	350' T_s	350' E_s	400' T_s	400' E_s	500' T_s	500' E_s	600' T_s	600' E_s	
1-30																	
2-00																	
2-30																	
3-00																	
3-30																	
4-00																	
5	1653.33	805.0	1679.19	806.1	1705.30	807.5	1721.64	809.2	1758.21	811.0	1785.01	813.5	1839.31	819.1	1894.50	825.8	70 mph
6	1390.68	671.4	1416.71	672.7	1443.03	674.3	1469.63	676.4	1496.75	678.8	1523.65	681.6	1578.75	688.2	1624.90	696.2	60 mph
7	1203.14	576.0	1229.34	577.5	1255.86	579.4	1282.72	581.8	1309.89	584.6	1337.38	587.9	1393.27	595.6	1450.35	605.1	
8	1062.53	504.5	1088.90	506.2	1115.63	508.5	1142.74	511.2	1170.20	514.4	1198.01	518.1	1254.68	526.9	1312.66	537.7	
9	953.22	449.0	979.75	450.9	1006.70	453.4	1034.05	456.5	1061.79	460.1	1089.94	464.2	1147.35	474.1	1206.20	486.2	50 mph
10	865.82	404.6	892.51	406.8	919.66	409.5	947.25	412.9	975.29	416.9	1003.75	421.5	1061.88	432.5	1121.57	445.9	
11	794.34	368.3	821.19	370.7	848.55	373.8	876.38	377.5	904.69	381.9	933.46	386.9	992.31	399.0	1052.80	413.7	
12	734.81	338.2	761.83	340.8	789.38	344.1	817.45	348.2	846.04	352.9	875.11	358.5	934.64	371.6	995.91	387.5	
13	684.48	312.7	711.65	315.5	739.40	319.1	767.71	323.5	796.56	328.7	825.92	334.6	886.13	348.8	948.12	366.0	
14	641.36	290.9	668.69	293.9	696.64	297.8	725.18	302.5	754.29	308.1	783.94	314.5	844.79	329.7	907.49	348.2	40 mph
15	604.02	272.0	631.50	275.3	659.64	279.4	688.41	284.2	717.78	290.4	747.71	297.3	809.18	313.6	872.56	333.2	
16	571.37	255.6	599.01	259.0	627.34	263.5	656.33	268.8	685.95	275.2	716.15	282.5	778.23	299.8	842.22	320.6	
17	542.59	241.1	570.38	244.7	598.90	249.4	628.11	255.2	657.97	261.9	688.45	269.6	751.08	287.9			
18	517.03	228.2	544.97	232.1	573.68	237.1	603.10	243.1	633.20	250.2	663.94	258.4	727.13	277.7			
19	494.17	216.8	522.27	220.8	551.16	226.1	580.79	232.4	611.13	239.9	642.12	248.5	705.83	268.8			
20	473.63	206.5	501.87	210.0	530.94	216.3	560.79	223.0	591.35	230.8	622.58	239.8	686.80	261.1			30 mph
21	455.05	197.2	483.45	201.7	512.70	207.5	542.74	214.5	573.53	222.7	605.00	232.1					
22	438.19	188.8	466.73	193.5	496.15	199.5	526.40	206.9	557.40	215.5	589.09	225.3					
23	422.81	181.1	451.50	186.0	481.07	192.3	511.53	200.0	542.74	209.2	574.65	219.2					
24	408.73	174.1	437.55	179.2	467.32	185.8	497.95	193.8	529.37	203.2	561.48	213.8					
25	395.78	167.7	424.75	173.0	454.69	179.9	485.51	188.1	517.12	197.8	549.44	208.9					

169

Δ=109°

TABLE IV
T_s AND E_s

Δ=109°

D_c	L_s=150' T_s	E_s	200' T_s	E_s	250' T_s	E_s	300' T_s	E_s	350' T_s	E_s	400' T_s	E_s	500' T_s	E_s	600' T_s	E_s
1-30																
2-00																
2-30																
3-00																
3-30																
4-00																
5	1682.65	828.8	1703.53	829.9	1734.65	831.3	1761.02	833.0	1787.62	835.1	1814.46	837.4	1868.84	843.0	1924.14	849.9
6	1415.12	691.2	1441.17	692.5	1467.52	694.3	1494.14	696.3	1521.05	698.7	1548.25	701.5	1603.45	708.2	1659.72	716.5
7	1224.09	595.0	1250.31	594.5	1276.87	596.5	1303.76	598.9	1330.97	601.7	1358.51	605.0	1414.52	612.9	1471.74	622.4
8	1030.88	519.4	1107.27	521.1	1134.04	523.4	1161.18	526.1	1188.70	529.4	1216.56	533.1	1273.36	542.1	1331.51	553.0
9	963.54	462.2	996.39	464.2	1023.08	466.7	1050.48	469.8	1078.28	473.6	1106.48	477.6	1164.04	487.7	1223.07	499.9
10	881.51	416.5	907.23	418.7	934.42	421.5	962.07	424.9	990.17	429.0	1018.69	433.7	1076.99	444.8	1136.88	458.4
11	807.70	379.2	834.59	381.6	861.99	384.7	889.89	388.5	918.26	392.9	947.10	398.0	1006.13	410.3	1066.84	425.1
12	747.07	348.1	774.12	350.8	801.72	354.1	829.86	358.2	858.52	363.1	887.67	368.6	947.40	382.0	1008.91	398.1
13	695.80	321.9	723.01	324.7	750.81	328.4	779.19	332.8	808.12	338.1	837.57	344.1	897.99	358.5	960.25	377.9
14	651.88	299.4	679.26	302.5	707.26	306.4	735.87	311.2	765.07	316.8	794.81	323.2	855.85	338.8	918.88	357.4
15	613.85	280.0	641.38	283.3	669.58	287.5	698.43	292.6	727.88	298.6	757.92	305.6	819.63	322.0	883.31	342.0
16	580.59	263.1	608.28	266.6	636.68	271.0	665.75	276.5	695.46	282.9	725.78	290.3	788.11	307.8	852.42	328.9
17	551.27	248.1	579.12	251.8	607.71	256.6	637.01	262.4	666.97	269.2	697.56	277.0	760.48	295.5		
18	525.24	234.9	550.24	238.8	582.02	243.8	611.54	250.0	641.74	257.2	672.60	265.4	736.09	285.0		
19	501.96	223.1	530.12	227.2	559.09	232.5	588.82	239.0	619.26	246.5	650.38	255.2	711.40	275.8		
20	481.03	212.5	509.35	216.2	538.50	221.4	568.44	229.2	599.12	237.1	630.49	246.2	695.03	267.8		
21	462.12	202.9	490.58	207.9	519.91	213.3	550.06	220.4	580.97	228.7	612.58	238.3				
22	444.94	194.2	473.55	199.0	503.07	205.1	533.42	212.6	564.55	221.3	596.39	231.2				
23	429.28	186.3	458.03	191.3	487.72	197.7	518.28	205.5	549.63	214.5	581.69	224.7				
24	414.93	179.1	443.84	184.3	473.70	191.0	504.45	199.0	536.01	208.5	568.28	219.3				
25	401.75	172.5	430.80	177.9	460.84	184.8	491.78	193.2	523.54	203.0	556.02	214.2				

Speed designation markers: 70 mph, 60 mph, 50 mph, 40 mph, 30 mph.

170

TABLE IV

T_s AND E_s   Δ = 110°

D_c	L_s = 150' T_s	E_s	200' T_s	E_s	250' T_s	E_s	300' T_s	E_s	350' T_s	E_s	400' T_s	E_s	500' T_s	E_s	600' T_s	E_s
1-30																
2-00																
2-30																
3-00																
3-30																
4-00																
5	1712.69	853.4	1738.59	854.5	1764.73	855.9	1791.13	857.6	1817.76	859.7	1844.63	862.1	1899.10	867.8	1954.50	874.7
6	1440.17	711.7	1466.24	713.0	1492.61	714.7	1519.26	716.8	1546.21	719.3	1573.45	722.1	1628.75	728.9	1685.15	737.2
7	1245.57	610.5	1271.81	612.1	1298.40	614.1	1325.33	616.5	1352.58	619.4	1380.17	622.7	1436.30	630.6	1493.67	640.3
8	1099.68	534.7	1126.09	536.5	1152.90	538.5	1180.08	541.6	1207.65	544.9	1235.57	548.6	1292.51	557.7	1350.82	568.7
9	986.26	475.2	1012.84	477.9	1039.86	480.4	1067.31	483.5	1095.16	487.2	1123.43	491.5	1181.15	501.7	1240.36	514.1
10	895.56	428.8	922.32	431.0	949.55	433.9	977.25	437.3	1005.41	441.4	1034.00	446.2	1092.47	457.4	1152.57	471.2
11	821.40	390.4	848.32	392.8	875.77	395.9	903.72	399.8	932.16	404.3	961.08	409.4	1020.30	421.8	1081.24	436.9
12	759.63	358.4	786.72	361.0	814.38	364.5	842.57	368.6	871.31	373.5	900.54	379.2	960.48	392.6	1022.23	409.0
13	707.40	331.4	734.66	334.2	762.52	337.9	790.96	342.4	819.97	347.7	849.51	353.8	910.15	368.4	972.67	386.0
14	662.66	308.3	690.08	311.3	718.15	315.3	746.83	320.2	776.11	325.7	805.96	332.4	867.27	348.0	930.54	367.0
15	623.92	288.3	651.50	291.6	679.77	295.8	708.69	301.0	738.24	307.1	768.38	311.1	830.34	330.8	894.32	351.0
16	590.04	270.8	617.79	274.3	646.25	278.9	675.41	284.4	705.22	290.9	735.64	298.3	798.24	316.1	862.87	337.4
17	560.18	255.4	588.08	259.2	616.74	264.0	646.13	269.8	676.19	276.8	706.91	284.6	770.10	303.4		
18	533.66	241.8	561.72	245.7	590.58	250.8	620.18	257.0	650.50	264.3	681.48	272.7	745.27	292.5		
19	509.94	229.6	538.16	233.8	567.21	239.2	597.04	245.7	627.60	253.3	658.85	262.1	723.18	283.0		
20	488.63	218.7	517.00	223.1	546.24	228.7	576.29	235.6	607.09	243.6	638.60	252.9	703.46	274.7		
21	469.36	208.8	497.89	213.4	527.31	219.4	557.57	226.5	588.60	235.0	620.36	244.6				
22	451.86	199.9	480.54	204.7	510.15	210.9	540.62	218.4	571.88	227.2	603.87	237.3				
23	435.90	191.7	464.74	196.8	494.52	203.3	525.11	211.1	556.68	220.1	588.90	230.8				
24	421.29	184.3	450.27	189.6	480.24	196.3	511.11	204.5	542.81	214.1	575.24	225.0				
25	407.86	177.5	436.99	183.0	467.13	190.0	498.20	198.5	530.11	208.4	562.77	219.7				

Design speed annotations (600'/500' region): 70 mph (rows 5–6), 60 mph (rows 6–7), 50 mph (rows 8–10), 40 mph (rows 14–16), 30 mph (500' lower rows).

171

L_s = 150 FT.   TABLE V

FUNCTIONS OF TRANSITIONS
USED IN TABLE IV

D_c	L.C.	S.T.	L.T.	y_c	x_c	k	p	θ_s	D_c
1-30	150.00	50.00	100.00	0.98	149.99	75.00	0.25	1.125	1-30
2-00	150.00	50.00	100.00	1.31	149.99	75.00	0.33	1.5	2-00
2-30	149.99	50.01	100.01	1.64	149.98	75.00	0.41	1.875	2-30
3-00	149.99	50.01	100.01	1.96	149.98	75.00	0.49	2.25	3-00
3-30	149.99	50.01	100.01	2.29	149.97	74.99	0.57	2.625	3-30
4-00	149.98	50.01	100.01	2.62	149.96	74.99	0.65	3.0	4-00
5	149.97	50.02	100.02	3.27	149.94	74.99	0.82	3.75	5
6	149.95	50.03	100.03	3.93	149.91	74.98	0.98	4.5	6
7	149.94	50.04	100.04	4.58	149.87	74.98	1.15	5.25	7
8	149.93	50.05	100.06	5.23	149.83	74.97	1.31	6.0	8
9	149.91	50.07	100.07	5.88	149.79	74.96	1.47	6.75	9
10	149.89	50.08	100.09	6.54	149.74	74.96	1.64	7.5	10
11	149.86	50.10	100.11	7.19	149.69	74.95	1.80	8.25	11
12	149.84	50.12	100.13	7.84	149.63	74.94	1.96	9.0	12
13	149.81	50.14	100.15	8.49	149.57	74.93	2.13	9.75	13
14	149.78	50.16	100.18	9.14	149.50	74.92	2.29	10.5	14
15	149.74	50.18	100.20	9.79	149.42	74.90	2.45	11.25	15
16	149.71	50.21	100.23	10.44	149.34	74.89	2.61	12.0	16
17	149.67	50.24	100.26	11.09	149.26	74.88	2.78	12.75	17
18	149.63	50.27	100.29	11.73	149.17	74.86	2.94	13.5	18
19	149.59	50.30	100.33	12.38	149.07	74.85	3.10	14.25	19
20	149.54	50.33	100.36	13.03	148.98	74.83	3.26	15.0	20
21	149.50	50.36	100.40	13.67	148.87	74.81	3.43	15.75	21
22	149.45	50.40	100.44	14.31	148.76	74.79	3.59	16.5	22
23	149.40	50.44	100.48	14.96	148.65	74.77	3.75	17.25	23
24	149.34	50.47	100.52	15.60	148.53	74.75	3.91	18.0	24
25	149.29	50.52	100.57	16.24	148.40	74.73	4.07	18.75	25

DEFLECTION ANGLES FROM T.S. TO POINTS ON TEN CHORD SPIRAL FOR TRANSITIONS USED IN TABLE IV

$L_s = 150$ FT. TABLE V

D_c	COL. A	10=S.C.	9	8	7	6	5	4	3	2	1	D_c
						TRANSIT ON T.S., SIGHT ON POINT NO.						
1-30		0-22.6	0-18.2	0-14.4	0-11.0	0-08.2	0-05.6	0-03.6	0-02.0	0-01.0	0-00.2	1-30
2-00		0-30.0	24.4	19.2	14.8	10.8	07.6	04.8	02.8	01.2	00.2	2-00
2-30		0-37.6	30.4	24.0	18.4	13.6	09.4	06.0	03.4	01.6	00.4	2-30
3-00		0-45.0	36.6	28.8	22.0	16.2	11.2	07.2	04.0	01.8	00.4	3-00
3-30		0-52.6	42.6	33.6	25.8	19.0	13.2	08.4	04.8	02.2	00.6	3-30
4-00	.02	1-00.0	0-48.6	38.4	29.4	21.6	15.0	09.6	05.4	02.4	00.6	4-00
5	.03	1-15.0	1-00.0	48.0	36.8	27.0	18.8	12.0	06.8	03.0	00.8	5
6	.03	1-30.0	1-13.0	0-57.4	44.2	32.4	22.6	14.4	08.2	03.6	00.8	6
7	.04	1-45.0	1-25.0	1-07.2	51.4	37.8	26.2	16.8	09.4	04.2	01.0	7
8	.04	2-00.0	1-37.4	1-16.8	0-58.8	43.2	30.0	19.2	10.8	04.8	01.2	8
9	.05	2-15.0	1-49.4	1-26.4	1-06.2	48.6	33.8	21.6	12.2	05.4	01.4	9
10	.05	2-30.0	2-01.6	1-36.0	1-13.6	54.0	37.6	24.0	13.6	06.0	01.6	10
11	.06	2-45.0	2-13.8	1-45.6	1-20.8	0-59.4	41.2	26.4	14.8	06.6	01.6	11
12	.07	3-00.0	2-25.8	1-55.6	1-28.2	1-04.8	45.0	28.8	16.2	07.2	01.8	12
13	.07	3-15.0	2-38.0	2-04.8	1-35.6	1-10.2	48.8	31.2	17.6	07.8	02.0	13
14	.08	3-30.0	2-50.2	2-14.4	1-43.0	1-15.6	52.6	33.6	19.0	08.4	02.2	14
15	.08	3-45.0	3-02.4	2-24.0	1-50.4	1-21.0	0-56.4	36.0	20.2	09.0	02.2	15
16	.09	4-00.0	3-14.4	2-33.6	1-57.6	1-26.4	1-00.0	38.4	21.6	09.6	02.4	16
17	.09	4-15.0	3-26.6	2-43.2	2-05.0	1-31.8	1-03.8	40.8	23.0	10.2	02.6	17
18	.10	4-30.0	3-38.8	2-52.8	2-12.4	1-37.2	1-07.6	43.2	24.4	10.8	02.8	18
19	.10	4-45.0	3-50.8	3-02.4	2-19.6	1-42.6	1-11.4	45.6	25.6	11.4	02.8	19
20	.11	5-00.0	4-03.0	3-12.0	2-27.0	1-48.0	1-15.0	48.0	27.0	12.0	03.0	20
21	.12	5-14.8	4-15.0	3-21.6	2-34.4	1-53.4	1-18.8	50.4	28.4	12.6	03.2	21
22	.12	5-29.8	4-27.2	3-31.2	2-41.8	1-58.8	1-22.6	52.8	29.8	13.2	03.4	22
23	.13	5-44.8	4-39.4	3-40.8	2-49.0	2-04.2	1-26.4	0-55.2	31.0	13.8	03.4	23
24	.13	5-59.8	4-51.4	3-50.4	2-56.4	2-09.6	1-30.0	0-57.6	32.4	14.4	03.6	24
25	.14	6-14.8	5-03.6	4-00.0	3-03.8	2-15.0	1-33.8	1-00.0	0-33.8	0-15.0	0-03.8	25

Note: Col. A.

For the deflection angle to a point other than a chord point simple interpolation may be used with no appreciable error provided a correction is made where necessary. The value in column A is the unit amount of this correction in minutes per foot of the distance from the nearest chord point. In all cases the correction should be subtracted from the interpolated result.

L_s = 200 FT. TABLE V

FUNCTIONS OF TRANSITIONS USED IN TABLE IV

D_c	L.C.	S.T.	L.T.	y_c	x_c	k	p	θ_s	D_c
1-30	199.99	66.67	133.34	1.75	199.99	100.00	0.44	1.5	1-30
2-00	199.99	66.67	133.34	2.33	199.98	100.00	0.58	2.0	2-00
2-30	199.98	66.68	133.35	2.91	199.96	99.99	0.73	2.5	2-30
3-00	199.98	66.68	133.35	3.49	199.95	99.99	0.87	3.0	3-00
3-30	199.97	66.69	133.36	4.07	199.93	99.99	1.02	3.5	3-30
4-00	199.96	66.70	133.37	4.65	199.90	99.98	1.16	4	4-00
5	199.93	66.72	133.39	5.81	199.85	99.97	1.45	5	5
6	199.90	66.74	133.41	6.98	199.78	99.96	1.74	6	6
7	199.87	66.76	133.44	8.14	199.70	99.95	2.04	7	7
8	199.83	66.79	133.47	9.30	199.61	99.93	2.33	8	8
9	199.78	66.82	133.51	10.45	199.51	99.92	2.62	9	9
10	199.73	66.86	133.55	11.61	199.39	99.90	2.91	10	10
11	199.67	66.90	133.59	12.77	199.26	99.88	3.20	11	11
12	199.61	66.95	133.64	13.92	199.12	99.85	3.49	12	12
13	199.54	67.00	133.69	15.07	198.97	99.83	3.77	13	13
14	199.47	67.05	133.75	16.22	198.81	99.80	4.06	14	14
15	199.39	67.11	133.82	17.37	198.63	99.77	4.35	15	15
16	199.31	67.17	133.88	18.51	198.45	99.74	4.64	16	16
17	199.22	67.23	133.95	19.66	198.25	99.71	4.93	17	17
18	199.12	67.30	134.03	20.80	198.04	99.67	5.22	18	18
19	199.02	67.37	134.11	21.93	197.81	99.63	5.50	19	19
20	198.92	67.45	134.19	23.07	197.58	99.60	5.79	20	20
21	198.81	67.53	134.28	24.20	197.33	99.55	6.08	21	21
22	198.69	67.62	134.38	25.33	197.07	99.51	6.37	22	22
23	198.57	67.71	134.48	26.46	196.80	99.47	6.65	23	23
24	198.44	67.80	134.58	27.58	196.52	99.42	6.94	24	24
25	198.31	67.90	134.69	28.70	196.23	99.37	7.22	25	25

Deflection Angles from T.S. to Points on Ten Chord Spiral for Transitions Used in Table IV

$L_s = 200$ FT. Table V

TRANSIT ON T.S., SIGHT ON POINT NO.

D_c	COL. A	10 = S.C.	9	8	7	6	5	4	3	2	1	D_c
1-30		0-30.0	0-24.4	0-19.2	0-14.8	0-10.8	0-07.6	0-04.8	0-02.8	0-01.2	0-00.2	1-30
2-00		0-40.0	32.4	25.6	19.6	14.4	10.0	06.4	03.6	01.6	00.4	2-00
2-30		0-50.0	40.6	32.0	24.6	18.0	12.6	08.0	04.6	02.0	00.6	2-30
3-00		1-00.0	48.6	38.4	29.4	21.6	15.0	09.6	05.4	02.4	00.6	3-00
3-30		1-10.0	0-56.8	44.8	34.4	25.2	17.6	11.2	06.4	02.8	00.8	3-30
4-00	.02	1-20.0	1-04.8	0-51.2	39.2	28.8	20.0	12.8	07.2	03.2	00.8	4-00
5	.03	1-40.0	1-21.0	1-04.0	49.0	36.0	25.0	16.0	09.0	04.0	01.0	5
6	.03	2-00.0	1-37.2	1-16.8	0-58.8	43.2	30.0	19.2	10.8	04.8	01.2	6
7	.04	2-20.0	1-53.4	1-29.6	1-08.6	50.4	35.0	22.4	12.6	05.6	01.4	7
8	.04	2-40.0	2-09.6	1-42.4	1-18.4	0-57.6	40.0	25.6	14.4	06.4	01.6	8
9	.05	3-00.0	2-25.8	1-55.2	1-28.2	1-04.8	45.0	28.8	16.2	07.2	01.8	9
10	.05	3-20.0	2-42.0	2-08.0	1-38.0	1-12.0	50.0	32.0	18.0	08.0	02.0	10
11	.06	3-40.0	2-58.2	2-20.8	1-47.8	1-19.2	0-55.0	35.2	19.8	08.8	02.2	11
12	.07	4-00.0	3-14.4	2-33.6	1-57.6	1-26.4	1-00.0	38.4	21.6	09.6	02.4	12
13	.07	4-20.0	3-30.6	2-46.4	2-07.4	1-33.6	1-05.0	41.6	23.4	10.4	02.6	13
14	.08	4-40.0	3-46.8	2-59.2	2-17.2	1-40.8	1-10.0	44.8	25.2	11.2	02.8	14
15	.08	4-59.8	4-03.0	3-12.0	2-27.0	1-48.0	1-15.0	48.0	27.0	12.0	03.0	15
16	.09	5-19.8	4-19.2	3-24.8	2-36.8	1-55.2	1-20.0	51.2	28.8	12.8	03.2	16
17	.09	5-39.8	4-35.4	3-37.6	2-46.6	2-02.4	1-25.0	54.4	30.6	13.6	03.4	17
18	.10	5-59.8	4-51.4	3-50.4	2-56.4	2-09.6	1-30.0	0-57.6	32.4	14.4	03.6	18
19	.10	6-19.8	5-07.6	4-03.2	3-06.2	2-16.8	1-35.0	1-00.8	34.2	15.2	03.8	19
20	.11	6-39.6	5-23.8	4-16.0	3-16.0	2-24.0	1-40.0	1-04.0	36.0	16.0	04.0	20
21	.12	6-59.6	5-40.0	4-28.8	3-25.8	2-31.2	1-45.0	1-07.2	37.8	16.8	04.2	21
22	.12	7-19.6	5-56.2	4-41.6	3-35.6	2-38.4	1-50.0	1-10.4	39.6	17.6	04.4	22
23	.13	7-39.4	6-12.4	4-54.2	3-45.4	2-45.6	1-55.0	1-13.6	41.4	18.4	04.6	23
24	.13	7-59.4	6-28.4	5-07.0	3-55.2	2-52.8	2-00.0	1-16.8	43.2	19.2	04.8	24
25	.14	8-19.2	6-44.6	5-19.8	4-05.0	3-00.0	2-05.0	1-20.0	0-45.0	0-20.0	0-05.0	25

L$_s$ = 250 FT. TABLE V

FUNCTIONS OF TRANSITIONS
USED IN TABLE IV

D$_c$	L.C.	S.T.	L.T.	y$_c$	x$_c$	k	p	θ$_s$	D$_c$
1-30	249.99	83.34	166.68	2.73	249.97	124.99	0.68	1.875	1-30
2-00	249.98	83.35	166.68	3.64	249.95	124.99	0.91	2.5	2-00
2-30	249.97	83.36	166.69	4.54	249.93	124.99	1.13	3.125	2-30
3-00	249.95	83.37	166.70	5.45	249.89	124.98	1.36	3.75	3-00
3-30	249.94	83.38	166.72	6.36	249.85	124.98	1.59	4.375	3-30
4-00	249.92	83.39	166.73	7.27	249.81	124.97	1.82	5.0	4-00
5	249.87	83.43	166.77	9.08	249.70	124.95	2.27	6.25	5
6	249.81	83.47	166.82	10.90	249.57	124.93	2.73	7.5	6
7	249.74	83.52	166.87	12.70	249.42	124.90	3.18	8.75	7
8	249.66	83.58	166.93	14.51	249.24	124.87	3.63	10.0	8
9	249.57	83.64	167.00	16.32	249.04	124.84	4.09	11.25	9
10	249.47	83.71	167.08	18.12	248.81	124.80	4.54	12.5	10
11	249.36	83.79	167.17	19.92	248.56	124.76	4.99	13.75	11
12	249.24	83.88	167.27	21.71	248.29	124.72	5.44	15.0	12
13	249.11	83.98	167.37	23.50	248.00	124.67	5.89	16.25	13
14	248.96	84.08	167.49	25.28	247.68	124.61	6.34	17.5	14
15	248.81	84.19	167.61	27.06	247.34	124.56	6.79	18.75	15
16	248.65	84.31	167.74	28.84	246.97	124.50	7.24	20.0	16
17	248.47	84.44	167.88	30.61	246.58	124.43	7.69	21.25	17
18	248.29	84.58	168.03	32.36	246.17	124.36	8.14	22.5	18
19	248.10	84.72	168.19	34.12	245.74	124.29	8.58	23.75	19
20	247.89	84.87	168.36	35.87	245.28	124.21	9.03	25.0	20
21	247.68	85.04	168.54	37.61	244.80	124.13	9.47	26.25	21
22	247.45	85.21	168.72	39.34	244.30	124.04	9.92	27.5	22
23	247.21	85.38	168.92	41.07	243.78	123.96	10.36	28.75	23
24	246.97	85.57	169.12	42.79	243.23	123.86	10.80	30.0	24
25	246.71	85.77	169.34	44.49	242.66	123.77	11.24	31.25	25

DEFLECTION ANGLES FROM T.S. TO POINTS ON TEN CHORD SPIRAL FOR TRANSITIONS USED IN TABLE IV

L_s = 250 FT. — TABLE V

D_c	COL. A	10=S.C.	9	8	7	6	5	4	3	2	1	D_c
					TRANSIT ON T.S., SIGHT ON POINT NO.							
1-30		0-37.6	0-30.4	0-24.0	0-18.4	0-13.6	0-09.4	0-06.0	0-03.4	0-01.6	0-00.4	1-30
2-00		0-50.0	0-40.6	32.0	24.6	18.0	12.6	08.0	04.6	02.0	00.6	2-00
2-30		1-02.6	0-50.6	40.0	30.6	22.6	15.6	10.0	05.6	02.6	00.6	2-30
3-00		1-15.0	1-00.8	48.0	36.8	27.0	18.8	12.0	06.8	03.0	00.8	3-00
3-30	.02	1-27.6	1-11.0	0-56.0	43.0	31.6	22.0	14.0	08.0	03.6	01.0	3-30
4-00		1-40.0	1-21.0	1-04.0	0-49.0	36.0	25.0	16.0	09.0	04.0	01.0	4-00
5	.03	2-05.0	1-41.2	1-20.0	1-01.2	45.0	31.2	20.0	11.2	05.0	01.2	5
6	.03	2-30.0	2-01.6	1-36.0	1-13.6	0-54.0	37.6	24.0	13.6	06.0	01.6	6
7	.04	2-55.0	2-21.8	1-52.0	1-25.8	1-03.0	43.8	28.0	15.8	07.0	01.8	7
8	.04	3-20.0	2-42.0	2-08.0	1-38.0	1-12.0	50.0	32.0	18.0	08.0	02.0	8
9	.05	3-45.0	3-02.2	2-24.0	1-50.2	1-21.0	0-56.2	36.0	20.2	09.0	02.2	9
10	.05	4-10.0	3-22.6	2-40.0	2-02.6	1-30.0	1-02.6	40.0	22.6	10.0	02.6	10
11	.06	4-35.0	3-42.8	2-56.0	2-14.8	1-39.0	1-08.8	44.0	24.8	11.0	02.8	11
12	.07	4-59.8	4-03.0	3-12.0	2-27.0	1-48.0	1-15.0	48.0	27.0	12.0	03.0	12
13	.07	5-24.8	4-23.2	3-28.0	2-39.2	1-57.0	1-21.2	52.0	29.2	13.0	03.2	13
14	.08	5-49.8	4-43.4	3-44.0	2-51.6	2-06.0	1-27.6	0-56.0	31.6	14.0	03.6	14
15	.08	6-14.8	5-03.6	4-00.0	3-03.0	2-15.0	1-33.8	1-00.0	33.8	15.0	03.8	15
16	.09	6-39.6	5-23.8	4-16.0	3-16.0	2-24.0	1-40.0	1-04.0	36.0	16.0	04.0	16
17	.09	7-04.6	5-44.0	4-32.0	3-28.2	2-33.0	1-46.2	1-08.0	38.2	17.0	04.2	17
18	.10	7-29.6	6-04.2	4-48.0	3-40.4	2-42.0	1-52.6	1-12.0	40.6	18.0	04.6	18
19	.10	7-54.4	6-24.6	5-03.8	3-52.8	2-51.0	1-58.8	1-16.0	42.8	19.0	04.8	19
20	.11	8-19.2	6-44.6	5-19.8	4-05.0	3-00.0	2-05.0	1-20.0	45.0	20.0	05.0	20
21	.12	8-44.2	7-04.8	5-35.8	4-17.2	3-09.0	2-11.2	1-24.0	47.2	21.0	05.2	21
22	.12	9-09.0	7-25.0	5-51.8	4-29.4	3-18.0	2-17.6	1-28.0	49.6	22.0	05.6	22
23	.13	9-33.8	7-45.2	6-07.8	4-41.8	3-27.0	2-23.8	1-32.0	51.8	23.0	05.8	23
24	.13	9-58.6	8-05.4	6-23.8	4-53.2	3-36.0	2-30.0	1-36.0	54.0	24.0	06.0	24
25	.14	10-23.4	8-25.4	6-39.6	5-06.0	3-45.0	2-36.2	1-40.0	0-56.2	0-25.0	0-06.2	25

$L_s = 300$ ft. Table V

Functions of Transitions
Used in Table IV

D_c	L.C.	S.T.	L.T.	y_c	x_c	k	p	θ_s	D_c
1-30	299.98	100.01	200.02	3.93	299.95	149.99	0.98	2.25	1-30
2-00	299.96	100.03	200.03	5.24	299.92	149.99	1.30	3.0	2-00
2-30	299.94	100.04	200.04	6.54	299.87	149.98	1.63	3.75	2-30
3-00	299.92	100.06	200.06	7.85	299.81	149.97	1.96	4.5	3-00
3-30	299.89	100.08	200.09	9.16	299.75	149.96	2.29	5.25	3-30
4-00	299.85	100.10	200.11	10.46	299.67	149.95	2.62	6.0	4-00
5	299.77	100.16	200.18	13.07	299.49	149.91	3.27	7.5	5
6	299.67	100.24	200.26	15.68	299.26	149.88	3.92	9.0	6
7	299.55	100.32	200.35	18.28	298.99	149.83	4.58	10.5	7
8	299.42	100.42	200.46	20.88	298.69	149.78	5.23	12.0	8
9	299.26	100.53	200.58	23.47	298.34	149.72	5.88	13.5	9
10	299.09	100.66	200.72	26.05	297.95	149.66	6.53	15.0	10
11	298.90	100.80	200.88	28.63	297.52	149.59	7.18	16.5	11
12	298.69	100.95	201.04	31.19	297.05	149.51	7.82	18.0	12
13	298.46	101.12	201.23	33.75	296.54	149.42	8.47	19.5	13
14	298.21	101.30	201.43	36.30	296.00	149.33	9.12	21.0	14
15	297.95	101.49	201.64	38.84	295.41	149.23	9.76	22.5	15
16	297.67	101.70	201.87	41.37	294.78	149.13	10.41	24.0	16
17	297.37	101.93	202.12	43.88	294.11	149.01	11.05	25.5	17
18	297.05	102.16	202.38	46.38	293.41	148.90	11.69	27.0	18
19	296.71	102.42	202.66	48.87	292.66	148.77	12.32	28.5	19
20	296.36	102.69	202.95	51.34	291.88	148.64	12.96	30.0	20
21	295.99	102.97	203.26	53.80	291.06	148.50	13.60	31.5	21
22	295.60	103.27	203.59	56.24	290.20	148.36	14.23	33.0	22
23	295.19	103.59	203.94	58.67	289.30	148.20	14.86	34.5	23
24	294.77	103.92	204.30	61.08	288.37	148.05	15.49	36.0	24
25	294.33	104.27	204.68	63.47	287.40	147.88	16.11	37.5	25

DEFLECTION ANGLES FROM T.S. TO POINTS ON TEN CHORD SPIRAL FOR TRANSITIONS USED IN TABLE IV

L = 300 FT. TABLE V

Dc	COL A	10=S.C.	9	8	7	6	5	4	3	2	1	Dc
						TRANSIT ON T.S. SIGHT ON POINT NO.						
1-30		0-45.0	0-36.6	0-28.8	0-22.0	0-16.2	0-11.2	0-07.2	0-04.0	0-01.8	0-00.4	1-30
2-00		1-00.0	0-48.6	38.4	29.4	21.6	15.0	09.6	05.4	02.4	00.6	2-00
2-30		1-15.0	1-00.8	48.0	36.8	27.0	18.8	12.0	06.8	03.0	00.8	2-30
3-00		1-30.0	1-13.0	0-57.6	44.2	32.4	22.6	14.4	08.2	03.6	01.0	3-00
3-30		1-45.0	1-25.0	1-07.2	51.4	37.8	26.2	16.8	09.4	04.2	01.0	3-30
4-00	.02	2-00.0	1-37.2	1-16.8	0-58.8	43.2	30.0	19.2	10.8	04.8	01.2	4-00
5	.03	2-30.0	2-01.6	1-36.0	1-13.6	0-54.0	37.6	24.0	13.6	06.0	01.6	5
6	.03	3-00.0	2-25.8	1-55.2	1-28.2	1-04.8	45.0	28.8	16.2	07.2	01.8	6
7	.04	3-30.0	2-50.2	2-14.4	1-43.0	1-15.6	0-52.6	33.6	19.0	08.4	02.2	7
8	.04	4-00.0	3-14.4	2-33.6	1-57.6	1-26.4	1-00.0	38.4	21.6	09.6	02.4	8
9	.05	4-30.0	3-38.8	2-52.8	2-12.4	1-37.2	1-07.6	43.2	24.4	10.8	02.8	9
10	.05	4-59.8	4-03.0	3-12.0	2-27.0	1-48.0	1-15.0	48.0	27.0	12.0	03.0	10
11	.06	5-29.8	4-27.2	3-31.2	2-41.8	1-58.8	1-22.6	52.8	29.8	13.2	03.4	11
12	.07	5-59.8	4-51.4	3-50.4	2-56.4	2-09.6	1-30.0	0-57.6	32.4	14.4	03.6	12
13	.07	6-29.6	5-15.8	4-09.6	3-11.2	2-20.4	1-37.6	1-02.4	35.2	15.6	04.0	13
14	.08	6-59.6	5-40.0	4-28.8	3-25.8	2-31.2	1-45.0	1-07.2	37.8	16.8	04.2	14
15	.08	7-29.4	6-04.2	4-48.0	3-40.4	2-42.0	1-52.6	1-12.0	40.6	18.0	04.6	15
16	.09	7-59.4	6-28.6	5-07.0	3-55.2	2-52.8	2-00.0	1-16.8	43.2	19.2	04.8	16
17	.09	8-29.2	6-52.8	5-26.2	4-09.8	3-03.6	2-07.6	1-21.6	46.0	20.4	05.2	17
18	.10	8-59.0	7-17.0	5-45.4	4-24.6	3-14.4	2-15.0	1-26.4	48.6	21.6	05.4	18
19	.10	9-28.8	7-41.2	6-04.6	4-39.2	3-25.2	2-22.6	1-31.2	51.4	22.8	05.8	19
20	.11	9-58.6	8-05.4	6-23.8	4-53.8	3-36.0	2-30.0	1-36.0	54.0	24.0	06.0	20
21	.12	10-28.4	8-29.4	6-42.8	5-08.6	3-46.8	2-37.6	1-40.8	0-56.8	25.2	06.4	21
22	.12	10-58.2	8-53.6	7-02.0	5-23.2	3-57.6	2-45.0	1-45.6	0-59.4	26.4	06.6	22
23	.13	11-28.0	9-17.8	7-21.2	5-38.0	4-08.4	2-52.6	1-50.4	1-02.2	27.6	07.0	23
24	.13	11-57.6	9-42.0	7-40.2	5-52.6	4-19.2	3-00.0	1-55.2	1-04.8	28.8	07.2	24
25	.14	12-27.2	10-06.2	7-59.4	6-07.2	4-30.0	3-07.6	2-00.0	1-07.6	0-30.0	0-07.6	25

L_s= 350 FT. TABLE V

FUNCTIONS OF TRANSITIONS
USED IN TABLE IV

D_c	L.C.	S.T.	L.T.	y_c	x_c	k	p	θ_s	D_c
1-30	349.97	116.69	233.36	5.34	349.93	174.99	1.33	2.625	1-30
2-00	349.94	116.71	233.38	7.13	349.87	174.98	1.78	3.5	2-00
2-30	349.91	116.73	233.40	8.91	349.80	174.97	2.22	4.375	2-30
3-00	349.87	116.76	233.44	10.68	349.71	174.95	2.67	5.25	3-00
3-30	349.82	116.79	233.47	12.46	349.60	174.93	3.12	6.125	3-30
4-00	349.77	116.83	233.52	14.24	349.48	174.91	3.56	7.0	4-00
5	349.64	116.93	233.62	17.79	349.18	174.86	4.45	8.75	5
6	349.48	117.04	233.75	21.33	348.83	174.80	5.34	10.5	6
7	349.29	117.18	233.89	24.86	348.40	174.73	6.23	12.25	7
8	349.07	117.33	234.07	28.38	347.92	174.65	7.11	14.0	8
9	348.83	117.51	234.26	31.90	347.36	174.56	7.99	15.75	9
10	348.55	117.71	234.48	35.40	346.75	174.46	8.88	17.5	10
11	348.25	117.94	234.73	38.88	346.07	174.34	9.76	19.25	11
12	347.91	118.18	235.00	42.35	345.33	174.22	10.64	21.0	12
13	347.55	118.45	235.29	45.80	344.52	174.09	11.52	22.75	13
14	347.16	118.74	235.61	49.24	343.65	173.94	12.39	24.5	14
15	346.75	119.05	235.95	52.65	342.72	173.78	13.26	26.25	15
16	346.30	119.39	236.32	56.05	341.73	173.62	14.13	28.0	16
17	345.82	119.75	236.72	59.42	340.68	173.44	15.00	29.75	17
18	345.32	120.13	237.14	62.77	339.57	173.25	15.86	31.5	18
19	344.79	120.54	237.59	66.09	338.39	173.05	16.72	33.25	19
20	344.23	120.98	238.06	69.39	337.16	172.85	17.58	35.0	20
21	343.64	121.44	238.57	72.66	335.87	172.63	18.43	36.75	21
22	343.03	121.93	239.10	75.90	334.52	172.40	19.28	38.5	22
23	342.38	122.44	239.67	79.11	333.12	172.16	20.13	40.25	23
24	341.71	122.99	240.26	82.30	331.66	171.91	20.98	42.0	24
25	341.01	123.56	240.88	85.44	330.14	171.65	21.81	43.75	25

DEFLECTION ANGLES FROM T.S. TO POINTS ON TEN CHORD SPIRAL FOR TRANSITIONS USED IN TABLE IV

L_s = 350 FT. TABLE V

Dc	COL. A	10=S.C.	9	8	7	6	5	4	3	2	1	Dc
1-30		0-52.6	0-42.6	0-33.6	0-25.8	0-19.0	0-13.2	0-08.4	0-04.8	0-02.2	0-00.6	1-30
2-00		1-10.0	0-56.8	0-44.8	34.4	25.2	17.6	11.2	06.4	02.8	00.8	2-00
2-30		1-27.6	1-11.0	0-56.0	43.0	31.6	22.0	14.0	08.0	03.6	01.0	2-30
3-00		1-45.0	1-25.0	1-07.2	0-51.4	37.8	26.2	16.8	09.6	04.2	01.0	3-00
3-30		2-02.6	1-39.2	1-18.4	1-00.0	44.2	30.6	19.6	11.0	05.0	01.2	3-30
4-00	.02	2-20.0	1-53.4	1-29.6	1-08.6	0-50.4	35.0	22.4	12.6	05.6	01.4	4-00
5	.03	2-55.0	2-21.8	1-52.0	1-25.8	1-03.0	43.8	28.0	15.8	07.0	01.8	5
6	.03	3-30.0	2-50.2	2-14.4	1-43.0	1-15.6	0-52.6	33.6	19.0	08.4	02.2	6
7	.04	4-05.0	3-18.4	2-36.8	2-00.0	1-28.2	1-01.2	39.2	22.0	09.8	02.4	7
8	.04	4-40.0	3-46.8	2-59.2	2-17.2	1-40.8	1-10.0	44.8	25.2	11.2	02.8	8
9	.05	5-14.8	4-15.2	3-21.6	2-34.4	1-53.4	1-18.8	50.4	28.4	12.6	03.2	9
10	.05	5-47.8	4-43.4	3-44.0	2-51.6	2-06.0	1-27.6	0-56.0	31.6	14.0	03.6	10
11	.06	6-24.8	5-11.6	4-06.4	3-08.6	2-18.6	1-36.2	1-01.6	34.6	15.4	03.8	11
12	.07	6-59.6	5-40.0	4-28.8	3-25.8	2-31.2	1-45.0	1-07.2	37.8	16.8	04.2	12
13	.07	7-34.4	6-08.2	4-51.0	3-43.0	2-43.8	1-53.8	1-12.8	41.0	18.2	04.6	13
14	.08	8-09.4	6-36.6	5-13.4	4-00.0	2-56.4	2-02.6	1-18.4	44.2	19.6	05.0	14
15	.08	8-44.2	7-04.8	5-35.8	4-17.2	3-09.0	2-11.2	1-24.0	47.2	21.0	05.2	15
16	.09	9-19.0	7-33.0	5-58.2	4-34.4	3-21.6	2-20.0	1-29.6	50.4	22.4	05.6	16
17	.09	9-53.6	8-01.4	6-20.6	4-51.4	3-34.2	2-28.8	1-35.2	53.6	23.8	06.0	17
18	.10	10-28.4	8-29.4	6-42.8	5-08.6	3-46.8	2-37.6	1-40.8	56.8	25.2	06.4	18
19	.10	11-03.2	8-57.6	7-05.2	5-25.6	3-59.4	2-46.2	1-46.4	0-59.8	26.6	06.6	19
20	.11	11-37.8	9-25.8	7-27.6	5-42.8	4-12.0	2-55.0	1-52.0	1-03.0	28.0	07.0	20
21	.12	12-12.4	9-54.0	7-49.8	6-00.0	4-24.6	3-03.8	1-57.6	1-06.2	29.4	07.4	21
22	.12	12-47.0	10-22.2	8-12.0	6-17.0	4-37.2	3-12.6	2-03.2	1-09.4	30.8	07.8	22
23	.13	13-21.6	10-50.2	8-34.4	6-34.0	4-49.6	3-21.2	2-08.8	1-12.4	32.2	08.0	23
24	.13	13-56.2	11-18.4	8-56.6	6-51.2	5-02.2	3-30.0	2-14.4	1-15.6	33.6	08.4	24
25	.14	14-30.6	11-46.4	9-19.0	7-08.4	5-14.8	3-38.8	2-20.0	1-18.8	0-35.0	0-08.8	25

TRANSIT ON T.S., SIGHT ON POINT NO.

L$_s$= 400 FT. TABLE V

FUNCTIONS OF TRANSITIONS
USED IN TABLE IV

Dc	L.C.	S.T.	L.T.	yc	xc	k	p	Θs	Dc
1-30	399.95	133.37	266.71	6.98	399.89	199.98	1.74	3.0	1-30
2-00	399.91	133.40	266.73	9.30	399.80	199.97	2.32	4.0	2-00
2-30	399.86	133.43	266.77	11.63	399.70	199.95	2.91	5.0	2-30
3-00	399.80	133.47	266.82	13.95	399.56	199.93	3.49	6.0	3-00
3-30	399.73	133.52	266.88	16.27	399.40	199.90	4.07	7.0	3-30
4-00	399.65	133.58	266.94	18.59	399.22	199.87	4.65	8.0	4-00
5	399.46	133.72	267.09	23.22	398.78	199.80	5.81	10.0	5
6	399.22	133.89	267.28	27.84	398.25	199.71	6.97	12.0	6
7	398.94	134.10	267.51	32.44	397.62	199.60	8.13	14.0	7
8	398.62	134.33	267.76	37.03	396.89	199.48	9.28	16.0	8
9	398.25	134.60	268.06	41.59	396.07	199.34	10.43	18.0	9
10	397.84	134.90	268.39	46.14	395.15	199.19	11.58	20.0	10
11	397.39	135.23	268.76	50.66	394.14	199.02	12.73	22.0	11
12	396.89	135.60	269.16	55.16	393.04	198.84	13.88	24.0	12
13	396.35	136.00	269.60	59.62	391.84	198.63	15.01	26.0	13
14	395.77	136.44	270.08	64.06	390.55	198.42	16.15	28.0	14
15	395.15	136.92	270.60	68.46	389.17	198.18	17.28	30.0	15
16	394.48	137.43	271.16	72.82	387.70	197.94	18.41	32.0	16
17	393.77	137.97	271.76	77.15	386.14	197.68	19.53	34.0	17
18	393.03	138.56	272.40	81.44	384.50	197.40	20.65	36.0	18
19	392.24	139.18	273.08	85.69	382.76	197.10	21.76	38.0	19
20	391.40	139.85	273.81	89.89	380.94	196.80	22.87	40.0	20
21	390.53	140.56	274.58	94.05	379.04	196.47	23.97	42.0	21
22	389.61	141.31	275.40	98.16	377.05	196.13	25.07	44.0	22
23	388.66	142.10	276.27	102.22	374.98	195.78	26.15	46.0	23
24	387.66	142.94	277.18	106.22	372.82	195.41	27.23	48.0	24
25	386.63	143.83	278.14	110.18	370.59	195.03	28.31	50.0	25

| | DEFLECTION ANGLES FROM T.S. TO POINTS ON TEN CHORD SPIRAL FOR TRANSITIONS USED IN TABLE IV | | | | | | | | | | | Lₛ = 400 FT. TABLE V |

DEFLECTION ANGLES FROM T.S. TO POINTS ON TEN CHORD SPIRAL FOR TRANSITIONS USED IN TABLE IV — $L_s = 400$ FT. — **TABLE V**

Dc	COL. A	10=S.C.	9	8	7	6	5	4	3	2	1	Dc
				TRANSIT ON T.S., SIGHT ON POINT NO.								
1-30		1-00.0	0-48.6	0-38.4	0-29.4	0-21.6	0-15.0	0-09.6	0-05.4	0-02.4	0-00.6	1-30
2-00		1-20.0	1-04.8	0-51.2	0-39.2	28.8	20.0	12.8	07.2	03.2	00.8	2-00
2-30		1-40.0	1-21.0	1-04.0	0-49.0	36.0	25.0	16.0	09.0	04.0	01.0	2-30
3-00		2-00.0	1-37.2	1-16.8	0-58.8	43.2	30.0	19.2	10.8	04.8	01.2	3-00
3-30		2-20.0	1-53.4	1-29.6	1-08.6	50.4	35.0	22.4	12.6	05.6	01.4	3-30
4-00	.02	2-40.0	2-09.6	1-42.4	1-18.4	0-57.6	40.0	25.6	14.4	06.4	01.6	4-00
5	.03	3-20.0	2-42.0	2-08.0	1-38.0	1-12.0	0-50.0	32.0	18.0	08.0	02.0	5
6	.03	4-00.0	3-14.4	2-33.6	1-57.6	1-26.4	1-00.0	38.4	21.6	09.6	02.4	6
7	.04	4-40.0	3-46.8	2-59.2	2-17.2	1-40.8	1-10.0	44.8	25.2	11.2	02.8	7
8	.04	5-19.8	4-19.2	3-24.8	2-36.8	1-55.2	1-20.0	51.2	28.8	12.8	03.2	8
9	.05	5-59.8	4-51.4	3-50.4	2-56.4	2-09.6	1-30.0	0-57.6	32.4	14.4	03.6	9
10	.05	6-39.6	5-23.8	4-16.0	3-16.0	2-24.0	1-40.0	1-04.0	36.0	16.0	04.0	10
11	.06	7-19.6	5-56.2	4-41.6	3-35.6	2-38.4	1-50.0	1-10.4	39.6	17.6	04.4	11
12	.07	7-59.4	6-28.6	5-07.0	3-55.2	2-52.8	2-00.0	1-16.8	43.2	19.2	04.8	12
13	.07	8-39.2	7-00.8	5-32.6	4-14.8	3-07.2	2-10.0	1-23.2	46.8	20.8	05.2	13
14	.08	9-19.0	7-33.0	5-58.2	4-34.4	3-21.6	2-20.0	1-29.6	50.4	22.4	05.6	14
15	.08	9-58.6	8-05.4	6-23.8	4-53.8	3-36.0	2-30.0	1-36.0	54.0	24.0	06.0	15
16	.09	10-38.4	8-37.6	6-49.2	5-13.4	3-50.4	2-40.0	1-42.4	0-57.6	25.6	06.4	16
17	.09	11-18.0	9-09.8	7-14.8	5-33.0	4-04.8	2-50.0	1-48.8	1-01.2	27.2	06.8	17
18	.10	11-57.6	9-42.0	7-40.2	5-52.6	4-19.2	3-00.0	1-55.2	1-04.8	28.8	07.2	18
19	.10	12-37.2	10-14.2	8-05.8	6-12.2	4-33.6	3-10.0	2-01.6	1-08.4	30.4	07.6	19
20	.11	13-16.8	10-46.2	8-31.2	6-31.6	4-48.0	3-20.0	2-08.0	1-12.0	32.0	08.0	20
21	.12	13-56.2	11-18.4	8-56.6	6-51.2	5-02.2	3-30.0	2-14.4	1-15.6	33.6	08.4	21
22	.12	14-35.6	11-50.4	9-22.2	7-10.8	5-16.6	3-40.0	2-20.8	1-19.2	35.2	08.8	22
23	.13	15-15.0	12-22.6	9-47.6	7-30.2	5-31.0	3-50.0	2-27.2	1-22.8	36.8	09.2	23
24	.13	15-54.2	12-54.6	10-13.0	7-49.8	5-45.4	4-00.0	2-33.6	1-26.4	38.4	09.6	24
25	.14	16-33.4	13-26.4	10-38.4	8-09.2	5-59.8	4-10.0	2-40.0	1-30.0	0-40.0	0-10.0	25

L_s = 500 FT.   TABLE V

FUNCTIONS OF TRANSITIONS
USED IN TABLE IV

D_c	L.C.	S.T.	L.T.	y_c	x_c	k	p	θ_s	D_c
1-30	499.90	166.74	333.41	10.90	499.78	249.96	2.72	3.75	1-30
2-00	499.83	166.79	333.47	14.54	499.62	249.94	3.64	5.0	2-00
2-30	499.73	166.86	333.54	18.16	499.40	249.90	4.54	6.25	2-30
3-00	499.62	166.94	333.63	21.79	499.14	249.86	5.46	7.5	3-00
3-30	499.48	167.04	333.74	25.41	498.84	249.80	6.36	8.75	3-30
4-00	499.32	167.15	333.87	29.02	498.48	249.74	7.26	10.0	4-00
5	498.94	167.43	334.17	36.24	497.62	249.60	9.08	12.5	5
6	498.48	167.76	334.54	43.42	496.58	249.43	10.88	15.0	6
7	497.93	168.16	334.98	50.56	495.36	249.22	12.68	17.5	7
8	497.30	168.63	335.49	57.68	493.94	248.99	14.48	20.0	8
9	496.58	169.15	336.07	64.73	492.34	248.72	16.27	22.5	9
10	495.78	169.75	336.72	71.74	490.56	248.42	18.06	25.0	10
11	494.90	170.41	337.45	78.69	488.60	248.09	19.84	27.5	11
12	493.93	171.14	338.25	85.57	486.46	247.73	21.60	30.0	12
13	492.89	171.95	339.13	92.39	484.15	247.34	23.36	32.5	13
14	491.76	172.83	340.09	99.13	481.66	246.92	25.12	35.0	14
15	490.55	173.78	341.14	105.79	479.00	246.48	26.86	37.5	15
16	489.25	174.81	342.26	112.36	476.18	246.00	28.59	40.0	16
17	487.88	175.92	343.48	118.86	473.18	245.48	30.30	42.5	17
18	486.43	177.12	344.78	125.24	470.02	244.95	32.02	45.0	18
19	484.89	178.41	346.18	131.53	466.71	244.38	33.70	47.5	19
20	483.28	179.78	347.68	137.72	463.24	243.79	35.39	50.0	20

DEFLECTION ANGLES FROM T.S. TO POINTS ON TEN CHORD SPIRAL FOR TRANSITIONS USED IN TABLE IV

L_s = 500 FT. — TABLE V

D_c	COL. A	10=S.C.	9	8	7	6	5	4	3	2.	1	D_c
				TRANSIT ON T.S. SIGHT ON POINT NO.								
1-30		1-15.0	1-00.8	0-48.0	0-36.8	0-27.0	0-18.8	0-12.0	0-06.8	0-03.0	0-00.8	1-30
2-00		1-40.0	1-21.0	1-04.0	0-49.0	0-36.0	25.0	16.0	09.0	04.0	01.0	2-00
2-30		2-05.0	1-41.2	1-20.0	1-01.2	0-45.0	31.2	20.0	11.2	05.0	01.2	2-30
3-00		2-30.0	2-01.6	1-36.0	1-13.6	0-54.0	37.6	24.0	13.6	06.0	01.6	3-00
3-30	.02	2-55.0	2-21.8	1-52.0	1-25.8	1-03.0	43.8	28.0	15.8	07.0	01.8	3-30
4-00		3-20.0	2-42.0	2-08.0	1-38.0	1-12.0	0-50.0	32.0	18.0	08.0	02.0	4-00
5	.03	4-10.0	3-22.6	2-40.0	2-02.6	1-30.0	1-02.6	40.0	22.6	10.0	02.6	5
6	.03	4-59.8	4-03.0	3-12.0	2-27.0	1-48.0	1-15.0	48.0	27.0	12.0	03.0	6
7	.04	5-49.8	4-43.4	3-44.0	2-51.6	2-06.0	1-27.6	0-56.0	31.6	14.0	03.6	7
8	.04	6-39.6	5-23.8	4-16.0	3-16.0	2-24.0	1-40.0	1-04.0	36.0	16.0	04.0	8
9	.05	7-29.6	6-04.2	4-48.0	3-40.4	2-42.0	1-52.6	1-12.0	40.6	18.0	04.6	9
10	.05	8-19.2	6-44.6	5-19.8	4-05.0	3-00.0	2-05.0	1-20.0	45.0	20.0	05.0	10
11	.06	9-09.0	7-25.0	5-51.8	4-29.4	3-18.0	2-17.6	1-28.0	49.6	22.0	05.6	11
12	.07	9-58.6	8-05.4	6-23.8	4-53.8	3-36.0	2-30.0	1-36.0	54.0	24.0	06.0	12
13	.07	10-48.2	8-45.6	6-55.6	5-18.4	3-54.0	2-42.6	1-44.0	0-58.6	26.0	06.6	13
14	.08	11-37.8	9-25.8	7-27.6	5-42.8	4-12.0	2-55.0	1-52.0	1-03.0	28.0	07.0	14
15	.08	12-27.2	10-06.2	7-59.4	6-07.2	4-30.0	3-07.6	2-00.0	1-07.6	30.0	07.6	15
16	.09	13-16.8	10-46.2	8-31.2	6-31.6	4-48.0	3-20.0	2-08.0	1-12.0	32.0	08.0	16
17	.09	14-06.0	11-26.4	9-03.0	6-56.0	5-05.8	3-32.6	2-16.0	1-16.6	34.0	08.6	17
18	.10	14-55.2	12-06.6	9-34.8	7-20.6	5-23.8	3-45.0	2-24.0	1-21.0	36.0	09.0	18
19	.10	15-44.4	12-46.6	10-06.6	7-45.0	5-41.8	3-57.4	2-32.0	1-25.6	38.0	09.6	19
20	.11	16-33.4	13-26.6	10-38.4	8-09.2	5-59.8	4-10.0	2-40.0	1-30.0	0-40.0	0-10.0	20

L$_s$=600 FT. TABLE V

FUNCTIONS OF TRANSITIONS
USED IN TABLE IV

D$_c$	L.C.	S.T.	L.T.	y$_c$	x$_c$	k	p	θ$_s$	D$_c$
1-30	599.84	200.12	400.13	15.70	599.63	299.94	3.92	4.5	1-30
2-00	599.71	200.21	400.23	20.93	599.34	299.89	5.23	6.0	2-00
2-30	599.54	200.33	400.36	26.15	598.97	299.83	6.55	7.5	2-30
3-00	599.34	200.47	400.52	31.36	598.52	299.75	7.85	9.0	3-00
3-30	599.10	200.64	400.71	36.56	597.99	299.66	9.16	10.5	3-30
4-00	598.83	200.84	400.92	41.75	597.37	299.56	10.46	12.0	4-00
5	598.17	201.32	401.45	52.10	595.90	299.32	13.06	15.0	5
6	597.37	201.90	402.09	62.39	594.11	299.02	15.65	18.0	6
7	596.42	202.59	402.85	72.61	591.99	298.66	18.24	21.0	7
8	595.33	203.40	403.74	82.73	589.56	298.25	20.81	24.0	8
9	594.10	204.33	404.75	92.76	586.81	297.79	23.38	27.0	9
10	592.72	205.37	405.90	102.68	583.76	297.28	25.93	30.0	10
11	591.20	206.54	407.18	112.49	580.40	296.71	28.46	33.0	11
12	589.54	207.84	408.60	122.17	576.74	296.09	30.98	36.0	12
13	587.74	209.27	410.16	131.70	572.80	295.43	33.47	39.0	13
14	585.79	210.83	411.87	141.08	568.55	294.71	35.96	42.0	14
15	583.71	212.55	413.74	150.29	564.03	293.94	38.42	45.0	15
16	581.49	214.41	415.77	159.34	559.24	293.11	40.85	48.0	16

DEFLECTION ANGLES FROM T.S. TO POINTS ON TEN CHORD SPIRAL FOR TRANSITIONS USED IN TABLE IV

Lₛ = 600 FT. TABLE V

TRANSIT ON T.S., SIGHT ON POINT NO.

Dc	COL. A	10=S.C.	9	8	7	6	5	4	3	2	1	Dc
1-30		1-30.0	1-13.0	0-57.6	0-44.2	0-32.4	0-22.4	0-14.4	0-08.2	0-03.6	0-01.0	1-30
2-00		2-00.0	1-37.2	1-16.8	0-58.8	0-43.2	30.0	19.2	10.8	04.8	01.2	2-00
2-30		2-30.0	2-01.6	1-36.0	1-13.6	0-54.0	37.6	24.0	13.6	06.0	01.6	2-30
3-00		3-00.0	2-25.8	1-55.2	1-28.2	1-04.8	45.0	28.8	16.2	07.2	01.8	3-00
3-30		3-30.0	2-50.2	2-14.4	1-43.0	1-15.6	0-52.6	33.6	19.0	08.4	02.2	3-30
4-00	.02	4-00.0	3-14.4	2-33.6	1-57.6	1-26.4	1-00.0	38.4	21.6	09.6	02.4	4-00
5	.03	4-59.8	4-03.0	3-12.0	2-27.0	1-48.0	1-15.0	48.0	27.0	12.0	03.0	5
6	.03	5-59.8	4-51.4	3-50.4	2-56.4	2-09.6	1-30.0	0-57.6	32.4	14.4	03.6	6
7	.04	6-59.6	5-40.0	4-28.8	3-25.8	2-31.2	1-45.0	1-07.2	37.8	16.8	04.2	7
8	.04	7-59.4	6-28.6	5-07.0	3-55.2	2-52.8	2-00.0	1-16.8	43.2	19.2	04.8	8
9	.05	8-59.0	7-17.0	5-45.4	4-24.6	3-14.4	2-15.0	1-26.4	48.6	21.6	05.4	9
10	.05	9-58.6	8-05.4	6-23.8	4-53.8	3-36.0	2-30.0	1-36.0	54.0	24.0	06.0	10
11	.06	10-58.2	8-53.6	7-02.0	5-23.2	3-57.6	2-45.0	1-45.6	0-59.4	26.4	06.6	11
12	.07	11-57.6	9-42.0	7-40.2	5-52.6	4-19.2	3-00.0	1-55.2	1-04.8	28.8	07.2	12
13	.07	12-57.0	10-30.2	8-18.4	6-22.0	4-40.8	3-15.0	2-04.8	1-10.2	31.2	07.8	13
14	.08	13-56.2	11-18.4	8-56.6	6-51.2	5-02.2	3-30.0	2-14.4	1-15.6	33.6	08.4	14
15	.08	14-55.2	12-06.6	9-34.8	7-20.6	5-23.8	3-45.0	2-24.0	1-21.0	36.0	09.0	15
16	.09	15-54.2	12-54.6	10-13.0	7-49.8	5-45.4	4-00.0	2-33.6	1-26.4	0-38.4	0-09.6	16

TABLE VI — Deflection Angle Coefficients for the 10 Chord Spiral

Spiral L = ½ Δ
Spiral L × no. m chart = DEF. L
Spiral L = ½ Δ (on full spiral)

CONSTANT FOR θ FOR PLUS CORRECTION — To Point No. 0: 1.00, 1: .81, 2: .64, 3: .49, 4: .36

TO POINT NO.	0=T.S.	1	2	3	4	5	6	7	8	9	10=S.C.
		INSTRUMENT SET UP ON POINT NUMBER									
0	0	.0067	.0267	.0600	.1067	.1667	.2400	.3267	.4267	.5400	.6667
1	.0033	0	.0167	.0467	.0900	.1437	.2167	.3000	.3967	.5067	.6300
2	.0133	.0133	0	.0267	.0667	.1200	.1867	.2667	.3600	.4667	.5867
3	.0300	.0333	.0233	0	.0367	.0867	.1500	.2267	.3167	.4200	.5367
4	.0533	.0600	.0533	.0333	0	.0467	.1067	.1800	.2667	.3667	.4800
5	.0833	.0933	.0900	.0733	.0433	0	.0567	.1267	.2100	.3067	.4167
6	.1200	.1333	.1333	.1200	.0933	.0533	0	.0667	.1467	.2400	.3467
7	.1633	.1800	.1833	.1733	.1500	.1133	.0633	0	.0767	.1667	.2700
8	.2133	.2333	.2400	.2333	.2133	.1800	.1333	.0733	0	.0867	.1867
9	.2700	.2933	.3033	.3000	.2833	.2533	.2100	.1533	.0833	0	.0967
10	.3333	.3600	.3733	.3733	.3600	.3333	.2933	.2400	.1733	.0933	0

CONSTANT FOR θ FOR MINUS CORRECTION — Point 6: .36, 7: .49, 8: .64, 9: .81, 10: 1.00

TABLE VII — Corrections for φ = θ/3 − C

CORRECTION C IN FORMULA φ = θ/3 − C

θ in degrees	15	20	25	30	35	40	45	50
C in minutes	0.2	0.4	0.8	1.4	2.2	3.4	4.8	6.6

TABLE VIII

DEFLECTION ANGLE COEFFICIENTS FOR THE 20 CHORD SPIRAL

CONSTANT FOR COMPUTING θ TO OBTAIN PLUS CORRECTION (TO POINT NO.):

TO POINT NO.	0	1	2	3	4	5	6	7
Constant	1.00	.90	.81	.72	.64	.56	.49	.42

INSTRUMENT SET UP ON POINT NUMBER

TO POINT NO.	0=T.S.	1	2	3	4	5	6	7	8	9	10	11	12	13	14	15	16	17	18	19	20=S.C.
0	0	.0017	.0067	.0150	.0267	.0417	.0633	.0817	.1067	.1350	.1667	.2017	.2400	.2817	.3267	.3750	.4267	.4817	.5400	.6017	.6667
1	.0008	0	.0042	.0117	.0225	.0367	.0542	.0750	.0992	.1267	.1575	.1917	.2292	.2700	.3142	.3617	.4125	.4667	.5242	.5850	.6492
2	.0033	.0033	0	.0067	.0167	.0300	.0467	.0667	.0900	.1167	.1467	.1800	.2167	.2567	.3000	.3467	.3967	.4500	.5067	.5667	.6300
3	.0075	.0083	.0058	0	.0092	.0217	.0375	.0567	.0792	.1050	.1342	.1667	.2025	.2417	.2842	.3300	.3792	.4317	.4875	.5467	.6092
4	.0133	.0150	.0133	.0083	0	.0117	.0267	.0450	.0667	.0917	.1200	.1517	.1867	.2250	.2667	.3117	.3600	.4117	.4667	.5250	.5867
5	.0208	.0233	.0225	.0183	.0108	0	.0142	.0317	.0525	.0767	.1042	.1350	.1692	.2067	.2475	.2917	.3392	.3900	.4442	.5017	.5625
6	.0300	.0333	.0333	.0300	.0233	.0133	0	.0167	.0367	.0600	.0867	.1167	.1500	.1867	.2267	.2700	.3167	.3667	.4200	.4767	.5367
7	.0408	.0450	.0458	.0433	.0375	.0283	.0158	0	.0192	.0417	.0675	.0967	.1292	.1650	.2042	.2467	.2925	.3417	.3942	.4500	.5092
8	.0533	.0583	.0600	.0583	.0533	.0450	.0333	.0183	0	.0217	.0467	.0750	.1067	.1417	.1800	.2217	.2667	.3150	.3667	.4217	.4800
9	.0675	.0733	.0758	.0750	.0708	.0633	.0525	.0383	.0208	0	.0242	.0517	.0825	.1167	.1542	.1950	.2392	.2867	.3375	.3917	.4492
10	.0833	.0900	.0933	.0933	.0900	.0833	.0733	.0600	.0433	.0233	0	.0267	.0567	.0900	.1267	.1667	.2100	.2567	.3067	.3600	.4167
11	.1008	.1083	.1125	.1133	.1108	.1050	.0958	.0833	.0675	.0483	.0258	0	.0292	.0617	.0975	.1367	.1792	.2250	.2742	.3267	.3825
12	.1200	.1283	.1333	.1350	.1333	.1283	.1200	.1083	.0933	.0750	.0533	.0283	0	.0317	.0633	.1050	.1467	.1917	.2400	.2917	.3467
13	.1408	.1500	.1558	.1583	.1575	.1533	.1458	.1350	.1208	.1033	.0825	.0583	.0308	0	.0342	.0717	.1125	.1567	.2042	.2550	.3092
14	.1633	.1733	.1800	.1833	.1833	.1800	.1733	.1633	.1500	.1333	.1133	.0900	.0633	.0333	0	.0367	.0767	.1200	.1667	.2167	.2700
15	.1875	.1983	.2058	.2100	.2108	.2083	.2025	.1933	.1808	.1650	.1458	.1233	.0975	.0683	.0358	0	.0383	.0817	.1275	.1767	.2292
16	.2133	.2250	.2333	.2383	.2400	.2383	.2333	.2250	.2133	.1983	.1800	.1583	.1333	.1050	.0733	.0383	0	.0417	.0867	.1350	.1867
17	.2408	.2533	.2625	.2683	.2708	.2700	.2658	.2583	.2475	.2333	.2158	.1950	.1708	.1433	.1125	.0783	.0408	0	.0442	.0917	.1425
18	.2700	.2833	.2933	.3000	.3033	.3033	.3000	.2933	.2833	.2700	.2533	.2333	.2100	.1833	.1533	.1200	.0833	.0433	0	.0467	.0967
19	.3008	.3150	.3258	.3333	.3375	.3383	.3358	.3300	.3208	.3083	.2925	.2733	.2508	.2250	.1958	.1633	.1275	.0883	.0458	0	.0492
20	.3333	.3483	.3600	.3683	.3733	.3750	.3733	.3683	.3600	.3483	.3333	.3150	.2933	.2683	.2400	.2083	.1733	.1350	.0933	.0483	0

CONSTANT FOR COMPUTING θ TO OBTAIN MINUS CORRECTION (TO POINT NO.):

TO POINT NO.	13	14	15	16	17	18	19	20
Constant	.42	.49	.56	.64	.72	.81	.90	1.00

TABLE IX – WIDENING FOR PAVEMENT ON CURVES

$$W = n \left[R - \sqrt{R^2 - 400} \right] + \frac{V}{\sqrt{R}}$$

D_c	R	W IN FEET	
		2-LANE	4-LANE
4	1432	2	3
5	1146	2	3
6	955	2	3
7	819	2	3
8	716	2	3
9	637	2	3
10	573	2	3
11	521	2	3
12	477	3	4
14	409	3	4
16	358	3	4
18	318	3	4
20	286	3	5
22	260	3	5
24	239	4	6
25	229	4	6

TABLE X
SAFE MAXIMUM CURVATURES FOR VARIOUS ASSUMED DESIGN SPEEDS

RATE OF SUPER-ELEVATION FEET PER FOOT (S)	ASSUMED DESIGN SPEED AND CORRESPONDING SAFE SIDE FRICTION FACTORS (F)									
	25 m.p.h. F=.16 D	30 F=.16 D	35 F=.16 D	40 F=.16 D	45 F=.16 D	50 F=.16 D	55 F=.16 D	60 F=.16 D	65 F=.15 D	70 m.p.h. F=.14 D
-.03	17.8	12.4	9.1	7.0	5.5	4.4	3.7	3.1	2.4	1.9
-.02	19.2	13.3	9.8	7.5	5.9	4.8	4.0	3.3	2.6	2.1
-.01	20.5	14.3	10.5	8.0	6.3	5.1	4.2	3.6	2.8	2.3
0.0	21.9	15.2	11.2	8.6	6.8	5.5	4.5	3.8	3.0	2.4
.01	23.3	16.2	11.9	9.1	7.2	5.8	4.8	4.0	3.2	2.6
.02	24.7	17.1	12.6	9.6	7.6	6.2	5.1	4.3	3.4	2.8
.03	26.0	18.1	13.3	10.2	8.0	6.5	5.4	4.5	3.6	3.0
.04	27.4	19.0	14.0	10.7	8.4	6.8	5.7	4.8	3.8	3.1
.05	28.8	20.0	14.7	11.2	8.9	7.2	5.9	5.0	4.0	3.3
.06	30.1	20.9	15.4	11.8	9.3	7.5	6.2	5.2	4.3	3.5
.07	31.4	21.9	16.1	12.3	9.7	7.9	6.5	5.5	4.5	3.7
.08	32.9	22.8	16.8	12.8	10.1	8.2	6.8	5.7	4.7	3.8
.09	34.3	23.8	17.5	13.4	10.6	8.6	7.1	5.9	4.9	4.0
.10	35.6	24.7	18.2	13.9	11.0	8.9	7.4	6.2	5.1	4.2

APPENDIX

Tables IV and V herein are extensions of the same numbered tables in the preceding pages for values of D_c of 26° to 38°, inclusive, for $L_s = 150$, 200, and 250 feet. These supplementary tables should be used in the same manner as the preceding tables bearing the same numbers.

All combinations of D_c and L_s shown are safe for assumed design speeds of 25 to 30 miles per hour when the pavements are superelevated to the practical maximum of 0.10 feet (1¼ inches) per foot.

192

TABLE IV - T_S AND E_S

All columns: $L_S = 150'$

D_C	$\Delta=42°$ T_S	$\Delta=42°$ E_S	$\Delta=41°$ T_S	$\Delta=41°$ E_S	$\Delta=40°$ T_S	$\Delta=40°$ E_S	$\Delta=39°$ T_S	$\Delta=39°$ E_S
26	160.93	20.2	158.69	19.4	156.46	18.7	154.25	17.90
27	157.84	19.8	155.67	19.0				
28	154.97	19.44						

D_C	$\Delta=46°$ T_S	$\Delta=46°$ E_S	$\Delta=45°$ T_S	$\Delta=45°$ E_S	$\Delta=44°$ T_S	$\Delta=44°$ E_S	$\Delta=43°$ T_S	$\Delta=43°$ E_S
26	170.05	23.6	167.75	22.7	165.46	21.9	163.19	21.0
27	166.63	23.1	164.41	22.2	162.20	21.4	160.01	20.6
28	163.46	22.6	161.32	21.8	159.18	21.0	157.07	20.2
29	160.51	22.2	158.43	21.4	156.37	20.6		
30	157.76	21.8	155.75	21.02				

TABLE IV - T$_S$ AND E$_S$

Upper band

Dc	Δ=47° Ls=150' T$_S$	E$_S$	200' T$_S$	E$_S$	Δ=48° Ls=150' T$_S$	E$_S$	200' T$_S$	E$_S$	Δ=49° Ls=150' T$_S$	E$_S$	200' T$_S$	E$_S$
26	172.37	24.5			174.71	25.5			177.07	26.5		
27	168.87	24.0			171.13	24.9			173.40	25.8		
28	165.62	23.5			167.80	24.4			170.00	25.3		
29	162.60	23.0			164.71	23.9			166.83	24.7		
30	159.78	22.6			161.82	23.4			163.88	24.3		
31	157.15	22.2			159.13	23.0			161.12	23.8		
32					156.60	22.64			158.53	23.4		

Lower band

Dc	Δ=50° Ls=150' T$_S$	E$_S$	200' T$_S$	E$_S$	Δ=51° Ls=150' T$_S$	E$_S$	200' T$_S$	E$_S$	Δ=52° Ls=150' T$_S$	E$_S$	200' T$_S$	E$_S$
26	179.45	27.5			181.84	28.5			184.26	29.5	210.46	33.17
27	175.69	26.8			178.00	27.8			180.33	28.8		
28	172.21	26.2			174.44	27.1			176.69	28.1		
29	168.97	25.6			171.13	26.6			173.31	27.5		
30	165.95	25.1			168.04	26.0			170.15	26.9		
31	163.13	24.7			165.15	25.5			167.20	26.4		
32	160.48	24.3			162.45	25.1			164.43	26.0		
33	158.00	23.9			159.91	24.7			161.83	25.5		
34					157.52	24.31			159.39	25.1		

TABLE IV - T_S AND E_S

Top panel — $\Delta = 55°$, $54°$, $53°$ (values in the 200′ blocks are Es, Ts; in the Ls = 150′ blocks are Ts, Es)

Dc	$\Delta=55°$ 200′ Es	200′ Ts	Ls=150′ Ts	Ls=150′ Es	$\Delta=54°$ 200′ Es	200′ Ts	Ls=150′ Ts	Ls=150′ Es	$\Delta=53°$ 200′ Es	200′ Ts	Ls=150′ Ts	Ls=150′ Es
26	36.5	217.94	191.63	32.8	35.4	215.42	189.15	31.7	34.3	212.93	186.70	30.6
27	35.8	213.79	187.45	32.0	34.70	211.36	185.06	30.9			182.68	29.8
28			183.56	31.2			181.25	30.2			178.96	29.1
29			179.95	30.5			177.71	29.5			175.50	28.5
30			176.58	29.8			174.42	28.8			172.27	27.9
31			173.43	29.2			171.33	28.3			169.26	27.3
32			170.48	28.7			168.45	27.7			166.43	26.8
33			167.71	28.2			165.73	27.3			163.78	26.4
34			165.11	27.7			163.19	26.8			161.28	26.0
35			162.66	27.3			160.78	26.4			158.93	25.6
36			160.34	26.9			158.52	26.03				

Bottom panel — $\Delta = 58°$, $57°$, $56°$

Dc	$\Delta=58°$ 200′ Es	200′ Ts	Ls=150′ Ts	Ls=150′ Es	$\Delta=57°$ 200′ Es	200′ Ts	Ls=150′ Ts	Ls=150′ Es	$\Delta=56°$ 200′ Es	200′ Ts	Ls=150′ Ts	Ls=150′ Es
26	40.2	225.63	199.21	36.4	38.9	223.04	196.66	35.2	37.7	220.48	194.14	34.0
27	39.3	221.21	194.76	35.4	38.1	218.71	192.30	34.3	37.0	216.24	189.86	33.1
28	38.6	217.11	190.62	34.5	37.4	214.70	188.25	33.4	36.27	212.31	185.89	32.3
29	37.88	213.30	186.77	33.7			184.48	32.6			182.20	31.5
30			183.19	33.0			180.97	31.9			178.76	30.8
31			179.84	32.3			177.68	31.2			175.55	30.2
32			176.70	31.6			174.61	30.6			172.53	29.6
33			173.75	31.0			171.72	30.0			169.71	29.1
34			170.98	30.5			169.00	29.5			167.05	28.6
35			168.37	30.0			166.45	29.0			164.54	28.1
36			165.91	29.5			164.04	28.6			162.18	27.7
37			163.58	29.1			161.76	28.2			159.95	27.3
38			161.38	28.7			159.60	27.80				

TABLE IV - T_s AND E_s

$\Delta = 59^\circ$, 60° , 61°

D_c	$\Delta=59^\circ$ $L_s=150'$ T_s	E_s	$200'$ T_s	E_s	$\Delta=60^\circ$ $L_s=150'$ T_s	E_s	$200'$ T_s	E_s	$\Delta=61^\circ$ $L_s=150'$ T_s	E_s	$200'$ T_s	E_s	D_c
26	201.79	37.7	228.24	41.5	204.39	39.0	230.88	42.8	207.01	40.3	233.54	44.1	26
27	197.24	36.7	223.73	40.6	199.75	37.9	226.28	41.8	202.28	39.2	228.85	43.1	27
28	193.02	35.7	219.55	39.8	195.44	36.9	222.01	41.0	197.89	38.2	224.50	42.2	28
29	189.09	34.9	215.66	39.0	191.44	36.0	218.05	40.2	193.80	37.2	220.45	41.4	29
30	185.43	34.1			187.70	35.2	214.35	39.52	189.99	36.3	216.68	40.7	30
31	182.01	33.3			184.21	34.4			186.43	35.5			31
32	178.81	32.7			180.94	33.7			183.10	34.8			32
33	175.80	32.0			177.87	33.1			179.97	34.1			33
34	172.98	31.5			174.99	32.4			177.03	33.5			34
35	170.31	30.9			172.27	31.9			174.25	32.9			35
36	167.80	30.4			169.71	31.4			171.64	32.3			36
37	165.43	30.0			167.29	30.9			169.17	31.8			37
38	163.18	29.5			164.99	30.4			166.83	31.4			38

$\Delta = 62^\circ$, 63° , 64°

D_c	$\Delta=62^\circ$ $L_s=150'$ T_s	E_s	$200'$ T_s	E_s	$\Delta=63^\circ$ $L_s=150'$ T_s	E_s	$200'$ T_s	E_s	$\Delta=64^\circ$ $L_s=150'$ T_s	E_s	$200'$ T_s	E_s	D_c
26	209.67	41.7	236.24	45.5	212.35	43.1	238.96	46.9	215.06	44.5	241.71	48.3	26
27	204.84	40.5	231.45	44.5	207.43	41.8	234.08	45.8	210.04	43.2	236.74	47.2	27
28	200.36	39.4	227.01	43.5	202.86	40.7	229.58	44.8	205.38	42.0	232.12	46.2	28
29	196.19	38.4	222.89	42.7	198.61	39.7	225.35	43.9	201.05	41.0	227.83	45.3	29
30	192.31	37.5	219.04	41.9	194.65	38.7	221.42	43.1	197.05	40.0	223.83	44.4	30
31	188.68	36.7	215.45	41.21	190.94	37.9	217.76	42.4	193.23	39.1	220.10	43.6	31
32	185.27	35.9			187.47	37.0			189.70	38.2	216.60	42.94	32
33	182.08	35.2			184.22	36.3			186.38	37.4			33
34	179.08	34.5			181.16	35.6			183.26	36.7			34
35	176.26	33.9			178.28	35.0			180.32	36.0			35
36	173.59	33.3			175.56	34.4			177.55	35.4			36
37	171.07	32.8			172.99	33.8			174.93	34.8			37
38	168.68	32.3			170.56	33.3			172.45	34.3			38

TABLE IV - Ts AND Es

Left section (Δ=65°, Δ=67°)

Dc	Ls=150' Ts	Ls=150' Es	200' Ts	200' Es	250' Ts	250' Es
Δ=65°						
26	217.80	45.9	244.49	49.8	271.51	54.77
27	212.68	44.6	239.42	48.6		
28	207.93	43.4	234.72	47.6		
29	203.52	42.3	230.34	46.6		
30	199.40	41.3	226.27	45.7		
31	195.55	40.3	222.46	44.9		
32	191.95	39.4	218.90	44.2		
33	188.56	38.6				
34	185.38	37.8				
35	182.39	37.1				
36	179.56	36.5				
37	176.89	35.9				
38	174.37	35.3				
Δ=67°						
26	223.37	49.0	250.14	52.9	277.26	57.9
27	218.06	47.5	244.88	51.6		
28	213.13	46.2	239.99	50.4		
29	208.54	45.0	235.45	49.4		
30	204.26	43.9	231.22	48.4		
31	200.26	42.9	227.27	47.5		
32	196.52	41.9	223.57	46.7		
33	193.01	41.0	220.10	46.0		
34	189.70	40.2				
35	186.59	39.4				
36	183.66	38.7				
37	180.89	38.0				
38	178.26	37.4				

Right section (Δ=66°, Δ=68°)

Dc	Ls=150' Ts	Ls=150' Es	200' Ts	200' Es	250' Ts	250' Es
Δ=66°						
26	220.57	47.4	247.30	51.3	274.37	56.3
27	215.35	46.1	242.13	50.1		
28	210.51	44.8	237.34	49.0		
29	206.01	43.6	232.89	48.0		
30	201.82	42.6	228.73	47.0		
31	197.89	41.6	224.85	46.2		
32	194.22	40.6	221.22	45.4		
33	190.77	39.8	217.82	44.71		
34	187.53	39.0				
35	184.48	38.3				
36	181.60	37.6				
37	178.88	36.9				
38	176.30	36.4				
Δ=68°						
26	226.21	50.6	253.02	54.5	280.19	59.5
27	220.79	49.1	247.66	53.2	274.88	58.4
28	215.77	47.7	242.68	51.9		
29	211.09	46.4	238.05	50.8		
30	206.73	45.3	233.74	49.8		
31	202.66	44.2	229.72	48.9		
32	198.84	43.2	225.95	48.0		
33	195.26	42.3	222.41	47.2		
34	191.90	41.4	219.09	46.53		
35	188.73	40.6				
36	185.74	39.9				
37	182.92	39.2				
38	180.24	38.5				

TABLE IV — T_S and E_S

$\Delta=69°$

D_c	$L_s=150'$ T_s	$L_s=150'$ E_s	$200'$ T_s	$200'$ E_s	$250'$ T_s	$250'$ E_s
26	229.08	52.2	255.93	56.1	283.16	61.2
27	223.56	50.6	250.47	54.7	277.74	60.0
28	218.44	49.2	245.40	53.5		
29	213.67	47.9	240.68	52.3		
30	209.23	46.7	236.29	51.2		
31	205.08	45.6	232.19	50.3		
32	201.20	44.5	228.35	49.4		
33	197.55	43.6	224.75	48.6		
34	194.12	42.7	221.37	47.8		
35	190.89	41.8	222.70	49.7		
36	187.85	41.1				
37	184.97	40.3				
38	182.25	39.7				

$\Delta=70°$

D_c	$L_s=150'$ T_s	$L_s=150'$ E_s	$200'$ T_s	$200'$ E_s	$250'$ T_s	$250'$ E_s
26	231.98	53.8	258.88	57.8	286.16	62.9
27	226.36	52.2	253.31	56.4	280.64	61.6
28	221.14	50.7	248.15	55.0	275.54	60.51
29	216.29	49.4	243.35	53.8		
30	211.77	48.1	238.87	52.7		
31	207.54	47.0	234.70	51.7		
32	203.58	45.9	230.78	50.8		
33	199.86	44.9	227.12	49.9		
34	196.37	43.9	223.67	49.1		
35	193.08	43.1	220.43	48.40		
36	189.98	42.3				
37	187.05	41.5				
38	184.28	40.8				

$\Delta=71°$

D_c	$L_s=150'$ T_s	$L_s=150'$ E_s	$200'$ T_s	$200'$ E_s	$250'$ T_s	$250'$ E_s
26	234.92	55.5	261.86	59.5		
27	229.19	53.9	256.19	58.0		
28	223.88	52.3	250.93	56.6		
29	218.94	50.9	246.04	55.4		
30	214.33	49.6	241.49	54.2		
31	210.02	48.4	237.23	53.2		
32	205.99	47.3	233.25	52.2		
33	202.21	46.2	229.52	51.3		
34	198.65	45.3	226.01	50.5		
35	195.30	44.4	222.70	49.7		
36	192.14	43.5				
37	189.15	42.7				
38	186.33	42.0				

$\Delta=72°$

D_c	$L_s=150'$ T_s	$L_s=150'$ E_s	$200'$ T_s	$200'$ E_s	$250'$ T_s	$250'$ E_s
26	237.90	57.3	264.88	61.3	292.27	66.5
27	232.06	55.5	259.10	59.7	286.55	65.1
28	226.65	53.9	253.75	58.3	281.26	63.8
29	221.62	52.5	248.77	57.0		
30	216.92	51.1	244.13	55.8		
31	212.54	49.9	239.80	54.7		
32	208.43	48.7	235.74	53.6		
33	204.58	47.6	231.94	52.7		
34	200.96	46.6	228.37	51.9		
35	197.54	45.7	225.01	51.1		
36	194.33	44.8	221.83	50.34		
37	191.29	44.0				
38	188.41	43.2				

TABLE IV — T_S AND E_S

$\Delta = 73°$

D_c	250 T_s	250 E_s	200' T_s	200' E_s	Ls=150 T_s	Ls=150 E_s
26	295.38	68.3	267.93	63.1	240.91	59.0
27	289.56	66.9	262.06	61.5	234.97	57.3
28	284.17	65.6	256.60	60.0	229.46	55.6
29	279.16	64.4	251.53	58.6	224.33	54.1
30			246.81	57.4	219.55	52.7
31			242.40	56.2	215.09	51.4
32			238.27	55.1	210.90	50.2
33			234.40	54.2	206.98	49.0
34			230.76	53.3	203.29	48.0
35			227.34	52.4	199.82	47.0
36			224.11	51.7	196.54	46.1
37					193.44	45.3
38					190.51	44.5

$\Delta = 74°$

D_c	250' T_s	250' E_s	200' T_s	200' E_s	Ls=150' T_s	Ls=150' E_s
26	298.54	70.2	271.03	65.0	243.96	60.9
27	292.61	68.7	265.05	63.3	237.91	59.0
28	287.12	67.3	259.49	61.7	232.30	57.3
29	282.02	66.1	254.33	60.3	227.08	55.7
30			249.52	59.0	222.21	54.3
31			245.03	57.8	217.67	52.9
32			240.83	56.7	213.41	51.7
33			236.89	55.7	209.41	50.5
34			233.18	54.7	205.66	49.4
35			229.70	53.9	202.12	48.4
36			226.41	53.1	198.78	47.4
37			223.31	52.32	195.63	46.6
38					192.65	45.7

$\Delta = 75°$

D_c	250 T_s	250 E_s	200' T_s	200' E_s	Ls=150 T_s	Ls=150 E_s
26	301.73	72.1	274.17	66.9	247.06	62.7
27	295.70	70.6	268.08	65.1	240.90	60.8
28	290.12	69.1	262.42	63.5	235.18	59.0
29	284.92	67.8	257.17	62.0	229.87	57.4
30	280.09	66.67	252.27	60.6	224.91	55.9
31			247.70	59.4	220.28	54.5
32			243.42	58.2	215.95	53.2
33			239.41	57.2	211.88	52.0
34			235.64	56.2	208.05	50.9
35			232.09	55.3	204.45	49.8
36			228.75	54.5	201.06	48.8
37			225.58	53.7	197.85	47.9
38					194.81	47.0

$\Delta = 76°$

D_c	250' T_s	250' E_s	200' T_s	200' E_s	Ls=150' T_s	Ls=150' E_s
26	304.97	74.1	277.35	68.8	250.19	64.7
27	298.83	72.5	271.15	67.0	243.92	62.7
28	293.15	71.0	265.39	65.3	238.10	60.8
29	287.86	69.6	260.04	63.8	232.69	59.1
30	282.94	68.4	255.06	62.3	227.65	57.6
31			250.41	61.0	222.93	56.1
32			246.05	59.9	218.52	54.8
33			241.97	58.7	214.38	53.5
34			238.13	57.7	210.48	52.3
35			234.52	56.8	206.82	51.3
36			231.11	55.9	203.36	50.2
37			227.89	55.1	200.09	49.3
38			224.86	54.37	197.00	48.4

TABLE IV - T$_S$ AND E$_S$

Δ=78°

D$_c$	250' T$_S$	250' E$_S$	200' T$_S$	200' E$_S$	L$_S$=150' T$_S$	L$_S$=150' E$_S$
26	311.58	78.2	283.85	72.9	256.59	68.6
27	305.22	76.4	277.42	70.9	250.09	66.5
28	299.34	74.8	271.45	69.1	244.06	64.5
29	293.86	73.4	265.91	67.4	238.46	62.7
30	288.77	72.0	260.75	65.9	233.23	61.0
31	284.01	70.8	255.93	64.5	228.34	59.5
32			251.41	63.2	223.77	58.0
33			247.18	62.0	219.48	56.7
34			243.21	60.9	215.44	55.4
35			239.47	59.9	211.64	54.3
36			235.94	58.9	208.06	53.2
37			232.61	58.0	204.68	52.1
38			229.46	57.2	201.47	51.2

Δ=80°

D$_c$	250' T$_S$	250' E$_S$	200' T$_S$	200' E$_S$	L$_S$=150' T$_S$	L$_S$=150' E$_S$
26	318.39	82.6	290.53	77.1	263.18	72.8
27	311.80	80.6	283.87	75.0	256.44	70.6
28	305.70	78.9	277.69	73.0	250.20	68.4
29	300.04	77.3	271.95	71.3	244.39	66.5
30	294.76	75.9	266.60	69.6	238.97	64.7
31	289.84	74.5	261.61	68.1	233.91	63.0
32	285.23	73.34	256.93	66.7	229.17	61.5
33			252.55	65.4	224.72	60.0
34			248.44	64.2	220.55	58.7
35			244.56	63.1	216.61	57.4
36			240.91	62.1	212.90	56.2
37			237.46	61.1	209.39	55.1
38			234.20	60.3	206.07	54.1

Δ=77°

D$_c$	L$_S$=150' T$_S$	L$_S$=150' E$_S$	200' T$_S$	200' E$_S$	250' T$_S$	250' E$_S$
26	253.37	66.6	280.58	70.8	308.26	76.1
27	246.98	64.6	274.26	68.9	302.01	74.4
28	241.06	62.7	268.40	67.2	296.22	72.9
29	235.55	60.9	262.96	65.6	290.84	71.5
30	230.42	59.3	257.88	64.1	285.84	70.2
31	225.62	57.8	253.15	62.7		
32	221.13	56.4	248.71	61.5		
33	216.91	55.1	244.56	60.4		
34	212.95	53.9	240.65	59.3		
35	209.21	52.7	236.98	58.3		
36	205.69	51.7	233.51	57.4		
37	202.37	50.7	230.24	56.6		
38	199.22	49.8	227.14	55.8		

Δ=79°

D$_c$	L$_S$=150' T$_S$	L$_S$=150' E$_S$	200' T$_S$	200' E$_S$	250' T$_S$	250' E$_S$
26	259.86	70.7	287.16	75.0	314.96	80.4
27	253.24	68.5	280.62	72.9	308.49	78.5
28	247.11	66.5	274.55	71.0	302.50	76.8
29	241.40	64.6	268.91	69.3	296.93	75.3
30	236.08	62.9	263.65	67.7	291.74	73.9
31	231.11	61.2	258.75	66.3	286.90	72.7
32	226.45	59.7	254.15	64.9		
33	222.08	58.3	249.85	63.7		
34	217.98	57.0	245.80	62.5		
35	214.11	55.8	242.00	61.5		
36	210.46	54.7	238.41	60.5		
37	207.02	53.6	235.02	59.6		
38	203.76	52.6	231.81	58.7		

TABLE IV — T_S AND E_S

Δ=82°

Dc	250′ Es	250′ Ts	200′ Es	200′ Ts	Ls=150′ Ts	Ls=150′ Es
26	87.1	325.39	81.6	297.40	269.96	77.2
27	85.0	318.57	79.3	290.51	262.98	74.8
28	83.1	312.26	77.2	284.11	256.51	72.5
29	81.4	306.39	75.3	278.16	250.49	70.5
30	79.9	300.93	73.5	272.63	244.88	68.5
31	78.4	295.83	71.9	267.46	239.64	66.8
32	77.1	291.07	70.4	262.61	234.73	65.1
33			69.0	258.08	230.13	63.5
34			67.7	253.82	225.80	62.1
35			66.5	249.81	221.72	60.7
36			65.4	246.03	217.88	59.5
37			64.4	242.45	214.25	58.3
38			63.4	239.08	210.81	57.2

Δ=84°

Dc	Ls=150′ Ts	Ls=150′ Es	200′ Ts	200′ Es	250′ Ts	250′ Es
26	276.95	81.9	304.50	86.3	332.61	91.9
27	269.72	79.3	297.35	83.8	325.55	89.7
28	263.02	76.9	290.73	81.6	319.02	87.6
29	256.79	74.6	284.57	79.5	312.94	85.8
30	250.98	72.6	278.84	77.6	307.29	84.1
31	245.55	70.7	273.48	75.9	302.02	82.5
32	240.47	68.9	268.47	74.3	297.09	81.1
33	235.70	67.2	263.78	72.8	292.46	79.8
34	231.22	65.7	259.37	71.4		
35	226.99	64.2	255.21	70.1		
36	223.01	62.9	251.30	68.9		
37	219.25	61.6	247.60	67.8		
38	215.69	60.4	244.11	66.8		

Δ=81°

Dc	Ls=150′ Ts	Ls=150′ Es	200′ Ts	200′ Es	250′ Ts	250′ Es
26	266.54	75.0	293.94	79.3	321.86	84.8
27	259.69	72.6	287.16	77.1	315.16	82.8
28	253.33	70.5	280.88	75.1	308.96	81.0
29	247.42	68.5	275.03	73.2	303.19	79.3
30	241.90	66.6	269.59	71.5	297.82	77.8
31	236.75	64.9	264.51	70.0	292.81	76.5
32	231.93	63.3	259.75	68.5	288.13	75.2
33	227.41	61.8	255.30	67.2		
34	223.15	60.4	251.11	65.9		
35	219.15	59.1	247.17	64.8		
36	215.37	57.8	243.45	63.7		
37	211.80	56.7	239.94	62.7		
38	208.42	55.6	236.62	61.8		

Δ=83°

Dc	Ls=150′ Ts	Ls=150′ Es	200′ Ts	200′ Es	250′ Ts	250′ Es
26	273.43	79.5	300.92	83.9	328.97	89.5
27	266.33	77.0	293.90	81.5	322.04	87.3
28	259.74	74.7	287.39	79.4	315.61	85.4
29	253.62	72.5	281.34	77.4	309.64	83.6
30	247.91	70.5	275.71	75.6	304.09	81.9
31	242.57	68.7	270.45	73.9	298.90	80.5
32	237.58	67.0	265.52	72.3	294.05	79.1
33	232.89	65.4	260.91	70.9	289.51	77.9
34	228.49	63.9	256.57	69.5		
35	224.34	62.5	252.49	68.3		
36	220.43	61.2	248.64	67.1		
37	216.73	59.9	245.01	66.1		
38	213.23	58.8	241.58	65.1		

TABLE IV — T_S AND E_S

Δ=86°

Dc	250' Ts	250' Es	200' Ts	200' Es	Ls=150' Ts	Ls=150' Es
26	340.06	96.9	311.81	91.2	284.16	86.7
27	332.76	94.5	304.42	88.6	276.68	84.0
28	325.99	92.3	297.56	86.2	269.74	81.4
29	319.71	90.3	291.19	84.0	263.28	79.0
30	313.86	88.5	285.25	82.0	257.27	76.8
31	308.40	86.8	279.71	80.1	251.65	74.8
32	303.29	85.3	274.52	78.4	246.38	72.9
33	298.51	83.9	269.66	76.7	241.44	71.1
34	294.02	82.6	265.09	75.3	236.80	69.5
35			260.79	73.9	232.43	67.9
36			256.74	72.6	228.31	66.5
37			252.92	71.4	224.42	65.1
38			249.30	70.3	220.73	63.8

Δ=88°

Dc	250' Ts	250' Es	200' Ts	200' Es	Ls=150' Ts	Ls=150' Es
26	347.76	102.2	319.37	96.4	291.61	91.9
27	340.20	99.6	311.72	93.6	283.86	88.9
28	333.20	97.3	304.61	91.1	276.68	86.2
29	326.69	95.1	298.02	88.7	269.99	83.6
30	320.64	93.2	291.87	86.5	263.77	81.3
31	314.99	91.4	286.13	84.5	257.94	79.1
32	309.71	89.7	280.76	82.7	252.50	77.1
33	304.76	88.2	275.73	80.9	247.38	75.2
34	300.11	86.8	271.00	79.3	242.58	73.4
35	295.74	85.5	266.56	77.8	238.05	71.8
36			262.36	76.5	233.79	70.2
37			258.40	75.2	229.75	68.8
38			254.67	74.0	225.94	67.4

Δ=85°

Dc	250' Ts	250' Es	200' Ts	200' Es	Ls=150' Ts	Ls=150' Es
26	336.31	94.4	308.12	88.7	280.52	84.3
27	329.13	92.1	300.86	86.2	273.17	81.6
28	322.48	90.0	294.12	83.9	266.35	79.1
29	316.30	88.0	287.85	81.7	260.01	76.8
30	310.55	86.3	282.02	79.8	254.10	74.7
31	305.18	84.7	276.57	78.0	248.57	72.7
32	300.17	83.2	271.47	76.3	243.40	70.9
33	295.46	81.8	266.69	74.7	238.55	69.1
34	291.05	80.60	262.20	73.3	233.99	67.5
35			257.98	72.0	229.69	66.0
36			254.00	70.7	225.64	64.6
37			250.24	69.6	221.81	63.3
38			246.69	68.5	218.19	62.1

Δ=87°

Dc	250' Ts	250' Es	200' Ts	200' Es	Ls=150' Ts	Ls=150' Es
26	343.88	99.5	315.56	93.8	287.85	89.3
27	336.45	97.1	308.04	91.1	280.24	86.4
28	329.57	94.8	301.06	88.6	273.18	83.8
29	323.17	92.7	294.57	86.3	266.61	81.3
30	317.22	90.8	288.53	84.2	260.49	79.0
31	311.66	89.1	282.89	82.3	254.77	76.9
32	306.48	87.5	277.61	80.5	249.41	75.0
33	301.61	86.0	272.67	78.8	244.39	73.1
34	297.04	84.7	268.02	77.3	239.67	71.4
35			263.65	75.8	235.22	69.8
36			259.53	74.5	231.03	68.3
37			255.64	73.2	227.06	66.9
38			251.96	72.1	223.32	65.6

TABLE IV - T_s AND E_s

$\Delta = 90°$

D_c	250' E_s	250' T_s	200' E_s	200' T_s	$L_s=150'$ T_s	$L_s=150'$ E_s
26	107.8	355.72	101.9	327.19	299.32	97.3
27	105.0	347.90	98.9	319.26	291.29	94.1
28	102.5	340.65	96.2	311.91	283.85	91.2
29	100.2	333.92	93.7	305.08	276.93	88.5
30	98.1	327.65	91.3	298.72	270.49	86.0
31	96.2	321.80	89.2	292.78	264.46	83.7
32	94.4	316.34	87.2	287.22	258.82	81.5
33	92.7	311.22	85.3	282.01	253.52	79.5
34	91.2	306.41	83.6	277.12	248.55	77.6
35	89.8	301.89	82.0	272.52	243.86	75.8
36	88.56	297.64	80.5	268.18	239.45	74.2
37			79.1	264.08	235.27	72.6
38			77.8	260.21	231.33	71.2

$\Delta = 92°$

D_c	250' E_s	250' T_s	200' E_s	200' T_s	$L_s=150'$ T_s	$L_s=150'$ E_s
26	113.7	363.97	107.7	335.29	307.30	103.0
27	110.7	355.87	104.5	327.08	298.99	99.6
28	108.0	348.37	101.6	319.47	291.29	96.5
29	105.6	341.40	98.9	312.40	284.12	93.6
30	103.3	334.92	96.4	305.81	277.44	91.0
31	101.2	328.86	94.1	299.67	271.20	88.5
32	99.3	323.21	92.0	293.91	265.36	86.2
33	97.5	317.91	90.0	288.52	259.88	84.0
34	95.9	312.94	88.0	283.46	254.73	82.0
35	94.4	308.26	86.4	278.69	249.88	80.1
36	93.0	303.86	84.8	274.20	245.31	78.4
37			83.3	269.96	240.99	76.7
38			81.9	265.96	236.90	75.1

$\Delta = 89°$

D_c	$L_s=150'$ T_s	$L_s=150'$ E_s	200' T_s	200' E_s	250' T_s	250' E_s
26	295.43	94.5	323.25	99.1	351.71	105.0
27	287.55	91.5	315.46	96.2	344.01	102.3
28	280.23	88.7	308.23	93.6	336.89	99.9
29	273.43	86.0	301.52	91.1	330.27	97.6
30	267.10	83.6	295.27	88.9	324.12	95.6
31	261.17	81.4	289.43	86.8	318.37	93.7
32	255.63	79.3	283.96	84.9	313.00	92.0
33	250.43	77.5	278.85	83.1	307.96	90.4
34	245.54	75.5	274.04	81.4	303.24	89.0
35	240.93	73.8	269.51	79.9	298.79	87.7
36	236.59	72.2	265.25	78.5		
37	232.49	70.7	261.22	77.1		
38	228.61	69.3	257.42	75.9		

$\Delta = 91°$

D_c	$L_s=150'$ T_s	$L_s=150'$ E_s	200' T_s	200' E_s	250' T_s	250' E_s
26	303.27	100.1	331.20	104.7	359.81	110.7
27	295.11	96.8	323.14	101.7	351.85	107.8
28	287.54	93.8	315.66	98.8	344.47	105.2
29	280.50	91.0	308.71	96.2	337.62	102.8
30	273.93	88.5	302.24	93.8	331.25	100.7
31	267.80	86.1	296.19	91.6	325.30	98.6
32	262.06	83.8	290.54	89.5	319.75	96.8
33	256.67	81.7	285.24	87.6	314.54	95.1
34	251.61	79.8	280.26	85.8	309.65	93.5
35	246.85	78.0	275.58	84.2	305.05	92.1
36	242.35	76.3	271.16	82.6	300.72	90.8
37	238.11	74.6	266.99	81.2		
38	234.09	73.1	263.06	79.9		

TABLE IV — T_s AND E_s

Δ = 93°

Dc	Ls=150' Ts	Ls=150' Es	200' Ts	200' Es	250' Ts	250' Es
26	311.40	105.9	339.45	110.7	368.20	116.7
27	302.94	102.5	331.10	107.4	359.96	113.7
28	295.10	99.3	323.35	104.4	352.33	110.9
29	287.81	96.3	316.16	101.6	345.24	108.3
30	281.02	93.6	309.46	99.0	338.65	106.0
31	274.67	91.0	303.20	96.6	332.49	103.8
32	268.73	88.6	297.35	94.4	326.74	101.8
33	263.15	86.4	291.86	92.4	321.35	100.0
34	257.91	84.3	286.71	90.5	316.29	98.3
35	252.97	82.4	281.86	88.7	311.53	96.8
36	248.32	80.5	277.29	87.1	307.06	95.3
37	243.92	78.8	272.98	85.5	302.83	94.0
38	239.77	77.2	268.91	84.1		

Δ = 94°

Dc	Ls=150' Ts	Ls=150' Es	200' Ts	200' Es	250' Ts	250' Es
26	315.57	109.0	343.68	113.8	372.52	119.9
27	306.97	105.4	335.18	110.4	364.13	116.7
28	298.99	102.1	327.31	107.3	356.37	113.8
29	291.57	99.0	319.99	104.4	349.15	111.2
30	284.66	96.2	313.17	101.7	342.45	108.7
31	278.20	93.6	306.80	99.3	336.18	106.5
32	272.15	91.1	300.85	97.0	330.33	104.4
33	266.48	88.8	295.27	94.9	324.85	102.5
34	261.14	86.7	290.02	92.9	319.71	100.8
35	256.12	84.7	285.09	91.1	314.87	99.2
36	251.39	82.8	280.44	89.4	310.31	97.7
37	246.91	81.0	276.06	87.8	306.01	96.3
38	242.68	79.3	271.91	86.3		

Δ = 95°

Dc	Ls=150' Ts	Ls=150' Es	200' Ts	200' Es	250' Ts	250' Es
26	319.82	112.1	348.00	116.9	376.91	123.1
27	311.07	108.4	339.35	113.4	368.38	119.8
28	302.96	105.0	331.33	110.2	360.48	116.8
29	295.41	101.9	323.89	107.2	353.14	114.1
30	288.37	98.9	316.95	104.5	346.32	111.6
31	281.79	96.2	310.47	102.0	339.95	109.3
32	275.64	93.7	304.41	99.6	334.00	107.1
33	269.87	91.3	298.73	97.4	328.42	105.2
34	264.44	89.1	293.40	95.4	323.18	103.3
35	259.33	87.0	288.38	93.5	318.26	101.7
36	254.51	85.1	283.65	91.7	313.63	100.1
37	249.96	83.2	279.19	90.1	309.26	98.7
38	245.66	81.5	274.97	88.5	305.13	97.35

Δ = 96°

Dc	Ls=150' Ts	Ls=150' Es	200' Ts	200' Es	250' Ts	250' Es
26	324.16	115.3	352.40	120.2	381.39	126.4
27	315.25	111.5	343.60	116.6	372.71	123.0
28	306.99	108.0	335.44	113.3	364.67	120.0
29	299.31	104.8	327.86	110.2	357.21	117.1
30	292.15	101.7	320.80	107.4	350.26	114.5
31	285.46	98.9	314.21	104.7	343.78	112.1
32	279.20	96.3	308.04	102.3	337.73	109.9
33	273.52	93.9	302.27	100.0	332.35	107.9
34	267.80	91.6	296.84	97.9	326.73	106.0
35	262.60	89.4	291.74	96.0	321.72	104.2
36	257.70	87.4	286.93	94.1	317.01	102.6
37	253.07	85.5	282.38	92.4	312.56	101.1
38	248.69	83.8	278.09	90.6	308.37	99.7

TABLE IV - Ts AND Es

Δ=98°

Dc	Ls=150' Ts	Es	200' Ts	Es	250' Ts	Es
26	333.09	122.0	361.46	127.0	390.62	133.3
27	323.87	118.0	354.34	123.1	381.63	129.7
28	315.31	114.2	343.90	119.6	373.31	126.4
29	307.35	110.8	336.05	116.3	365.58	123.4
30	299.94	107.6	328.74	113.3	358.39	120.6
31	293.01	104.6	321.92	110.5	351.68	118.0
32	286.52	101.8	315.53	107.9	345.42	115.7
33	280.44	99.2	309.55	105.5	339.54	113.5
34	274.72	96.8	303.93	103.2	334.03	111.4
35	269.33	94.5	298.64	101.1	328.85	109.6
36	264.26	92.3	293.66	99.2	323.98	107.8
37	259.46	90.3	288.96	97.3	319.37	106.2
38	254.92	88.4	284.52	95.6	315.03	104.7

Δ=100°

Dc	Ls=150' Ts	Es	200' Ts	Es	250' Ts	Es
26	342.39	129.1	370.89	134.1	400.22	140.6
27	332.83	124.8	361.45	130.1	390.91	136.8
28	323.97	120.8	352.70	126.3	382.30	133.3
29	315.72	117.1	344.57	122.8	374.29	130.0
30	308.04	113.7	337.00	119.6	366.85	127.0
31	300.87	110.6	329.93	116.6	359.90	124.3
32	294.15	107.6	323.32	113.8	353.42	121.7
33	287.84	104.8	317.13	111.2	347.34	119.4
34	281.92	102.2	311.31	108.8	341.63	117.2
35	276.34	99.8	305.84	106.6	336.27	115.2
36	271.09	97.5	300.68	104.5	331.23	113.4
37	266.12	95.4	295.81	102.5	326.46	111.6
38	261.42	93.4	291.21	100.7	321.97	110.0

Δ=97°

Dc	Ls=150' Ts	Es	200' Ts	Es	250' Ts	Es
26	328.58	118.6	356.88	123.5	385.96	129.8
27	319.52	114.7	347.93	119.8	377.12	126.3
28	311.11	111.1	339.63	116.4	368.95	123.1
29	303.29	107.7	331.91	113.2	361.35	120.2
30	296.01	104.6	324.73	110.3	354.29	117.5
31	289.20	101.7	318.03	107.6	347.69	115.0
32	282.82	99.0	311.75	105.1	341.53	112.7
33	276.84	96.5	305.87	102.7	335.76	110.6
34	271.23	94.1	300.35	100.5	330.34	108.7
35	265.93	91.9	295.16	98.5	325.25	106.9
36	260.95	89.9	290.26	96.6	320.46	105.2
37	256.23	87.9	285.64	94.8	315.93	103.6
38	251.77	86.1	281.28	93.2	311.67	102.2

Δ=99°

Dc	Ls=150' Ts	Es	200' Ts	Es	250' Ts	Es
26	337.69	125.5	366.12	130.5	395.37	136.9
27	328.30	121.3	356.85	126.5	386.22	133.2
28	319.59	117.5	348.25	122.9	377.76	129.8
29	311.50	113.9	340.27	119.5	369.89	126.7
30	303.95	110.6	332.83	116.4	362.58	123.8
31	296.90	107.5	325.88	113.5	355.75	121.1
32	290.30	104.7	319.38	110.4	349.38	118.7
33	284.10	102.0	313.30	108.3	343.40	116.4
34	278.28	99.5	307.58	106.0	337.79	114.3
35	272.80	97.1	302.20	103.8	332.52	112.4
36	267.64	94.9	297.14	101.8	327.57	110.6
37	262.76	92.8	292.35	99.9	322.8	108.9
38	258.14	90.9	287.83	98.1	318.46	107.3

TABLE IV - T_S AND E_S

Upper section

D_C	$\Delta=102°$ 250' T_S	E_S	200' T_S	E_S	$L_S=150'$ T_S	E_S	$\Delta=104°$ 250' T_S	E_S	200' T_S	E_S	$L_S=150'$ T_S	E_S	D_C
26	410.23	148.4	380.72	141.7	352.08	136.5	420.69	156.5	390.98	149.8	362.19	144.5	26
27	400.59	144.3	370.94	137.4	342.17	132.0	410.69	152.2	380.85	145.1	351.93	139.6	27
28	391.67	140.5	361.88	133.4	332.99	127.8	401.45	148.1	371.46	140.9	342.41	135.2	28
29	383.38	137.0	353.45	129.7	324.45	123.9	392.86	144.4	362.73	136.9	333.56	131.0	29
30	375.67	133.8	345.61	126.2	316.49	120.3	384.88	141.0	354.60	133.3	325.32	127.2	30
31	368.48	130.9	338.29	123.0	309.06	116.9	377.42	137.9	347.02	129.9	317.61	123.6	31
32	361.76	128.2	331.44	120.1	302.10	113.7	370.47	135.0	339.92	126.7	310.40	120.2	32
33	355.46	125.7	325.03	117.3	295.57	110.8	363.95	132.3	333.27	123.8	303.63	117.1	33
34	349.56	123.3	319.00	114.8	289.43	108.0	357.83	129.8	327.03	121.1	297.27	114.2	34
35	344.00	121.2	313.33	112.4	283.65	105.5	352.08	127.5	321.16	118.5	291.28	111.4	35
36	338.78	119.2	307.99	110.2	278.21	103.0	346.67	125.4	315.62	116.1	285.64	108.8	36
37	333.85	117.3	302.95	108.1	273.06	100.8	341.57	123.4	310.40	113.9	280.30	106.4	37
38	329.20	115.6	298.19	106.1	268.19	98.6	336.75	121.5	305.47	111.8	275.26	104.1	38

Lower section

D_C	$\Delta=101°$ $L_S=150'$ T_S	E_S	200' T_S	E_S	250' T_S	E_S	$\Delta=103°$ 250' T_S	E_S	200' T_S	E_S	$L_S=150'$ T_S	E_S	D_C
26	347.18	132.7	375.75	137.9	405.17	144.4	415.40	152.4	385.79	145.7	357.08	140.4	26
27	337.45	128.3	366.14	133.7	395.70	140.5	405.59	148.2	375.84	141.2	347.00	135.7	27
28	328.43	124.2	357.24	129.8	386.93	136.8	396.50	144.3	366.61	137.1	337.65	131.4	28
29	320.04	120.5	348.97	126.2	378.79	133.5	388.07	140.7	358.04	133.2	328.96	127.4	29
30	312.22	116.9	341.26	122.9	371.21	130.4	380.22	137.4	350.06	129.7	320.86	123.7	30
31	304.92	113.7	334.07	119.8	364.14	127.5	372.90	134.3	342.61	126.4	313.29	120.2	31
32	298.08	110.6	327.34	116.9	357.54	124.9	366.07	131.5	335.63	123.4	306.20	116.9	32
33	291.67	107.8	321.03	114.2	351.36	122.5	359.66	128.9	329.11	120.5	299.55	113.9	33
34	285.64	105.1	315.11	111.8	345.55	120.2	353.55	126.5	322.97	117.9	293.31	111.1	34
35	279.96	102.6	309.54	109.5	340.10	118.2	348.00	124.3	317.20	115.4	287.43	108.4	35
36	274.61	100.2	304.30	107.3	334.97	116.2	342.69	122.2	311.77	113.1	281.88	105.9	36
37	269.55	98.0	299.34	105.3	330.12	114.4	337.67	120.3	306.63	110.9	276.64	103.5	37
38	266.77	96.0	294.66	103.4	325.55	112.8	332.93	118.5	301.79	108.9	271.69	101.3	38

TABLE IV - Ts AND Es

Δ = 105°

Dc	Ls=150' Ts	Ls=150' Es	200' Ts	200' Es	250' Ts	250' Es
26	367.42	148.6	396.29	154.0	426.09	160.8
27	356.97	143.6	385.97	149.2	415.92	156.3
28	347.29	139.0	376.41	144.8	406.51	152.1
29	338.27	134.7	367.53	140.7	397.77	148.3
30	329.88	130.8	359.25	136.9	389.64	144.8
31	322.03	127.1	351.53	133.4	382.05	141.6
32	314.69	123.6	344.30	130.2	374.97	138.6
33	307.80	120.4	337.54	127.2	368.33	135.8
34	301.32	117.4	331.18	124.3	362.11	133.2
35	295.23	114.5	325.20	121.7	356.25	130.8
36	289.48	111.9	319.57	119.2	350.75	128.6
37	284.05	109.4	314.25	116.9	345.55	126.5
38	278.91	107.0	309.23	114.8	340.65	124.6

Δ = 106°

Dc	Ls=150' Ts	Ls=150' Es	200' Ts	200' Es	250' Ts	250' Es
26	372.77	152.8	401.72	158.3	431.62	165.2
27	362.13	147.7	391.21	153.4	421.26	160.5
28	352.27	143.0	381.48	148.8	411.68	156.3
29	343.09	138.6	372.43	144.6	402.78	152.3
30	334.54	134.5	364.01	140.7	394.51	148.7
31	326.55	130.7	356.15	137.1	386.78	145.3
32	319.08	127.1	348.79	133.8	379.57	142.2
33	312.06	123.8	341.90	130.6	372.82	139.3
34	305.47	120.7	335.43	127.7	366.48	136.7
35	299.26	117.8	329.34	125.0	360.53	134.2
36	293.41	115.0	323.61	122.5	354.92	131.9
37	287.88	112.4	318.19	120.1	349.63	129.8
38	282.65	110.0	313.08	117.8	344.65	127.8

Δ = 107°

Dc	Ls=150' Ts	Ls=150' Es	200' Ts	200' Es	250' Ts	250' Es
26	378.25	157.2	407.27	162.7	437.27	169.7
27	367.41	151.9	396.58	157.6	426.73	164.9
28	357.37	147.1	386.66	153.0	416.97	160.5
29	348.02	142.5	377.45	148.6	407.91	156.4
30	339.32	138.3	368.87	144.6	399.49	152.7
31	331.18	134.4	360.87	140.9	391.63	149.2
32	323.57	130.7	353.38	137.4	384.29	146.0
33	316.42	127.3	346.36	134.2	377.41	143.0
34	309.71	124.1	339.77	131.2	370.96	140.3
35	303.39	121.1	333.58	128.4	364.90	137.7
36	297.43	118.2	327.74	125.8	359.19	135.3
37	291.80	115.6	322.23	123.3	353.81	133.1
38	286.48	113.1	317.02	121.0	348.73	131.0

Δ = 108°

Dc	Ls=150' Ts	Ls=150' Es	200' Ts	200' Es	250' Ts	250' Es
26	383.85	161.8	412.96	167.3	443.06	174.4
27	372.82	156.3	402.07	162.1	432.33	169.4
28	362.59	151.3	391.97	157.2	422.39	164.9
29	353.07	146.6	382.59	152.8	413.17	160.7
30	344.21	142.2	373.86	148.6	404.59	156.8
31	335.92	138.2	365.71	144.8	396.59	153.2
32	328.17	134.4	358.08	141.2	389.11	149.9
33	320.89	130.9	350.93	137.9	382.11	146.8
34	314.06	127.6	344.22	134.8	375.54	144.0
35	307.62	124.5	337.91	131.9	369.37	141.3
36	301.55	121.6	331.97	129.2	363.57	138.9
37	295.82	118.8	326.36	126.6	358.09	136.6
38	290.39	116.2	321.06	124.3	352.92	134.4

TABLE IV - T_S AND E_S

$\Delta = 110°$

D_c	250' E_S	250' T_S	200' T_S	200' E_S	$L_S=150'$ E_S	$L_S=150'$ T_S
26	184.2	455.08	424.75	176.9	171.2	395.48
27	178.9	443.94	413.46	171.4	165.4	384.03
28	174.0	433.64	402.98	166.2	160.1	373.42
29	169.5	424.07	393.25	161.5	155.1	363.55
30	165.4	415.17	384.19	157.1	150.5	354.35
31	161.6	406.87	375.73	153.0	146.2	345.75
32	158.0	399.12	367.82	149.2	142.2	337.71
33	154.8	391.86	360.41	145.6	138.4	330.16
34	151.7	385.05	353.45	142.3	134.9	323.07
35	148.9	378.65	346.91	139.2	131.6	316.39
36	146.2	372.63	340.74	136.3	128.5	310.04
37	143.8	366.95	334.92	133.6	125.6	304.14
38	141.5	361.60	329.43	131.1	122.8	298.52

$\Delta = 109°$

D_c	250' T_S	250' E_S	200' T_S	200' E_S	$L_S=150'$ T_S	$L_S=150'$ E_S
26	443.00	171.2	418.78	172.0	389.60	166.4
27	438.06	174.1	407.69	166.6	378.36	160.8
28	427.95	169.4	397.41	161.7	367.94	155.6
29	418.55	165.0	387.86	157.1	358.25	150.8
30	409.82	161.0	378.96	152.8	349.21	146.3
31	401.67	157.3	370.66	148.8	340.78	142.1
32	394.06	153.9	362.89	145.1	332.88	138.2
33	386.93	150.7	355.62	141.7	325.47	134.6
34	380.24	147.8	348.78	138.5	318.51	131.2
35	372.95	145.0	342.36	135.5	311.95	128.0
36	368.04	142.5	336.30	132.7	305.77	125.0
37	362.46	140.1	330.59	130.1	299.93	122.1
38	357.20	137.9	325.19	127.6	294.41	119.5

TABLE V

Functions of Transitions Used in Table IV

$L_s = 150$ FT. D_c $L_s = 150$ FT.

D_c	L.C.	S.T.	L.T.	y_c	x_c	k	p	θ_s
26	149.23	50.56	100.51	16.88	148.27	74.71	4.24	19.5
27	149.17	50.60	100.56	17.51	148.14	74.69	4.40	20.25
28	149.11	50.65	100.71	18.15	148.00	74.67	4.56	21.0
29	149.04	50.70	100.77	18.79	147.85	74.64	4.72	21.75
30	148.97	50.75	100.82	19.42	147.70	74.62	4.88	22.5
31	148.91	50.80	100.88	20.05	147.55	74.59	5.04	23.25
32	148.83	50.85	100.94	20.68	147.39	74.56	5.20	24.0
33	148.76	50.91	101.00	21.31	147.23	74.54	5.36	24.75
34	148.68	50.96	101.06	21.94	147.06	74.51	5.52	25.5
35	148.61	51.02	101.12	22.57	146.88	74.48	5.68	26.25
36	148.53	51.08	101.19	23.19	146.70	74.45	5.84	27.0
37	148.44	51.14	101.26	23.81	146.52	74.42	6.00	27.75
38	148.26	51.21	101.33	24.44	146.33	74.39	6.16	28.5

Deflection Angles from T.S. to Pts. on Ten Chord Spiral for Transitions Used in Table IV

SIGHT ON POINT NO. — TRANSIT ON T.S.

D_c	COL. A	10=S.T.	9	8	7	6	5	4	3	2	1
26	.15	6°-29.6'	5-15.8	4-09.6	3-11.2	2-20.4	1-37.6	1-02.4	0-35.2	0-15.6	0-04.0
27	.15	6°-44.6'	5-27.8	4-18.2	3-18.4	2-25.8	1-41.2	1-04.8	0-36.4	0-16.2	0-04.0
28	.16	6°-59.6'	5-40.0	4-28.8	3-25.8	2-31.2	1-45.0	1-07.2	0-37.8	0-16.8	0-04.2
29	.17	7°-14.6'	5-52.2	4-38.4	3-33.2	2-36.6	1-48.8	1-09.6	0-39.2	17.4	04.4
30	.17	7°-29.4'	6-04.2	4-47.8	3-40.4	2-42.0	1-52.6	1-12.0	0-40.6	18.0	04.6
31	.18	7°-44.4'	6-16.4	4-57.4	3-47.8	2-47.4	1-56.2	1-14.4	0-41.8	18.6	04.6
32	.18	7°-59.4'	6-28.6	5-07.0	3-55.2	2-52.8	2-00.0	1-16.8	0-43.2	19.2	04.8
33	.19	8°-14.2'	6-40.6	5-16.6	4-02.6	2-58.2	2-03.8	1-19.2	0-44.6	19.8	05.0
34	.19	8°-29.2'	6-52.6	5-26.2	4-09.8	3-03.6	2-07.6	1-21.6	0-46.0	20.4	05.2
35	.20	8°-44.0'	7-04.8	5-35.8	4-17.2	3-09.0	2-11.2	1-24.0	0-47.2	21.0	05.2
36	.21	8°-59.0'	7-16.8	5-45.4	4-24.6	3-14.4	2-15.0	1-26.4	0-48.6	21.6	0-05.4
37	.21	9°-14.0'	7-29.0	5-55.0	4-32.0	3-19.8	2-18.8	1-28.8	0-50.0	22.2	0-05.6
38	.22	9°-28.8'	7-41.2	6-04.6	4-39.2	3-25.2	2-22.6	1-31.2	0-51.4	22.8	0-05.8

Note· Col. A.

For the deflection angle to a point other than a chord point simple interpolation may be used with no appreciable error provided a correction is made where necessary. The value in column A is the unit amount of this correction in minutes per foot of the distance from the nearest chord point. In all cases the correction should be subtracted from the interpolated result.

TABLE V

FUNCTIONS OF TRANSITIONS USED IN TABLE IV

Dc	θs	p	k	xc	yc	L.T.	S.T.	L.C.	Dc
26	26.	7.51	99.32	195.92	29.81	134.80	68.00	198.18	26
27	27.	7.79	99.26	195.60	30.92	134.92	68.11	198.03	27
28	28.	8.07	99.21	195.28	32.03	135.04	68.22	197.89	28
29	29.	8.36	99.15	194.94	33.13	135.17	68.34	197.73	29
30	30.	8.64	99.09	194.59	34.23	135.30	68.46	197.57	30
31	31.	8.92	99.03	194.22	35.32	135.44	68.58	197.41	31
32	32.	9.20	98.97	193.85	36.41	135.58	68.71	197.24	32
33	33.	9.49	98.90	193.47	37.50	135.73	68.85	197.07	33
34	34.	9.77	98.84	193.07	38.58	135.88	68.99	196.89	34
35	35.	10.05	98.77	192.66	39.65	136.04	69.13	196.70	35
36	36.	10.33	98.70	192.25	40.72	136.20	69.28	196.51	36
37	37.	10.60	98.63	191.82	41.79	136.37	69.43	196.32	37
38	38.	10.88	98.55	191.38	42.85	136.54	69.59	196.12	38

DEFLECTION ANGLES FROM T.S. TO PTS. ON TEN CHORD SPIRAL FOR TRANSITIONS USED IN TABLE IV

Dc	COL. A	10=S.T.	9	8	7	6	5	4	3	2	1	Dc
26	.15	8°-39.0'	7-00.8	5-32.6	4-14.8	3-07.2	2-10.0	1-23.2	0-46.8	0-20.8	0-05.2	26
27	.15	8°-59.0'	7-17.0	5-45.4	4-24.6	3-14.4	2-15.0	1-26.4	0-48.6	0-21.6	0-05.4	27
28	.16	9°-19.0'	7-33.0	5-58.2	4-34.4	3-21.6	2-20.0	1-29.6	0-50.4	0-22.4	05.6	28
29	.17	9°-38.8'	7-49.2	6-11.0	4-44.2	3-28.8	2-25.0	1-32.8	0-52.2	0-23.2	05.8	29
30	.17	9°-58.6'	8-05.4	6-23.8	4-53.8	3-36.0	2-30.0	1-36.0	0-54.0	0-24.0	06.0	30
31	.18	10°-18.6'	8-21.4	6-36.4	5-03.6	3-43.2	2-35.0	1-39.2	0-55.8	0-24.8	06.2	31
32	.18	10°-38.2'	8-37.6	6-49.2	5-13.4	3-50.4	2-40.0	1-42.4	0-57.6	0-25.6	06.4	32
33	.19	10°-58.0'	8-53.6	7-02.0	5-23.2	3-57.6	2-45.0	1-45.6	0-59.4	0-26.4	06.6	33
34	.19	11°-18.0'	9-09.8	7-14.8	5-33.0	4-04.8	2-50.0	1-48.8	1-01.2	0-27.2	06.8	34
35	.20	11°-37.8'	9-25.8	7-27.6	5-42.8	4-12.0	2-55.0	1-52.0	1-03.0	0-28.0	07.0	35
36	.21	11°-57.6'	9-42.0	7-40.2	5-52.6	4-19.2	3-00.0	1-55.2	1-04.8	0-28.8	07.2	36
37	.21	12°-17.4'	9-58.0	7-53.0	6-02.4	4-26.4	3-05.0	1-58.4	1-06.6	0-29.6	0-07.4	37
38	.22	12°-37.0'	10-14.2	8-05.8	6-12.2	4-33.6	3-10.0	2-01.6	1-08.4	0-30.4	0-07.6	38

Column labels: SIGHT ON POINT NO. — columns 6–9; T.S. — column 5; TRANSIT ON — columns 1–4.

TABLE V L_s=250 FT.

Functions of Transitions Used in Table IV — L_s=250 FT.

Dc	L.C.	S.T.	L.T.	yc	xc	k	p	θs	Dc
26	246.44	85.98	169.57	46.20	242.08	123.67	11.68	32.5	26
27	246.17	86.19	169.80	47.89	241.46	123.57	12.12	33.75	27
28	245.88	86.41	170.05	49.57	240.83	123.46	12.56	35.0	28
29	245.58	86.65	170.30	51.24	240.18	123.35	12.99	36.25	29
30	245.27	86.89	170.57	52.90	239.50	123.24	13.43	37.5	30
31	244.96	87.14	170.84	54.55	238.81	123.12	13.86	38.75	31
32	244.63	87.41	171.13	56.18	238.09	123.00	14.30	40.0	32
33	244.29	87.68	171.43	57.81	237.35	122.87	14.72	41.25	33
34	243.94	87.96	171.74	59.43	236.59	122.74	15.15	42.5	34
35	243.58	88.26	172.06	61.03	235.81	122.61	15.58	43.75	35
36	243.21	88.56	172.39	62.62	235.01	122.48	16.01	45.0	36
37	242.84	88.88	172.74	64.20	234.19	122.33	16.43	46.25	37
38	242.45	89.20	173.09	65.77	233.36	122.19	16.86	47.5	38

Deflection Angles from T.S. to Pts. on Ten Chord Spiral for Transitions Used in Table IV

SIGHT ON POINT NO. / TRANSIT ON T.S.

Dc	COL. A	10=S.C.	9	8	7	6	5	4	3	2	1	Dc
26	.15	10-48.2	8-45.6	6-55.6	5-18.4	3-54.0	2-42.6	1-44.0	0-58.6	0-26.0	0-06.6	26
27	.15	11-13.0	9-05.6	7-11.6	5-30.6	4-03.0	2-48.8	1-48.0	1-00.8	0-27.0	0-06.8	27
28	.16	11-37.8	9-25.8	7-27.6	5-42.8	4-12.0	2-55.0	1-52.0	1-03.0	0-28.0	07.0	28
29	.17	12-02.6	9-46.0	7-43.4	5-55.0	4-21.0	3-01.2	1-56.0	1-05.2	0-29.0	07.2	29
30	.17	12-27.2	10-06.0	7-59.4	6-07.2	4-30.0	3-07.6	2-00.0	1-07.6	0-30.0	07.6	30
31	.18	12-52.0	10-26.0	8-15.2	6-19.4	4-39.0	3-13.8	2-04.0	1-09.8	0-31.0	07.8	31
32	.18	13-16.8	10-46.2	8-31.2	6-31.6	4-48.0	3-20.0	2-08.0	1-12.0	0-32.0	08.0	32
33	.19	13-41.4	11-06.4	8-47.0	6-43.8	4-56.8	3-26.4	2-12.0	1-14.2	0-33.0	08.2	33
34	.19	14-06.0	11-26.6	9-03.0	6-56.0	5-05.8	3-32.4	2-16.0	1-16.6	0-34.0	08.6	34
35	.20	14-30.6	11-46.4	9-19.0	7-08.2	5-14.8	3-38.8	2-20.0	1-18.8	0-35.0	08.8	35
36	.21	14-55.2	12-06.6	9-34.8	7-20.6	5-23.8	3-45.0	2-24.0	1-21.0	0-36.0	09.0	36
37	.21	15-19.8	12-26.6	9-50.8	7-32.6	5-32.8	3-51.2	2-28.0	1-23.2	0-37.0	0-09.2	37
38	.22	15-44.4	12-46.4	10-06.6	7-44.8	5-41.8	3-57.4	2-32.0	1-25.6	0-38.0	0-09.6	38

SUPPLEMENT

DEFLECTION ANGLES FOR SET-UP ON ANY POINT

WHEN SET UP ON ANY POINT OF A
TRANSITION THE DEFLECTION ANGLE FROM ANY
BACKSIGHT TO ANY FORESIGHT MAY BE FOUND
BY THE FORMULA

$$\phi = (L_1 + L_2 + L_3)(L_3 - L_1)\frac{\theta_s}{3L_s^2}$$

VALUES ARE REASONABLY ACCURATE FOR ALL PRACTICAL PURPOSES EXCEPT
WHERE "C" CORRECTIONS FOR SHARP TRANSITIONS ARE APPRECIABLE. WHEN T.S.
AND S.C. ARE LOCATED DIRECTLY AND NOT BY CARRYING TRANSITION STATIONS
FROM T.S. TO S.C. ERRORS ARE NOT CUMULATIVE AND "C" CORRECTIONS RARELY ARE
NECESSARY.

WHEN SET UP ON T.S. $L_1 = L_2 = 0$ AND BACKSIGHT IS ON TANGENT.

WHEN SET UP ON S.C. $L_2 = L_3 = L_s$ AND FORESIGHT IS ON THE LOCAL TANGENT.

WHEN SET UP ON ANY POINT, DEFLECTION ANGLE FROM BACKSIGHT TO LOCAL
TANGENT CAN BE COMPUTED BY MAKING $L_3 = L_2$; AND FROM FORESIGHT BY MAKING $L_1 = L_2$.

Taken from article by
Orville Kofoid in
"WESTERN CONSTRUCTION NEWS"
V. 14 - No.6   June, 1939